INQUIRY JOURNAL

IMPACT™
CALIFORNIA
SOCIAL STUDIES

UNITED STATES
HISTORY & GEOGRAPHY

CONTINUITY & CHANGE

Joyce Appleby, Ph.D.

Alan Brinkley, Ph.D.

Albert S. Broussard, Ph.D.

James M. McPherson, Ph.D.

Donald A. Ritchie, Ph.D.

Mc
Graw
Hill

mheducation.com/prek-12

Send all inquiries to:
McGraw-Hill Education
8787 Orion Place
Columbus, OH 43240

ISBN: 978-0-07-906376-2
MHID: 0-07-906376-4

Printed in the United States of America.

7 8 9 10 11 LWI 23 22 21 20

Table of Contents

Dear Student,

Many of us are curious, and we have questions about many things. We have the more personal questions, such as, "What type of job or career might I be suited for?" or "How do I learn the best way to save money to buy the things I want or need?" to questions of a larger nature about the world around us. These might include questions such as the following: "What does being treated like an adult mean? Why do nations go to war with one another? How do I understand what I see or read about in history or online or in the news? Why do political parties clash with one another so frequently?"

Asking good questions helps us take charge of our own learning. Learning to ask good questions is a process, as "yes" or "no" types of questions don't get us very far in discovering why events happened or why people feel as they do. Once we master this process, however, we become better thinkers and researchers and can find out more about subjects that interest us. Asking good questions is also important if we want to understand and affect the world around us.

In this book, as in other parts of the program, there will be "Essential Questions" that you will research. These are universal questions. Examples of such questions include: "How do new ideas change the way people live?" and "What makes a culture unique?" and "What characteristics make a good leader?" and "Why does conflict develop?" You will choose some of your own supporting questions to help you answer the Essential Question.

As you move through the study of history, you will be reading primary and secondary sources about a specific time period. **Primary sources**—whether they are diaries, poetry, letters, or artwork—were created by people who saw or experienced the event they are describing. **Secondary sources**—whether they are biographies, or history books, or your student text, are created after an event, by people who were not part of the original event.

Once you have completed the readings and the text notes, there is a "Report Your findings" project in which you answer the Essential Question. You will work on some parts of the project by yourself, and you will work on other parts of the project with your classmates. You will be given many opportunities to take informed action. This means that you will use what you have learned and apply it to a current issue in a way that interests you. You will share this information with other students or with people in your community.

Creating a Nation

ESSENTIAL QUESTION

How should societies settle disputes?

Think about how this question might relate to the disputes that colonists faced when they began to form a nation.

TALK ABOUT IT

Discuss with a partner what type of information you would need to know to answer this question. For example, one question might be: What kind of disputes did colonists face?

DIRECTIONS: Now write down three additional questions that would help you explain some of the strategies that colonists used to settle disputes.

MY RESEARCH QUESTIONS

Supporting Question 1:

_____

_____

Supporting Question 2:

_____

_____

Supporting Question 3:

_____

_____

Origins of the American Nation

DIRECTIONS Search for evidence in Chapter 1, Lesson 1 to help you answer the following questions.

1A GEOGRAPHY Where did the earliest civilizations of North America arise, and who were they?

_____

_____

_____

_____

ESSENTIAL QUESTION

How should societies settle disputes?

As you gather evidence to answer the Essential Question, think about:

- how settlers to North America caused and resolved conflict with native peoples.

- how the settlers of Jamestown and the early colonies used laws and rules to help settle disputes.

- what the central dispute in the American Revolution was, and how it came about.

1B GEOGRAPHY What geographical features helped support their cultures?

_____

_____

_____

_____

2A **EXPLAINING** What need drove Europeans to explore the Atlantic Ocean?

_____

_____

_____

My Notes

_____

_____

_____

_____

2B **IDENTIFYING CAUSE AND EFFECT** What was the effect of European exploration on those early cultures and civilizations?

_____

_____

_____

_____

3 DETERMINING CENTRAL IDEAS What factors compelled the settlers of the thirteen colonies to settle in colonies of North America?

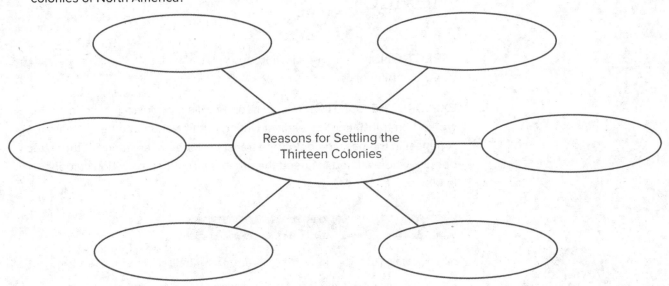

Reasons for Settling the Thirteen Colonies

4 SEQUENCING As the colonies grew, what events contributed to the war for independence from England? Complete the time line by filling in the events.

1750   1760   1770   1780

1755   1765   1775

5 DRAWING CONCLUSIONS What was the alternative to the War for Independence? Was the war inevitable?

_____

_____

_____

_____

_____

ESSENTIAL QUESTION

How should societies settle disputes?

Aztec Account of the Conquest of Mexico

DIRECTIONS: Read the following excerpt, from a book. Then respond to the questions that follow.

EXPLORE THE CONTEXT: Miguel Leon-Portilla is a Mexican historian who worked on translating the earliest writing of the Nahua people of Central America. In the passage below, he translated the observations of the Aztec people, who watched firsthand the arrival of the Spanish conquistadors in Mexico.

PRIMARY SOURCE: DOCUMENT

❝A thing like a ball of stone comes out of its **entrails**: it comes out shooting sparks and raining fire. . . . If it is aimed against a tree, it shatters the tree into **splinters**. This is a most unnatural sight, as if the tree had exploded from within. . . They dress in iron . . . Their deer carry them on their back wherever they wish to go. These deer, our lord, are as tall as the roof of a house. ❞

—from *The Broken Spears: The Aztec Account of the Conquest of Mexico* by Miguel Leon-Portilla

VOCABULARY

entrails: the insides of something, such as an animal or machine

splinters: small, sharp pieces

1 **DETERMINING CONTEXT** What are the items that the narrator is describing in the passage?

_____

_____

_____

2 INFERRING Why did the translator choose this passage to include in his collection of Aztec writings? What historical inference does the translator wish to offer the reader?

_____

_____

_____

_____

3 ANALYZING TEXT How do the conquistadors demonstrate their power to the native people?

_____

_____

_____

_____

4 HISTORY What important things were going on at the time these observations about the Spanish conquistadors were written? How do the historical events help you understand the document?

_____

_____

_____

_____

5 IDENTIFYING What can you tell about the way the narrator lives from his description of the animal in the passage?

_____

_____

_____

_____

ESSENTIAL QUESTION

How should societies settle disputes?

VOCABULARY

commonwealth: community

divulging: giving away; telling

divers: diverse; very different

prejudicial: bias for or against something or someone

obstinate: stubborn

Case Against Anne Hutchinson

DIRECTIONS: Read the passage, and answer the accompanying questions.

EXPLORE THE CONTEXT: In the passage below, Judge Winthrop, the governor of Massachusetts Bay Colony, confronts Anne Hutchinson at a trial. She had been holding meetings of women to discuss religious topics. He and others in the Puritan colony objected to her criticism of the clergy. Mrs. Hutchinson and John Wheelwright both objected to some of the teachings of the Puritan religion. As a result, they were both tried and banished from the colony in 1637.

PRIMARY SOURCE: TRIAL TRANSCRIPT

66 Judge Winthrop: Mrs. Hutchinson, . . . you are called here as one of those that have troubled the peace of the **commonwealth** and the churches here; you are known to be a woman that hath had a great share in the promoting and **divulging** of those opinions that are causes of this trouble. . . . [You have] spoken **divers** things . . . **prejudicial** to the honour of the churches and ministers. Therefore we have thought good to send for you to understand how things are, that if you be in an erroneous way we may reduce you that so you may become a profitable member here among us[.] Otherwise, if you be **obstinate** in your course that then the court may take such course that you may trouble us no further. . . . Therefore I would entreat you to express whether you do not assent and hold in practice to those opinions and factions that have been handled in court already, that is to say, whether you do not justify Mr. Wheelwright's sermon and the petition. 99

—from *The Massachusetts Bay Colony Case against Anne Hutchinson*, 1637

1 **DETERMINING MEANING** What is the central message of the statement? What does the speaker ask of Mrs. Hutchinson?

Battis, Emery John. Saints and sectaries: Anne Hutchinson and the Antinomian controversy in the Massachusetts Bay Colony. Chapel Hill: Published for the Institute of Early American History and Culture at Williamsburg, Va., by the University of North Carolina Press, 1962.

2 **ANALYZING** What does Judge Winthrop accuse Mrs. Hutchinson of? Identify instances in the excerpt that explicitly state his accusation and also write them on the line below.

_____

_____

_____

_____

3 **EVALUATING EVIDENCE** What type of document is this? How does this information help you understand the document?

_____

_____

_____

_____

4 **DETERMINING CONTEXT** Where was this document written? When was it written?

_____

_____

_____

_____

5 **INFERRING** What important details about the place and time this document was written help you understand the document?

_____

_____

_____

_____

6 CIVICS What democratic principle might have guided Anne Hutchinson's actions? What principle might have guided Judge Winthrop's actions?

_____

_____

_____

The Young Republic

DIRECTIONS Search for evidence in Chapter 1, Lesson 2 to help you answer the following questions.

1A **COMPARING** The founders realized that the Articles of Confederation was a flawed plan. How did they improve on the plan with the U.S. Constitution? What improvements did they make?

_____

_____

_____

_____

1B **CIVICS** What did some Anti-Federalists demand be added to the Constitution before ratifying it, and why?

_____

_____

_____

_____

2A **EXPLAINING ISSUES** What basic differences in founders' views led to the establishment of different political parties?

_____

_____

_____

_____

2B **CITING TEXT EVIDENCE** Give an example from the student text of how the two-party system works.

_____

_____

_____

_____

ESSENTIAL QUESTION

How should societies settle disputes?

As you gather evidence to answer the Essential Question, think about:

- how the U.S. Constitution helps settle disputes.
- the strength and weaknesses of political parties.
- the power wielded by the courts under the U.S. Constitution.

My Notes

_____

_____

_____

_____

_____

_____

_____

3 HISTORY Use the Cornell Notes organizer to take notes about the expansion of the United States in the nineteenth century.

Main Ideas	Notes
Marbury v. *Madison*	
Treaty of Paris	
Northwest Territory	
Louisiana Territory	

4 **IDENTIFYING CAUSES AND EFFECTS** Use the cause-and-effect organizer below to take notes about the War of 1812.

Causes	War of 1812	Effects

5 **MAKING INFERENCES** What inferences can you make about how the stature of the United States changed on the world stage after the War of 1812?

_____

_____

_____

_____

ESSENTIAL QUESTION

How should societies settle disputes?

VOCABULARY

accoutrements: clothing or equipment

peltry: animal pelts

Lewis and Clark Expedition

DIRECTIONS: Study the following excerpt from a letter. Then respond to the questions that follow.

EXPLORE THE CONTEXT: Thomas Jefferson was fascinated by the West, and he dreamed of seeing the country grow. In 1803, hoping to find an easy route to the Pacific Ocean, he sent a secret request to Congress asking for money to pay for an expedition to explore the West. At the time, the United States did not own the Louisiana Territory. A treaty to purchase it was not signed until May 2, 1803 and was ratified by Congress in December of that same year.

PRIMARY SOURCE: LETTER

" The river Missouri, and the Indians inhabiting it, are not as well known . . . It is, however, understood, that the country on that river is inhabited by numerous tribes, who furnish great supplies of furs and **peltry** to the trade of another nation, . . . through an infinite number of portages and lakes, shut up by ice through a long season. . . . An intelligent officer, with ten or twelve chosen men, fit for the enterprise, and willing to undertake it, taken from our posts, where they may be spared without inconvenience, might explore the whole line, even to the Western Ocean, have conferences with the natives on the subject of commercial intercourse, get admission among them for our traders, as others are admitted, agree on convenient deposits for an interchange of articles, and return with the information acquired, in the course of two summers. Their arms and **accoutrements**, some instruments of observation, and light and cheap presents for the Indians, would be all the apparatus they could carry, and with an expectation of a soldier's portion of land on their return, would constitute the whole expense. . . . While other civilized nations have encountered great expense to enlarge the boundaries of knowledge by undertaking voyages of discovery, . . . that it should incidentally advance the geographical knowledge of our own continent, cannot be but an additional gratification. . . . The appropriation of two thousand five hundred dollars, "for the purpose of extending the external commerce of the United States," while understood and considered by the Executive as giving the legislative sanction, would cover the undertaking from notice, and prevent the obstructions which interested individuals might otherwise previously prepare in its way. "

—from *Jefferson's Secret Message to Congress Regarding the Lewis & Clark Expedition,* January 18, 1803

Jefferson, Thomas. "Secret Message to Congress Regarding the Lewis & Clark Expedition (1803)." Letter, Washington, D.C., 1803.

1 `ECONOMICS` Underline the details in the passage that reveal Jefferson's economic motivation for exploring the Louisiana Territory.

_____

_____

_____

_____

2 `GEOGRAPHY` What natural resources does Jefferson expect to find and explore? What is his motivation for that exploration?

_____

_____

_____

_____

3 **EVALUATING EVIDENCE** How does Jefferson propose to compensate the explorers for their journey? How do you think the members of Congress will respond to his suggestion? What criticisms is Jefferson heading off with his suggestions?

_____

_____

_____

_____

4 **INFERRING** For whom was the document written? How does that information help you understand it?

_____

_____

_____

_____

5 **DETERMINING CONTEXT** What important things were going on at the time that relate to the document? How does this information help you understand the document?

_____

_____

_____

ESSENTIAL QUESTION

How should societies settle disputes?

The Federalist Papers

DIRECTIONS: Study the following excerpt from an essay. Then respond to the questions that follow.

EXPLORE THE CONTEXT: This passage comes from a larger body of work called *The Federalist Papers*. *The Federalist Papers* is a collection of 85 essays that were written in support of the effort in New York to ratify the Constitution of the United States. The essays were written by Alexander Hamilton, James Madison, and John Jay. They were first printed in newspapers in New York and later collected and reprinted as a book.

PRIMARY SOURCE: ESSAYS

❝ It may be a reflection on human nature, that such devices should be necessary to control the abuses of government. But what is government itself, but the greatest of all reflections on human nature? If men were angels, no government would be necessary. If angels were to govern men, neither external nor internal controls on government would be necessary. In framing a government which is to be administered by men over men, the great difficulty lies in this: you must first enable the government to control the governed; and in the next place oblige it to control itself. ❞

—from *The Federalist Papers, no. 51: The Structure of the Government Must Furnish the Proper Checks and Balances Between the Different Departments,* by James Madison

1 **HISTORY**　What type of document is this? How does this help you understand it?

_____

_____

_____

_____

_____

_____

Madison, James. "Federalist No. 51: The Structure of the Government Must Furnish the Proper Checks and Balances Between the Different Departments." Independent Journal, February 6, 1788.

2 CITING TEXT EVIDENCE What is the central argument of the passage? Underline the part that explains the central argument best.

_____

_____

_____

_____

3 DETERMINING CONTEXT Does the author want something specific to happen by writing this document? If so, what? And how does he go about accomplishing his purpose?

_____

_____

_____

_____

4 INFERRING What does this document infer was happening at the time it was written? How does this information help you understand the document?

_____

_____

_____

_____

5 DRAWING CONCLUSIONS What does the author suggest is government's responsibility to its citizens?

_____

_____

_____

_____

6 CIVICS What are the civic virtues that are demonstrated in this document?

_____

_____

_____

_____

Antebellum America

DIRECTIONS Search for evidence in Chapter 1, Lesson 3 to help you answer the following questions.

1A **DESCRIBING** What was happening in the northern states during the early and mid-1800s?

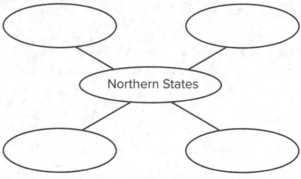

Northern States

1B **DESCRIBING** What was happening in the southern states during the early and mid-1800s?

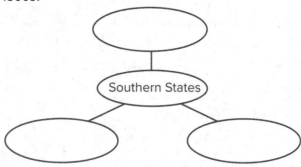

Southern States

2A ECONOMICS The cotton gin brought an age of mechanization to the cotton fields. How did the cotton gin change the economy of the South?

_____

_____

_____

2B **ANALYZING** How did inventions such as the cotton gin contribute to laws that kept enslaved African Americans in servitude?

_____

_____

_____

ESSENTIAL QUESTION

How should societies settle disputes?

As you gather evidence to answer the Essential Question, think about:

- why nationalism emerged after the War of 1812.
- how immigration in the mid-1800s led to political disputes.
- the impact of an agricultural economy on society.

My Notes

_____

_____

_____

_____

_____

_____

_____

3 SEQUENCING How did President Jackson settle the dispute with Native Americans? Complete the chart.

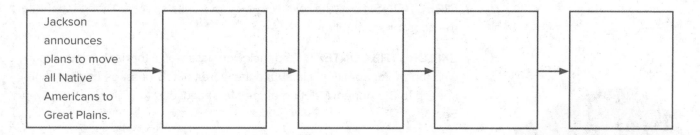

Jackson announces plans to move all Native Americans to Great Plains. → ☐ → ☐ → ☐ → ☐

4 EXPLAINING Complete the following chart by explaining the purpose of each reform movement.

Reform Movement	Purpose
Temperance	
Women's Rights	
Abolition	

ESSENTIAL QUESTION
How should societies settle disputes?

Frederick Douglass

DIRECTIONS: Read the following excerpt from a speech. Then respond to the questions that follow.

EXPLORE THE CONTEXT: Frederick Douglass was a former enslaved man who fought for abolition. He spoke the words of this passage as part of his speech to the Annual Meeting of the Massachusetts Anti-Slavery Society in Boston.

PRIMARY SOURCE: SPEECH

❝It may be asked, "Why do you want it? Some men have got along very well without it. Women have not this right." Shall we justify one wrong by another? That is a sufficient answer. . . . I hold that women, as well as men, have the right to vote, and my heart and my voice go with the movement to extend **suffrage** to woman; but that question rests upon another basis than that on which our right rests. We may be asked, I say, why we want it. I will tell you why we want it. We want it because it is our right, first of all. No class of men can, without insulting their own nature, be content with any deprivation of their rights. We want it, again, as a means for educating our race. Men are so **constituted** that they derive their conviction of their own possibilities largely from the estimate formed of them by others. If nothing is expected of a people, that people will find it difficult to contradict that expectation. By depriving us, of suffrage, you affirm our **incapacity** to form an intelligent judgment respecting public men and public measures; you declare before the world that we are unfit to exercise the elective franchise, and by this means lead us to undervalue ourselves, to put a low estimate upon ourselves, and to feel that we have no possibilities like other men. ❞

—from *What the Black Man Wants,* by Frederick Douglass, 1865

VOCABULARY

suffrage: the right to vote

constituted: made up of

incapacity: inability

Douglass, Frederick. *What the Black Man Wants.* In *The Library of oratory, ancient and modern,* edited by Chauncey M. Depew, Nathan Haskell Dole, Caroline Ticknor, and Thomas Charles Quinn, 134-144. New York: Du Mont, 1902.

1 **CITING TEXT EVIDENCE** What is the reason Frederick Douglass argues that black men should have the vote? Underline the part of the passage that helps you understand the reason.

_____

_____

_____

_____

_____

2 **HISTORY** What historical events does the passage suggest were happening at the time it was written to help us understand Douglass's speech?

_____

_____

_____

_____

_____

3 **ANALYZING SOURCES** Where was the speech delivered? What aspects of the speech were targeted specifically for the audience of the speech?

_____

_____

_____

_____

_____

4 **MAKING CONNECTIONS** Frederick Douglass voices this point of view: "Men are so constituted that they derive their conviction of their own possibilities largely from the estimate formed of them by others." Do you agree with his point of view? Explain your answer.

_____

_____

_____

_____

_____

ESSENTIAL QUESTION

How should societies settle disputes?

The Monroe Doctrine

DIRECTIONS: Study the following excerpt from a speech. Then respond to the questions that follow.

EXPLORE THE CONTEXT: The Monroe Doctrine was part of President James Monroe's annual address to Congress in 1823. In his message, he declared that he intended to stay out of the affairs of European countries and to refrain from meddling in their existing colonial settlements. He considered the Western Hemisphere closed to further colonization, and he intended to maintain this policy with force. The primary reason he made these statements was that he feared Spain would try to establish more colonies in Central America.

PRIMARY SOURCE: SPEECH

“ We owe it, therefore, to **candor** and to the **amicable** relations existing between the United States and those powers to declare that we should consider any attempt on their part to extend their system to any portion of this hemisphere as dangerous to our peace and safety. With the existing colonies or dependencies of any European power we have not interfered and shall not interfere. But with the Governments who have declared their independence and maintain it, and whose independence we have, on great consideration and on just principles, acknowledged, we could not view any interposition for the purpose of oppressing them, or controlling in any other manner their destiny, by any European power in any other light than as the **manifestation** of an unfriendly disposition toward the United States. ”

—from *The Monroe Doctrine,* by James Monroe, 1823

VOCABULARY

candor: honesty, frankness

amicable: friendly

manifestation: a sign or appearance that shows something clearly

Daniel, John W. The Monroe Doctrine. Washington, 1896.

1 **CITING TEXT EVIDENCE** In what lines does President Monroe threaten to use military power to maintain his policy?

_____

_____

_____

_____

_____

2 **IDENTIFYING CAUSES AND EFFECTS** In what position might the Monroe Doctrine place the country? Why is this important?

_____

_____

_____

_____

_____

3 **DRAWING CONCLUSIONS** How might events at the time help reveal the meaning of Monroe's words?

_____

_____

_____

_____

4 **CIVICS** What branch of government is on display in this document? Explain your answer.

_____

_____

_____

_____

ESSENTIAL QUESTIONS

How should societies settle disputes?

① Think About It

Review the supporting questions you developed at the beginning of the chapter. Review the evidence you found in Chapter 1. Were you able to answer each of your Supporting Questions?

If you didn't find enough evidence to answer your Supporting Questions, what do you think you need to consider?

_____

_____

_____

_____

② Organize Your Evidence

Use a web such as the one below to organize the evidence you will use to support your Position Statement.

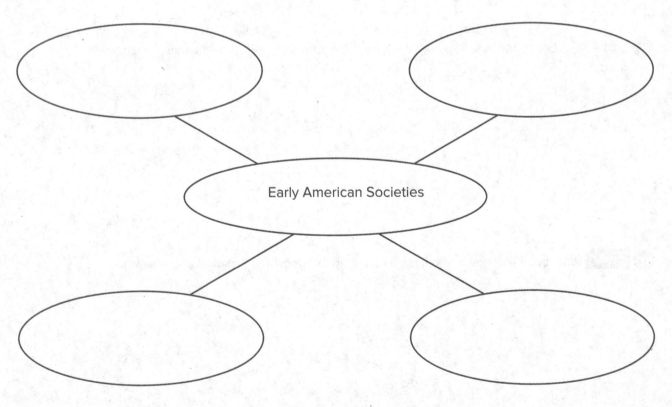

Early American Societies

3 Write About It

Create a position statement focused on the Essential Question: How should societies settle disputes? Use the evidence you gathered and organized in Step 2 to guide you in developing your statement.

_____

_____

_____

_____

_____

_____

_____

4 Talk About It

Discuss the evidence you have gathered with a small group. Check your group's understanding of how societies should resolve disputes, and answer any questions members may have. Consider any additional advice or input they may have.

_____

_____

_____

5 Connect to the Essential Question

On a separate piece of paper, write a mock newspaper interview with a person from American colonial times. Imagine the questions you would ask and some of the answers you would get, and write the interview using details from the text. Your questions should answer the Essential Question: _How should societies settle disputes?_

TAKING ACTION

MAKE CONNECTIONS The actor and composer Lin-Manuel Miranda wrote a musical focused on founder Alexander Hamilton. The story is about an immigrant who comes to America and helps shape a young nation. Miranda's unique interpretation for the musical is that the story is conveyed in a modern hip-hop musical style. He also casts people of color in many leading and supporting roles. This artistic decision has allowed millions of people to learn a civics lesson in a new way. The narrative of the musical is historically accurate, but the interpretation is modern and edgy.

DIRECTIONS: Use what you have learned in Chapter 1 about the founding of the United States and how the founders settled their disputes. Choose one dispute from the chapter and one historical figure who played a role in the dispute. Research how that figure influenced the historical event. Then work with a team to draft a hip-hop riff, poem, or song that captures the conflict, as well as how it impacted the early foundation of the country and how it was resolved.

Your hip-hop riff should include at least three verses and a repeating chorus that describes your central historical figure. Practice presenting your hip-hop song, and perform it or record it to share with other classes in your school.

War and the West

ESSENTIAL QUESTION

How should societies settle disputes?

Think about how this question might relate to the Civil War and the settlement of the American West. What kind of disputes arose that led to war and conflict? In what different ways did government leaders and citizens handle those disputes? What worked, and what didn't?

TALK ABOUT IT

Discuss with a partner the type of information you would need to know to answer these questions. For example, one question might be: What were the main disputes that led to the Civil War?

DIRECTIONS: Now write three additional questions that would help you describe the conflicts that occurred between the Northerners and the Southerners and the settlers and Native Americans during this time period.

MY RESEARCH QUESTIONS

Supporting Question 1:

_____

_____

Supporting Question 2:

_____

_____

Supporting Question 3:

_____

_____

The Sectional Crisis

DIRECTIONS Search for evidence in Chapter 2, Lesson 1 to help you answer the following questions.

1A **IDENTIFYING CONNECTIONS** What lured thousands of Americans to move west?

_____

_____

1B **RELATING EVENTS** How did Manifest Destiny influence these settlers?

_____

_____

2A **IDENTIFYING CONNECTIONS** What was the idea of popular sovereignty?

_____

_____

2B **UNDERSTANDING CONTEXT** How did the idea of popular sovereignty influence the Compromise of 1850?

_____

_____

3 **GEOGRAPHY** Fill in the graphic organizer below to identify events and their influence on western expansion.

Historical Event	Impact on Western Expansion
Louisiana Purchase	
	gave people a sense of a God-given right to settle the West
Battle of San Jacinto	
	ended the war with Mexico and gave the United States a great deal of territory, including what is now California, Nevada, and Utah, and parts of Arizona, New Mexico, Colorado, and Wyoming

ESSENTIAL QUESTION

How should societies settle disputes?

As you gather evidence to answer the Essential Question, think about:

• the ways in which land was divided as Americans settled the West

• the main events and disputes that led to the Civil War

My Notes

_____

_____

_____

_____

_____

_____

_____

4A **IDENTIFYING CAUSE AND EFFECT** Use the graphic organizer below to outline some of the reasons that led Kansas to earn the name "Bleeding Kansas."

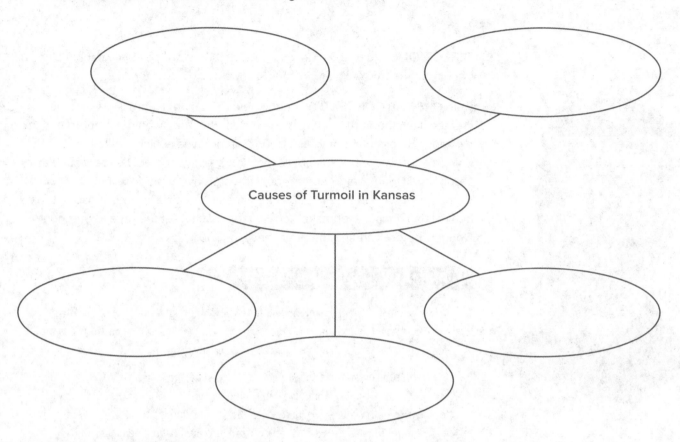

Causes of Turmoil in Kansas

4B **DETERMINING CONTEXT** How did the turmoil in Kansas reflect the struggle facing the entire country? Describe some of the key nationwide events that led to the secession of the South.

_____

_____

_____

_____

_____

Lincoln, Abraham. "Draft of Speech on Popular Sovereignty." May 18, 1858. Papers at the Library of Congress, Transcribed and Annotated by the Lincoln Studies Center, Knox College, Galesburg, Illinois. Accessed May 3, 2017. http://memory.loc.gov/cgi-bin/query/r?ammem/mal:@field(DOCID+@lit(d4339400))

ESSENTIAL QUESTION

How should societies settle disputes?

Draft of Speech on Popular Sovereignty

DIRECTIONS: Read the following excerpt from a speech by Abraham Lincoln. Then respond to the questions that follow.

EXPLORE THE CONTEXT: When the new territory of Nebraska was to be created, key southern leaders made it clear that they would not approve of its existence unless parts of the Missouri Compromise, which would have made Kansas a free state because of its location, were repealed. Leaders such as Stephen A. Douglas agreed to repeal the antislavery portion of the Missouri Compromise. Abraham Lincoln, at the time an obscure lawyer, spoke out against this Kansas-Nebraska Act. He later lost his senate race to Stephen A. Douglas before winning the presidency in 1860.

PRIMARY SOURCE: SPEECH

“Now, I take it, nearly everybody does care something about slavery—is either for it, or against it; and that the statesmanship of a measure which **conforms** to the sentiments of nobody, might well be doubted in advance—

But Nebraskaism did not originate as a piece of statesmanship—Gen. Cass, in 1848, invented it, as a political maneuver, to secure himself the democratic nomination for the presidency—It served its purpose then, and sunk out of sight—Six years later, Judge Douglas fished it up, and **glozed** it over with what he called, and still persists in calling 'sacred right of self-government'—

Well, I too, believe in self-government as I understand it; but I do not understand that the privilege one man takes of making a slave of another, or holding him as such, is any part of "self-government"—To call it so is, to my mind, simply absurd, and ridiculous—

I am for the people of the whole nation doing just as they please, in all matters which concern the whole nation; for those of each part, doing just as they choose, in all matters which concern no other part; and for each individual doing just as he chooses in all matters which concern no body else—

This is the principle—Of course I am content with any exception, which the Constitution, or the actually existing state of things, makes a necessity—

But neither the principle, nor the exception, will admit the indefinite spread and **perpetuity** of human slavery—

I think the true magnitude of the slavery element in this nation is scarcely appreciated by anyone—Four years ago the Nebraska policy was adopted, professedly, to drive the **agitation** of the subject into the territories, and out of every other place, and, especially out of Congress. ”

—from "Draft of Speech on Popular Sovereignty," by Abraham Lincoln, May 18, 1858

VOCABULARY

conforms: acts like others of a certain place and time

glozed: to gloss, or to glaze

perpetuity: time that continues forever

agitation: a state of anxiety or nervousness

1 **IDENTIFYING PERSPECTIVES** According to Lincoln, what motives did General Cass and Judge Douglas have for supporting "Nebraskaism"?

_____

_____

_____

_____

2 **COMPARING** What distinction does Lincoln make between his views and the views of others?

_____

_____

_____

_____

3 **CITING TEXT EVIDENCE** What are some of Lincoln's leadership characteristics? Cite evidence from the text to support your answer.

_____

_____

_____

_____

_____

_____

4 CIVICS How did government leaders use compromise in this situation?

_____

_____

_____

_____

5 **ANALYZING** Why do you think that Lincoln wrote that the Nebraska policy would be unable to "drive the agitation of the subject into the territories, and out of every other place, and, especially out of Congress"?

_____

_____

_____

_____

ESSENTIAL QUESTION

How should societies settle disputes?

Dred Scott v. Sanford

DIRECTIONS: Read the following excerpt from a court ruling. Then respond to the questions that follow.

EXPLORE THE CONTEXT: In 1846 Dred Scott and his wife, Harriet, sued for his freedom after having lived with his slaveholder in a free territory. His 11-year legal battle grew in significance as slavery became the dominant issue of the war. His case made it to the Supreme Court.

PRIMARY SOURCE: COURT RULING

" V. 1. The **plaintiff** himself acquired no title to freedom by being taken, by his owner, to Rock Island, in Illinois, and brought back to Missouri. This court has heretofore decided that the status or condition of a person of African descent depended on the laws of the State in which he resided.

2. It has been settled by the decisions of the highest court in Missouri, that by the laws of that State, a slave does not become entitled to his freedom, where the owner takes him to reside in a State where slavery is not permitted, and afterwards brings him back to Missouri.

Conclusion. It follows that it is apparent upon the record that the court below erred in its judgment on the plea **in abatement** and also erred in giving judgment for the defendant, when the exception shows that the plaintiff was not a citizen of the United States. And as the Circuit Court had no **jurisdiction**, either in the case stated in the plea in abatement, or in the one stated in the exception, its judgment in favor of the defendant is **erroneous**, and must be reversed. "

—from the *Dred Scott* Decision by Chief Justice Taney, 1857

VOCABULARY

plaintiff: a person who starts the complaint in a legal case

in abatement: made in error by failing to follow procedure

jurisdiction: the authority to explain and use the law

erroneous: mistaken

Chief Justice Taney, "Transcript of Dred Scott v. Sanford." The United States Supreme Court (1857)

1 **IDENTIFYING** Who ultimately had the power to decide the fate of Dred Scott?

_____

_____

_____

_____

2 **DETERMINING CENTRAL IDEAS** What was the Court's justification for denying Scott his freedom?

_____

_____

_____

_____

_____

3 **HISTORY** How do you think the _Dred Scott_ decision influenced the course of the country?

_____

_____

_____

_____

_____

4 **MAKING CONNECTIONS** What would you do if you disagreed with a decision made by the U.S. Supreme Court?

_____

_____

_____

_____

_____

The Civil War and Reconstruction

DIRECTIONS Search for evidence in Chapter 2, Lesson 2 to help you answer the following questions.

1A **IDENTIFYING** What was the Emancipation Proclamation?

_____

_____

_____

_____

1B **ANALYZING** How did Lincoln's issuance of the Emancipation Proclamation change the meaning of the war?

_____

_____

_____

_____

2A **IDENTIFYING CONNECTIONS** Describe new military technology. How did it impact soldiers during the Civil War?

_____

_____

_____

_____

2B **SUMMARIZING** What were some of the challenges facing battlefield physicians during the Civil War?

_____

_____

_____

_____

ESSENTIAL QUESTION

How should societies settle disputes?

As you gather evidence to answer the Essential Question, think about:

- ways in which the differing sides chose to fight for what they believed in
- some of the devastating effects of a major war

My Notes

_____

_____

_____

_____

_____

_____

_____

3 GEOGRAPHY As you read, use the graphic organizer below to record the advantages and disadvantages facing each side during the Civil War.

	Advantages	Disadvantages
North		
South		

4 DETERMINING CENTRAL IDEAS Complete the graphic organizer below with details about some of the major battles of the Civil War and their outcomes.

Battle	Details	Outcome
First Battle of Bull Run		
Antietam		
Vicksburg		
Gettysburg		

5 DESCRIBING What was Lincoln's plan for Reconstruction, and why did Radical Republicans oppose it?

_____

_____

_____

_____

ESSENTIAL QUESTION

How should societies settle disputes?

The Fourteenth Amendment

DIRECTIONS: Read the following amendment to the Constitution. Then respond to the questions that follow.

EXPLORE THE CONTEXT: After the Civil War, Congress submitted to the states three amendments guaranteeing equal civil and legal rights to African American citizens. They are the Thirteenth, Fourteenth, and Fifteenth amendments to the Constitution. The amendments were part of the Reconstruction process.

PRIMARY SOURCE: THE CONSTITUTION

❝AMENDMENT XIV Section 1.

All persons born or naturalized in the United States, and subject to the jurisdiction thereof, are citizens of the United States and of the State wherein they reside. No State shall make or enforce any law which shall **abridge** the privileges or **immunities** of citizens of the United States; nor shall any State **deprive** any person of life, liberty, or property, without due process of law; nor deny to any person within its jurisdiction the equal protection of the laws. ❞

—from the United States Constitution

VOCABULARY

abridge: reduce or make fewer

immunities: protections

deprive: to withhold from

① **DETERMINING CENTRAL IDEAS** What right was guaranteed by the Fourteenth Amendment? Which branch of government guaranteed this right?

_____

_____

_____

② **COMPARING** How does this amendment compare with the Supreme Court's ruling in *Dred Scott* v. *Sanford*?

_____

_____

_____

_____

3 **ANALYZING** Why do you think the writers of the amendment refer multiple times to single "States"?

_____

_____

_____

_____

4 CIVICS What other rights were extended by the Fourteenth Amendment? Cite evidence from the text to support your answer.

_____

_____

_____

_____

5 **COMPARING AND CONTRASTING** Fill in the graphic organizer with the primary purpose of the Thirteenth, Fourteenth, and Fifteenth Amendments.

Amendment	Purpose
Thirteenth	
Fourteenth	
Fifteenth	

ESSENTIAL QUESTION

How should societies settle disputes?

Circular No. 8 Regarding Requirements for Female Nursing Applicants; 7/14/1862; MM 1430; Court Martial Case Files, 12/1800 - 10/1894; Records of the Office of the Judge Advocate General (Army), Record Group 153; National Archives Building, Washington, D.C. [Online Version, https://www.docsteach.org/documents/document/circular-no-8-regarding-requirements-for-female-nursing-applicants, May 30, 2017]

Regarding Requirements for Female Nursing Applicants

DIRECTIONS: Read the following excerpt from a circular used to recruit nurses during the Civil War. Then respond to the questions that follow.

EXPLORE THE CONTEXT: Dorothea Dix served as the Superintendent of U.S. Army Nurses during the Civil War. Hoping to avoid any scandal that might occur with young unmarried women tending soldiers, Ms. Dix developed strict criteria for judging a woman's suitability for a nursing position.

PRIMARY SOURCE: CIRCULAR

❝ No candidate for service in the Women's Department for nursing in the military hospitals of the United States, will be received below the age of thirty-five years, (35) nor above fifty.

Only women of strong health, not subjects of **chronic** disease, nor liable to sudden illnesses, need apply. The duties of the station make large and continued demands on strength.

Matronly persons of experience, good conduct, or superior education and serious **disposition**, will always have preference; habits of neatness, order, sobriety, and **industry**, are **prerequisites**.

All applicants must present certificates of qualification and good character from at least two persons of trust, testifying to morality, integrity, seriousness, and capacity for the care of the sick.

Obedience to rules of service, and conformity to special regulations, will be required and enforced.

Compensation, as regulated by act of Congress, forty cents a day and subsistence. ❞

—from *Circular No.8 Regarding Requirements for Female Nursing Applicants* by Dorothea Dix

VOCABULARY

chronic: long-lasting

disposition: character, temperament

industry: hard work

prerequisites: qualifications, necessities

1 HISTORY From the information in this circular, what do we know about the role of women during this time in history?

_____

_____

_____

2 **EVALUATING EVIDENCE** Ms. Dix claims that there will be "continued demands on strength." What do you think some of those demands might be?

_____

_____

_____

3 **UNDERSTANDING CONTEXT** Forty cents per day in 1861 is approximately $10.60 in 2017. Why do you think women would undertake such serious and demanding work for "40 cents a day and subsistence"?

_____

_____

_____

_____

_____

4 **DESCRIBING** How would you describe the perfect candidate for the position advertised in the circular?

_____

_____

_____

5 **MAKING CONNECTIONS** The laws of the United States generally prohibit job discrimination based on age unless it can be shown that age corresponds to the performance of an essential duty of the position. Why do you think that the age requirement stated in this circular would be subject to a discrimination lawsuit today?

_____

_____

_____

ESSENTIAL QUESTION

How should societies settle disputes?

As you gather evidence to answer the Essential Question, think about:

- the different motivations people had for settling the West

- how various groups of people interacted with one another and with natural resources

My Notes

Miners and Ranchers

DIRECTIONS Search for evidence in Chapter 2, Lesson 3 to help you answer the following questions.

1A ANALYZING How did mining lead to the rise of boomtowns?

1B IDENTIFYING CAUSES Why were boomtowns rowdy?

2A GEOGRAPHY Which states joined the Union because of population growth based on mining?

2B RELATING EVENTS How did hydraulic mining affect the environment of these states?

3 **DRAWING CONCLUSIONS** Fill in the graphic organizer below with reasons the long cattle drive became popular.

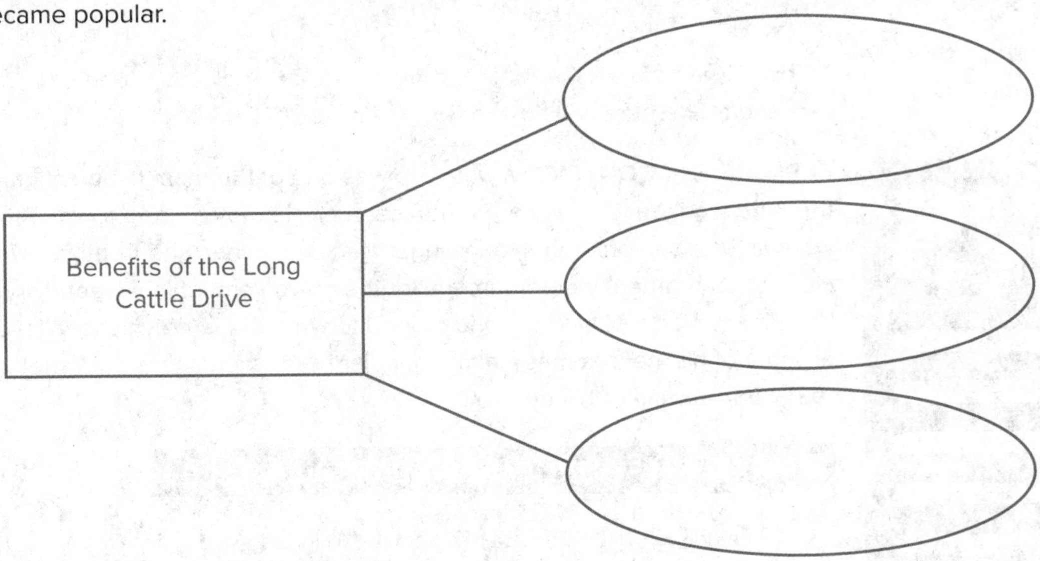

Benefits of the Long Cattle Drive

4A **IDENTIFYING** What was the result of the Treaty of Guadalupe Hidalgo?

_____

_____

_____

_____

4B **INFERRING** Was the Treaty of Guadalupe Hidalgo effective in settling the questions of the territory and rights of Mexican Americans?

_____

_____

_____

_____

ESSENTIAL QUESTION

How should societies settle disputes?

Earp's Frontier Life

DIRECTIONS: Read the following excerpt from a newspaper article. Then respond to the questions that follow.

EXPLORE THE CONTEXT: Wyatt Earp was one of the most famous figures of the American West in the nineteenth century. He moved from town to town working as a saloonkeeper, gunslinger, gambler, miner, and frontier lawman. He and his brothers were infamous for their involvement in violent disputes. Later he moved to California and helped to write the largely fictionalized account of his life that made him a popular hero when it was published in 1931, two years after his death.

PRIMARY SOURCE: NEWSPAPER ARTICLE

66 EARP'S FRONTIER LIFE. Leaves from the Whirling Past of a Man with a Remarkable Record. by Alfred Henry Lewis. Washington, Dec. 3, 1896—In the early eighties I was a neighbor of the Earp family. They **abode** at Tombstone, Ariz., and did much toward making the hamlet a thrilling place of residence. . . Wyatt Earp, and for that matter, all the Earps, were gunfighters and men of prompt and bitter courage. Wyatt Earp himself is credited with ten men; one his own brother-in-law, Clanton. Every one of the Earps had killed his men—not man—and were famed in Tombstone and in the Cochise country round about as qualified to pull and make a center shot in less than one-tenth of a second. They had all filed the sights from their six-shooters when I knew them in '81 and '82; and, in **eschewing** the intervention of a trigger, were prone to that prowess known as 'fanning' their pistols in a fight, whereby a Colt's six-shooter becomes for the nonce a miniature Gatling.

STAGE ROBBER LEADER In the early '80s there were two factions in Tombstone. Virgil and Wyatt Earp led one—the Stage Robbers. Johnny Behan, Ike Clanton, and Jack Ringo led the other—the Rustlers. The Stage Robbers were in politics Republican, and stood up stages and **plundered** express companies for a livelihood. The Rustlers were Democrats, and devoted themselves to cattle stealing, murder, whiskey, and **faro bank** as steady pursuits. In these days Johnny Behan was Sheriff of Cochise County and Virgil Earp was the Marshal of Tombstone. Behan, as stated, belonged to the Cow Thief Democracy party, while Earp robbed stages and voted with the Republicans. The Earps, Wyatt, Virgil, Warren, and Julian had treated themselves to many a killing. But there was no money in murder; nothing but relaxation. So they devoted themselves to holding up the stage. Virgil Earp had a combination with Barshel Williams, then the Wells-Fargo agent at Tombstone. When big money went out on the stage, Williams tipped it off to Virgil Earp. The hold-ups were then planted in a convenient canyon. When the stage came along, at the words, 'Hands up!' Warren Earp, who was a stage company guard, meekly put his hands over his head. There was never any shooting; it was from all standpoints a family affair on the part of the Earps. Often they got as high as $25,000. 99

—from "Earp's Frontier Life," by Alfred Henry Lewis,
New York Journal, December 4, 1896

VOCABULARY

abode: lived

eschewing: avoiding

plundered: stole from

faro bank: a place where the gambling card game faro is played

Lewis, Alfred Henry. "EARP'S FRONTIER LIFE." *New York Journal,* December 4, 1896.

1 **DETERMINING MAIN IDEAS** What impression does this article give you about the rule of law in western boomtowns?

_____

_____

_____

_____

_____

2 **INFERRING** What do the author's use of the words "thrilling" place to live and the Earps being "credited" with men tell you about their society at the time?

_____

_____

_____

_____

_____

3 **ECONOMICS** Why did the Earps shift their focus from murder to stage robberies? Cite evidence from the text to support your answer.

_____

_____

_____

_____

4 **DESCRIBING** How did politics play a role in the Earps' feud with the Rustlers?

_____

_____

_____

_____

The Treaty of Guadalupe Hidalgo

ESSENTIAL QUESTION
How should societies settle disputes?

DIRECTIONS: Read the following excerpt from a treaty and answer the accompanying questions.

EXPLORE THE CONTEXT: The Treaty of Guadalupe Hidalgo formally ended the war between the United States and Mexico. It was signed in 1848 at the city of Guadalupe Hidalgo, a city to which Mexicans had retreated because of the advance of U.S. forces. The treaty called for Mexico to cede 55 percent of its territory, including parts of present-day Arizona, California, New Mexico, Texas, Colorado, Nevada, and Utah, to the United States.

VOCABULARY
disposing: getting rid of

subjected: forced to undergo

inviolably: without exception

PRIMARY SOURCE: TREATY

❝ARTICLE VIII Mexicans now established in territories previously belonging to Mexico, and which remain for the future within the limits of the United States, as defined by the present treaty, shall be free to continue where they now reside, or to remove at any time to the Mexican Republic, retaining the property which they possess in the said territories, or **disposing** thereof, and removing the proceeds wherever they please, without their being **subjected**, on this account, to any contribution, tax, or charge whatever.

Those who shall prefer to remain in the said territories may either retain the title and rights of Mexican citizens, or acquire those of citizens of the United States. But they shall be under the obligation to make their election within one year from the date of the exchange of ratifications of this treaty; and those who shall remain in the said territories after the expiration of that year, without having declared their intention to retain the character of Mexicans, shall be considered to have elected to become citizens of the United States.

In the said territories, property of every kind, now belonging to Mexicans not established there, shall be **inviolably** respected. The present owners, the heirs of these, and all Mexicans who may hereafter acquire said property by contract, shall enjoy with respect to it guarantees equally ample as if the same belonged to citizens of the United States. ❞

—from the Treaty of Guadalupe Hidalgo, 1848

Treaty of Peace, Friendship, Limits, and Settlement with the Republic of Mexico, U.S.-Mex., February 2, 1848, 9 I.S. 929.

1 **IDENTIFYING** What options did Mexicans living in the newly acquired American land have?

_____

_____

_____

_____

2 CIVICS What was to happen to Mexicans who did not declare their intention one way or the other after a year?

_____

_____

_____

_____

3 **ANALYZING** In your opinion, were the treaty's attempts to protect the rights of Mexicans currently living in the newly acquired land enough?

_____

_____

_____

_____

4 **IDENTIFYING CONNECTIONS** Mexico is a border country and close ally of the United States. How would you describe the way in which our relationship has evolved since the time of the treaty?

_____

_____

_____

_____

Farming the Plains

DIRECTIONS Search for evidence in Chapter 2, Lesson 4 to help you answer the following questions.

1A **ECONOMICS** How did the conditions on the Great Plains lead to innovation?

_____

_____

_____

_____

1B **IDENTIFYING** What were some of the innovations that made farming on the Great Plains possible?

_____

_____

_____

_____

2A **DESCRIBING** What was the Homestead Act?

_____

_____

_____

_____

2B **RELATING EVENTS** How did the Homestead Act encourage settlers to move to the Plains?

_____

_____

_____

_____

ESSENTIAL QUESTION

How should societies settle disputes?

As you gather evidence to answer the Essential Question, think about:

- how the government attempted to control the settlement of the West
- what life was like as a homesteader on the plains

My Notes

_____

_____

_____

_____

_____

_____

3 **ANALYZING** As you read, use the graphic organizer below to analyze the advantages and disadvantages of settling in the West.

Advantages	Disadvantages

4 **IDENTIFYING CAUSES AND EFFECTS** Use the cause-effect graphic organizer below to explain the rise of tenant farming on the plains.

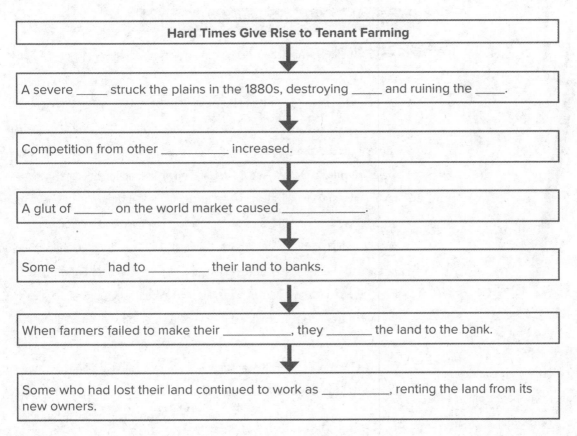

Hard Times Give Rise to Tenant Farming

⬇

A severe _____ struck the plains in the 1880s, destroying _____ and ruining the _____.

⬇

Competition from other _____ increased.

⬇

A glut of _____ on the world market caused _____.

⬇

Some _____ had to _____ their land to banks.

⬇

When farmers failed to make their _____, they _____ the land to the bank.

⬇

Some who had lost their land continued to work as _____, renting the land from its new owners.

5 **IDENTIFYING PERSPECTIVES** Why do you think Frederick Jackson Turner called the frontier a "safety valve of social discontent"?

_____

_____

ESSENTIAL QUESTION
How should societies settle disputes?

The Homestead Act

DIRECTIONS: Read the following excerpt from a piece of legislation. Then respond to the questions that follow.

EXPLORE THE CONTEXT: The Homestead Act was passed by Congress in order to encourage the settlement of western lands. It granted the adult head of a family 160 acres of public land for a minimal fee and a five-year commitment of continual residence. Despite the low price of the land, few farmers and ranchers could afford the materials necessary to build and run a farm. Most of the land went to speculators, cattlemen, miners, lumbermen, and railroads. Of the 500 million acres dispersed by the General Land Office between 1862 and 1904, only 80 million acres went to homesteaders.

PRIMARY SOURCE: LEGISLATION

❝CHAP. LXXV. —An Act to secure Homesteads to actual Settlers on the Public Domain.

Be it enacted by the Senate and House of Representatives of the United States of America in Congress assembled, That any person who is the head of a family, or who has arrived at the age of twenty-one years, and is a citizen of the United States, or who shall have filed his declaration of intention to become such, as required by the naturalization laws of the United States, and who has never **borne arms** against the United States Government or given aid and comfort to its enemies, shall, from and after the first January, eighteen hundred and sixty-three, be entitled to enter one quarter section or a less quantity of **unappropriated** public lands, upon which said person may have filed a preemption claim, or which may, at the time the application is made, be subject to preemption at one dollar and twenty-five cents, or less, per acre; or eighty acres or less of such unappropriated lands, at two dollars and fifty cents per acre, to be located in a body, in conformity to the legal subdivisions of the public lands, and after the same shall have been surveyed: Provided, That any person owning and residing on land may, under the provisions of this act, enter other land lying **contiguous** to his or her said land, which shall not, with the land so already owned and occupied, exceed in the aggregate one hundred and sixty acres. ❞

—from the Homestead Act of May 20, 1862

VOCABULARY

borne arms: fought, as in war

unappropriated: not chosen for a certain purpose

preemption: the right to buy before others

contiguous: next to, as in sharing a border

Act of May 20, 1862, ch. 75, 12 Stat. 392.

Copyright © McGraw-Hill Education

1 CIVICS In your opinion, was the Homestead Act clearly written?

_____

_____

_____

_____

_____

2 **ANALYZING** Why do you think the government wanted western lands to be settled?

_____

_____

_____

_____

_____

3 **IDENTIFYING POINT OF VIEW** Whose viewpoint was it that the land being distributed was "unappropriated"? Give an example of a group who may have had a different point of view.

_____

_____

_____

_____

_____

4 **DETERMINING CENTRAL IDEAS** Did the Homestead Act successfully help the poor?

_____

_____

_____

_____

Stewart, Elinore Pruitt. Letters of a Woman Homesteader. Boston: Houghton Mifflin Company, 1914.

Copyright © McGraw-Hill Education

ESSENTIAL QUESTION
How should societies settle disputes?

Letter of a Woman Homesteader

DIRECTIONS: Read the following letter. Then respond to the questions that follow.

EXPLORE THE CONTEXT: When Elinore Pruitt lost her husband in a railroad accident, she moved to Denver to find a way to make a living for herself and her two-year-old daughter, Jerrine. She began as a house cleaner and later became a housekeeper for a wealthy cattleman in Wyoming—Mr. Stewart, whom she eventually married. She wrote many letters to Mrs. Coney, her former employer in Denver, describing her life in the new territory.

PRIMARY SOURCE: LETTER

January 23, 1913

Dear Mrs. Coney,

. . . When I read of the hard times among the Denver poor, I feel like urging them every one to get out and file on land. I am very enthusiastic about women **homesteading**. It really requires less strength and labor to raise plenty to satisfy a large family than it does to go out to wash, with the added satisfaction of knowing that their job will not be lost to them if they care to keep it. Even if improving the place does go slowly, it is that much done to stay done. Whatever is raised is the homesteader's own, and there is no house-rent to pay. . . .

To me, homesteading is the solution of all poverty's problems, but I realize that **temperament** has much to do with success in any undertaking, and persons afraid of coyotes and work and loneliness had better let ranching alone. At the same time, any woman who can stand her own company, can see the beauty of the sunset, loves growing things, and is willing to put in as much time at careful labor as she does over the washtub, will certainly succeed; will have independence, plenty to eat all the time, and a home of her own in the end.

Experimenting need cost the homesteader no more than the work, because by applying to the Department of Agriculture at Washington he can get enough of any seed and as many kinds as he wants to make a thorough trial, and it doesn't even cost postage. Also one can always get bulletins from there and from the Experiment Station of one's own State concerning any problem or as many problems as may come up. I would not, for anything, allow Mr. Stewart to do anything toward improving my place, for I want the fun and the experience myself. And I want to be able to speak from experience when I tell others what they can do. Theories are very beautiful, but facts are what must be had, and what I intend to give some time.

Here I am boring you to death with things that cannot interest you! You'd think I wanted you to homestead, wouldn't you? But I am only thinking of the troops of tired, worried women, sometimes even cold and hungry, scared to death of losing their places to work, who could have plenty to eat, who could have good fires by gathering the wood, and comfortable homes of their own, if they but had the courage and determination to get them.

. . . .With much love to you from Jerrine and myself, I am

Yours affectionately,

Elinore Pruitt Stewart

—from *Letters of a Woman Homesteader*, by Elinore Pruitt Stewart

VOCABULARY

homesteading: living on and cultivating a tract of land received from the U.S. government

temperament: personality

1 ECONOMICS Would Elinore recommend homesteading to women? Cite evidence from the text to support your answer.

_____

_____

_____

2 SUMMARIZING According to Elinore, what kind of people are best suited for homesteading?

_____

_____

_____

3 INFERRING Does Elinore think Mrs. Coney is a good fit for homesteading?

_____

_____

_____

_____

_____

4 UNDERSTANDING CONTEXT Considering that this letter was written in 1913, what was unusual about Elinore Stewart?

_____

_____

_____

5 EVALUATING ARGUMENTS What do you think Elinore would say to someone who argues that homesteading is too difficult and too costly for the poor?

_____

_____

_____

_____

ESSENTIAL QUESTION

How should societies settle disputes?

As you gather evidence to answer the Essential Question, think about:

- the conflicts that arose between settlers and Native Americans
- what attempts were made to try to settle their disagreements

My Notes

Native Americans

DIRECTIONS Search for evidence in Chapter 2, Lesson 5 to help you answer the following questions.

1A **RELATING EVENTS** How was Native American society structured prior to the arrival of American settlers?

_____

_____

_____

1B **IDENTIFYING CAUSES** What led to Native American uprisings against the settlers?

_____

_____

_____

2A **EXPLAINING** What is "Americanization"?

_____

_____

_____

_____

2B **IDENTIFYING CONNECTIONS** How did boarding schools, the Dawes Act, the Citizenship Act, and the Indian Reorganization Act each promote or discourage Americanization?

_____

_____

_____

_____

_____

_____

3 GEOGRAPHY Use the graphic organizer below to record information about some of the conflicts between settlers and Native Americans.

	Reason	Action	Outcome
The Dakota Sioux Uprising			
Red Cloud's War			
The Sand Creek Massacre			
Advantages Battle of the Little Bighorn			
Tragedy at Wounded Knee			

4A IDENTIFYING What did the Indian Peace Commission propose?

_____

_____

_____

4B ANALYZING Why was the Indian Peace Commission's plan for peace doomed to failure?

_____

_____

_____

Smith, John. "Massacre of the Cheyenne Indians." In Report of the Joint Committee on the Conduct of the War at the Second Session Thirty-Eighth Congress, 85–86. Washington: Government Printing Office, 1865.

ESSENTIAL QUESTION
How should societies settle disputes?

Affidavit of John Smith

DIRECTIONS: Read the following excerpt from an affidavit. Then respond to the questions that follow.

EXPLORE THE CONTEXT: In 1864, tensions in Colorado were high between miners entering the territory and the Cheyenne and Arapaho groups already there. Native Americans raided the settlers' wagon trains and ranches, burning homes and killing an estimated 200 settlers. The governor persuaded the Native Americans to surrender. When Chief Black Kettle brought several hundred Cheyenne to Fort Lyon to negotiate a peace deal, Colonel John Chivington began an attack on the unsuspecting Native Americans known as the Sand Creek Massacre. The following affidavit was recorded in September 1864, two months before the Sand Creek Massacre.

VOCABULARY

inevitable: unable to avoid

retaliate: to fight back

depredations: attacks

PRIMARY SOURCE: AFFADAVIT

"Black Kettle, the head chief of the Cheyenne nation, replied as follows: . . . .While a hunting party of their young men were proceeding north in the neighborhood of South Platte river, having found some loose stock [cattle] belonging to white men, which they were taking to a ranch to deliver up, they were suddenly confronted by a party of United States soldiers and ordered to deliver up their arms. A difficulty immediately ensued which resulted in the killing and wounding of several on both sides.

A short time after this occurrence took place, a village of papooses, squaws, and old men, located at what is known as Cedar cañon a short distance north of the South Platte river, who were perfectly unaware of any difficulty having occurred between any portion of their tribe, Cheyenne, and the whites, were attacked by a large party of soldiers and some of them killed and their ponies driven off. After this, while a body of United States troops were proceeding from Smoky Hill to the Arkansas river, they reached the neighborhood of Lean Bear's band of the Cheyenne nation. Lean Bear, second chief of the Cheyenne nation, approached the column of troops alone, his warriors remaining off some distance, he not dreaming that there was any hostility between his nation and the whites. He was immediately shot down and fire opened upon his band, the result of which was a fight between the two parties. Presuming from all these circumstances that war was **inevitable**, the young men of the Cheyenne nation commenced to **retaliate**, committing various **depredations** all the time, which he, Black Kettle, and other principal chiefs of the Cheyenne nation were opposed to, and endeavored by all means in their power to restore pacific relations between that tribe and their white brethren; but, at various times when endeavoring to approach the military posts for the purpose of accomplishing the same, he was fired upon and driven off.

The young men of the Arapahoe nation, supposing it was the intention of the whites to make war upon them as well as the Cheyennes, also commenced retaliating, as well as they were able, and against the desire of most of their principal chiefs, who, as well as Black Kettle and other chiefs of the Cheyennes, were bitterly opposed to hostilities with the whites. "

—from "Report to Colonel Ford, Affidavit of John Smith," Fort Lyon Territory, January 15, 1865

1 ANALYZING POINT OF VIEW Whose perspective does this affidavit represent?

_____

_____

_____

2 IDENTIFYING According to Black Kettle, what initiated the fight between the settlers and Native Americans?

_____

_____

_____

_____

3 CITING TEXT EVIDENCE How can miscommunication lead to disputes? Cite evidence from the text to support your answer.

_____

_____

_____

_____

_____

4 CIVICS How would you describe Black Kettle's view of how to settle a dispute?

_____

_____

_____

_____

5 RELATING EVENTS How could the Sand Creek Massacre have been avoided?

_____

_____

_____

_____

ESSENTIAL QUESTION

How should societies settle disputes?

Educating the Indians—a Female Pupil of the Government School at Carlisle Visits Her Home at Pine Ridge Agency

DIRECTIONS: Examine the following illustration. Then respond to the questions that follow.

EXPLORE THE CONTEXT: In 1860, the Bureau of Indian Affairs began establishing boarding schools to further the process of Native Americans' "assimilation" and convince them to adopt the white people's beliefs and values. In 1879, Henry Pratt established Carlisle, one of the most well-known, off-reservation boarding schools. His motto was "Kill the Indian, Save the Man." Native American people often resisted their children's placement in these boarding schools. In some cases police forcibly seized children from their parents to enforce the policy of Americanization.

PRIMARY SOURCE: IMAGE

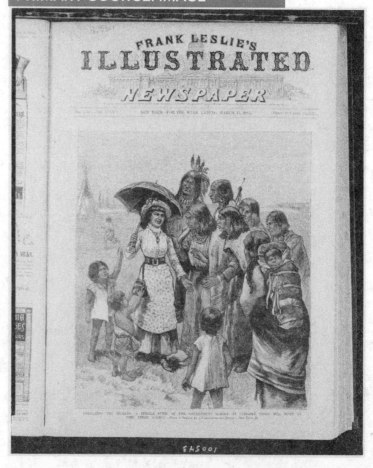

—from *Frank Leslie's Illustrated Newspaper*, March 15, 1884

1 **ANALYZING SOURCES** What techniques does the illustrator use to portray a social contrast?

_____

_____

_____

2 **IDENTIFYING BIAS** What possible biases might readers of this magazine have had as they interpreted this image?

_____

_____

_____

_____

3 GEOGRAPHY What do you think Henry Pratt meant by "Kill the Indian, Save the Man"?

_____

_____

_____

4 **DETERMINING CONTEXT** Why would this illustration be chosen for a magazine in 1884?

_____

_____

_____

5 **RESEARCHING FOR INQUIRY** What is the Pine Ridge Agency responsible for today? How does the government support Native Americans now? Research online and write your answer below.

_____

_____

_____

_____

ESSENTIAL QUESTION

How should societies settle disputes?

1 Think About It

Review the Supporting Questions that you developed at the beginning of the chapter. Review the evidence that you gathered in Chapter 2. Were you able to answer each Supporting Question?

If there was not enough evidence to answer your Supporting Questions, what additional evidence do you think you need to consider?

_____

_____

_____

2 Organize Your Evidence

Use a chart such as the one below to organize the evidence you will use to support your findings about how societies should settle disputes.

Dispute	What kind of action was taken to try and settle the dispute?	Was it successful?	Cite evidence from the text	

3 Write About It

Choose one of the conflicts from the graphic organizer. Write two paragraphs. In the first paragraph, briefly describe how the event actually unfolded. In the second paragraph, consider what steps would have had to occur to lead to a different result.

_____

_____

_____

_____

_____

_____

_____

_____

4 Connect to the Essential Question

Work in small groups. Briefly discuss the conflicts each group member chose and how they could have been resolved differently. Then, choose one of these conflicts that most interests the group. On a separate piece of paper, write the script for a play that helps to answer the ESSENTIAL QUESTION: *How should societies settle disputes?* Create three to five characters, including at least one historical figure. Your group can write the script as events actually unfolded or a script as events could have unfolded (either better or worse). Remember to be respectful when writing about different cultures.

Perform the skit for your class. Through your play, the audience should be able to understand the historical dispute and how it was handled or could have been handled.

_____

_____

_____

_____

_____

_____

CITIZENSHIP
TAKE ACTION

MAKE CONNECTIONS Societies have always dealt with disputes, and writers play an important role in highlighting and analyzing those issues. Think of examples from the chapter such as Helen Hunt Jackson, Frederick Jackson Turner, Frederick Williams, and Harriet Beecher Stowe. Writers today share their opinions through books, newspapers, or social media. Think of some of the disputes that are currently happening on a local or national level. Is there a dispute that you feel strongly about? Do you have ideas for a solution, or do you support solutions that are currently being discussed?

DIRECTIONS: Write a newspaper editorial to share your opinion about how a current dispute should be handled. Outline ways in which you think the dispute could be solved and steps that would need to be taken in order to carry out your plan. Urge others to support your solution. Volunteers may wish to share their editorials with the class.

Creating a Modern America

ESSENTIAL QUESTION

How did the United States become an industrialized society after the Civil War?

Think about how this question might relate to business, commerce, and forms of transportation and shipping.

TALK ABOUT IT

Discuss with a partner what type of information you would need to know to answer this question. For example, one question might be: Why are the events and ideas that occurred during this era so significant?

DIRECTIONS: Now write down three additional questions that you need to answer to explain the importance of the post–Civil War United States and the changes that occurred during this time.

MY RESEARCH QUESTIONS

Supporting Question 1:

_____

_____

Supporting Question 2:

_____

_____

Supporting Question 3:

_____

_____

Industry and the Railroads

DIRECTIONS Search for evidence in Chapter 3, Lesson 1 to help you answer the following questions.

1A ECONOMICS How did petroleum contribute to economic expansion in the United States?

_____

_____

_____

_____

1B DETERMINING CENTRAL IDEAS What factors contributed to the growing workforce, and therefore the economy, in the United States?

_____

_____

_____

_____

2A ANALYZING EVENTS What were some of Thomas Alva Edison's inventions, and how did they help improve people's lives?

_____

_____

_____

_____

2B ANALYZING EVENTS How did Lewis Latimer improve the standard of living?

_____

_____

_____

_____

ESSENTIAL QUESTION

How did the United States become an industrialized society after the Civil War?

As you gather evidence to answer the Essential Question, think about:

- how natural resources contributed to changes in industry.
- how new technology affected commerce and daily life.
- the principles of laissez-faire economics.
- the rise of the railroad industry.

My Notes

_____

_____

_____

_____

_____

_____

3 **CITING TEXT EVIDENCE** In what ways did the United States practice laissez-faire economics in the late 1800s?

_____

_____

_____

_____

4 **ECONOMICS** How did railroads spur economic growth?

_____

_____

_____

5 **DESCRIBING** Complete the graphic organizer by explaining how land grants and robber barons either contributed to or took from society.

Land grants	
Robber barons	

Morrill, Justin S. "The Tariff Bill." Speech of Hon. Justin S. Morrill, of Vermont, Delivered in the Senate of the United States, March 20, 1872. Washington: F. & J. Rives & Geo. A. Bailly, 1872.

ESSENTIAL QUESTION

How did the United States become an industrialized society after the Civil War?

VOCABULARY

tangible: real, concrete

discriminates: is biased

incidental: related, secondary

The Tariff Bill

DIRECTIONS: Read the following excerpt from a speech. Then answer the questions that follow.

EXPLORE THE CONTEXT: Justin Smith Morrill was a Republican from Vermont who served for 31 years as a U.S. senator. The following is from a speech Senator Morrill delivered to the U.S. Senate on March 20, 1872.

PRIMARY SOURCE: SPEECH

66 The only **tangible** benefit we can confer upon labor in this country is by a tariff that **discriminates** in favor of American industry, and our country is now, as it should be hereafter, among all nations the paradise of the laboring man. Not only does he here receive much greater wages, but taking into account the character and quality of his food, clothing, and lodgings, these, as a whole, are cheaper here than anywhere else. He can here support his family, and have more left for their education, travel, and taste than falls to the lot of any French, German, Italian, or English workman. So far as what is called 'revenue reform' conceals free trade under its cloak, it conceals a dagger aimed at the American laborer. The **incidental** protection given by our tariff—and the main purpose has been always to obtain revenue—has elevated labor throughout half the civilized world. 99

—from "The Tariff Bill," speech of the Honorable Justin S. Morrill of Vermont, 1872

1 **DETERMINING CENTRAL IDEAS** What is Senator Morrill promoting in his speech?

_____

_____

_____

_____

2 `ECONOMICS` Why does Senator Morrill consider the United States "the paradise of the laboring man"?

_____

_____

_____

_____

_____

3 **CITING TEXT EVIDENCE** Which sentence demonstrates that Senator Morrill believes the current economy affords Americans more luxuries than those living in other countries?

_____

_____

_____

_____

_____

4 **DETERMINING MEANING** What do you think Senator Morrill meant by "'revenue reform' conceals free trade under its cloak, it conceals a dagger aimed at the American laborer"?

_____

_____

_____

_____

_____

5 **MAKING CONNECTIONS** Do the principles Senator Morrill speaks about still apply to U.S. commerce and industry today?

_____

_____

_____

_____

_____

Nimmo, Jr., Joseph. Internal Commerce of the United States, submitted December 31, 1884. Washington: Government Printing Office, 1885.

ESSENTIAL QUESTION

How did the United States become an industrialized society after the Civil War?

Department of the Treasury on the Railroad

DIRECTIONS: Read the following excerpt from a government report. Then answer the questions that follow.

EXPLORE THE CONTEXT: The ever-expanding railroad had both positive and negative points. Railroads carried goods to distant places that were once hard to reach, but there was also little regulation of the railroad system. In some ways, the railroad system was much like any other large corporation, and people feared its power.

PRIMARY SOURCE: REPORT

66 Thus the railroad, with its vast possibilities for the advancement of the commercial, industrial, and social interests of the world, ran directly counter to the pre-existing order of things. But from the beginning the great efficiency of the railroad as a highway of commerce has **begotten** a public sentiment in favor of its **unimpeded** extension. From the time of the **inauguration** of railroad enterprises in Europe and in this country to the present day there has been, however, a deep feeling of public concern as to the possible or actual abuses of the powers granted to railroad companies touching the determination of transportation charges, such abuses having reference both to **exorbitant** rates and unjustly discriminating rates. The very fact that the conservative and self-regulating influences of competition on free highways was lacking on railroads implied the necessity of governmental supervision and regulation. 99

—from *Report On the Internal Commerce of the United States*, United States Department of the Treasury Bureau of Statistics, 1884

VOCABULARY

begotten: caused

unimpeded: not hindered

inauguration: creation

exorbitant: extremely high

1 **DETERMINING CENTRAL IDEAS** What does this report find about people's feelings concerning the railroad?

_____

_____

_____

2 `ECONOMICS` What was one key concern people had about the railroad?

_____

_____

_____

_____

3 **CITING TEXT EVIDENCE** What phrase from the excerpt supports your answer from Question 2?

_____

_____

_____

_____

4 **ANALYZING ISSUES** Why did the government feel the need to step in to supervise and regulate the railroads?

_____

_____

_____

_____

5 **MAKING CONNECTIONS** Do you believe the government should step in to regulate commerce or transportation in the twenty-first century? Explain your answer.

_____

_____

_____

_____

Big Business and Unions

DIRECTIONS Search for evidence in Chapter 3, Lesson 2 to help you answer the following questions.

1A **DETERMINING MEANING** What are economies of scale?

_____

_____

_____

_____

1B **CITING TEXT EVIDENCE** How did corporations achieve economies of scale?

_____

_____

_____

_____

2A **COMPARING** How is vertical integration and horizontal integration similar and different?

_____

_____

_____

_____

2B **ECONOMICS** How did Andrew Carnegie use vertical integration to expand the steel industry?

_____

_____

_____

_____

ESSENTIAL QUESTION

How did the United States become an industrialized society after the Civil War?

As you gather evidence to answer the Essential Question, think about:

- the differences between types of corporate structures.
- how Andrew Carnegie revolutionized the steel industry.
- why unions were met with such fierce resistance by businesses.

My Notes

_____

_____

_____

_____

_____

_____

_____

3 ANALYZING IDEAS Explain three ways that businesses tried to prevent or break up unions.

_____

_____

_____

4 INFERRING In the graphic organizer, write one cause and one effect that helped lead to laws that were friendlier to unions.

Cause	Effect

Miscellaneous Items in High Demand - Library of Congress - LC-USZ62-61237

Copyright © McGraw-Hill Education

ESSENTIAL QUESTION

How did the United States become an industrialized society after the Civil War?

The Great Railroad Strike of July 1887

DIRECTIONS: Study the image related to the Great Railroad Strike. Then respond to the questions that follow.

EXPLORE THE CONTEXT: When the Baltimore and Ohio Railroad announced it was cutting wages for the third time in July 1877, the workers fought back, first in Martinsburg, West Virginia, and then in other cities. Roughly 80,000 railroad workers went on strike in cities such as Chicago and New York City.

PRIMARY SOURCE: WOOD ENGRAVING

1 **DESCRIBING** Describe the scenes shown in the image.

_____

_____

_____

_____

2 **ANALYZING** How are the figures in the engraving depicted?

_____

_____

_____

_____

3 **INTEGRATING VISUAL INFORMATION** How is this engraving similar to the image illustrating "Coxey's Army" in the student text?

_____

_____

_____

_____

4 **DETERMINING POINT OF VIEW** How do you think the engraver felt about the railroad strikes?

_____

_____

_____

_____

5 CIVICS How do the actions in the engraving pertain to modern-day strikes?

_____

_____

_____

_____

Tarbell, Ida M. The History of the Standard Oil Company. Vol. 1. New York: McClure, Phillips & Co., 1904.

ESSENTIAL QUESTION

How did the United States become an industrialized society after the Civil War?

Ida M. Tarbell on Standard Oil

DIRECTIONS: Read the following excerpt from a book. Then respond to the questions that follow.

EXPLORE THE CONTEXT: Born in 1857, Ida M. Tarbell was an American journalist who led the way for what is now called investigative reporting. A price-fixing scheme in the 1870s, which involved John D. Rockefeller's Standard Oil Company, negatively affected her father, who made his living as an oil refiner and producer. Later, Tarbell's investigation into Standard Oil's practices led to the U.S. Supreme Court breaking up the oil giant's monopoly.

PRIMARY SOURCE: BOOK

❝Here he was shipping Eastward over one road between 4,000 and 5,000 barrels of refined oil a day—oil wrung from his neighbors by an outrageous conspiracy, men said bitterly. This feeling was still **keen** when Mr. Rockefeller and several of his colleagues in the South Improvement scheme suddenly, in May, 1873, appeared on the streets of Titusville. The men who had fought him so desperately now stared in amazement at the smiling, **unruffled** countenance with which he greeted them. Did not the man know when he was beaten? Did he not realise the opinion the Oil Regions held of him? His placid demeanor in the very teeth of their violence was **disconcerting**.❞

—excerpt from *The History of the Standard Oil Company*, by Ida M. Tarbell, 1904

VOCABULARY

keen: intense

unruffled: calm

disconcerting: disturbing

1 **EXPLAINING** What does Tarbell mean by the phrase "oil wrung from his neighbors by an outrageous conspiracy"?

_____

_____

2 **DETERMINING CENTRAL IDEAS** What does the reader know about the men of Titusville?

_____

_____

_____

_____

3 **ANALYZING INDIVIDUALS** What is the men's general opinion of Rockefeller?

_____

_____

_____

_____

4 **ANALYZING CENTRAL IDEAS** What does the sentence "The men who had fought him so desperately now stared in amazement at the smiling, unruffled countenance with which he greeted them" tell the reader about Rockefeller?

_____

_____

_____

_____

_____

5 ECONOMICS Do small businesses today have an easier time competing with large businesses? Why or why not?

_____

_____

_____

_____

_____

ESSENTIAL QUESTION

How did the United States become an industrialized society after the Civil War?

As you gather evidence to answer the Essential Question, think about:

- the role of immigrants in the expanding economy of the United States.
- the opposition immigrants faced as they tried to build better lives.
- the role the government played in both encouraging and preventing immigration.

My Notes

Immigration

DIRECTIONS Search for evidence in Chapter 3, Lesson 3 to help you answer the following questions.

1A **CONTRASTING** In which industries did Italian immigrants commonly work, and how did those industries compare to the industries in which Jewish immigrants commonly worked?

_____

_____

_____

_____

1B **COMPARING** In which industries did Polish immigrants commonly work, and how did these industries compare to those in which Italian and Jewish immigrants worked?

_____

_____

_____

_____

2A **COMPARING** How were Ellis Island and Angel Island similar?

_____

_____

_____

_____

2B **RELATING EVENTS** After immigrants left Ellis Island or Angel Island, where did they typically settle?

_____

_____

_____

_____

3 GEOGRAPHY Complete the Venn diagram by writing where the majority of immigrants in each state came from.

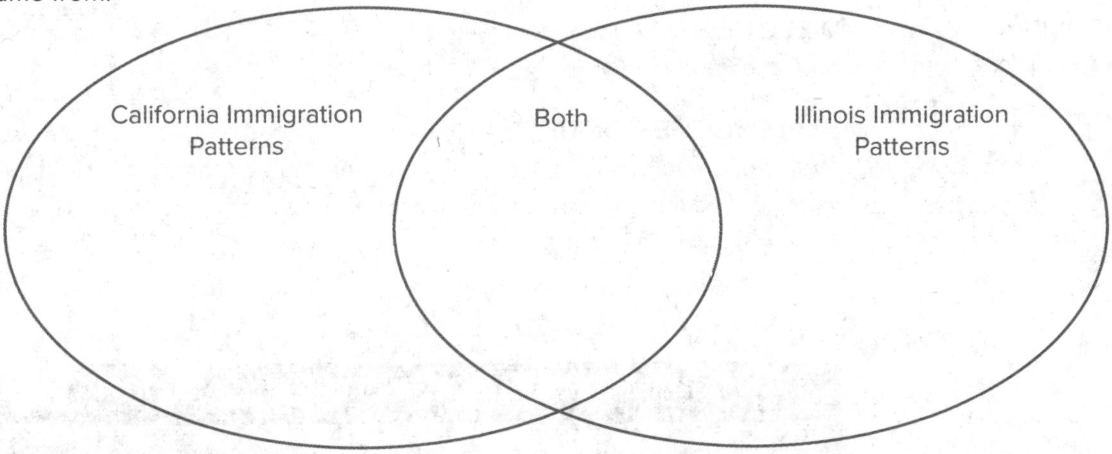

California Immigration Patterns | Both | Illinois Immigration Patterns

4 **ANALYZING IDEAS** What did the American Protective Association and the Workingman's Party of California stand for?

_____
_____
_____
_____

5 CIVICS How did the Chinese Exclusion Act of 1882 seek to prevent Chinese immigration?

_____
_____
_____
_____

How did the United States become an industrialized society after the Civil War?

Welcome to All!

DIRECTIONS: Read the following political cartoon. Then respond to the questions that follow.

EXPLORE THE CONTEXT: The post–Civil War era was filled with a great deal of upheaval. Among the changes to the United States was the influx of immigrants coming from many countries around the world. Political cartoons of the era depicted immigration in various ways.

PRIMARY SOURCE: POLITICAL CARTOON

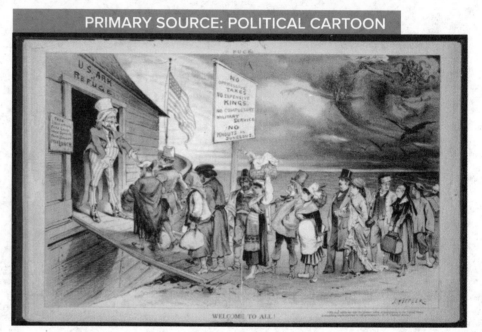

1 **DESCRIBING** Describe the scene shown in the image.

_____

_____

_____

2 GEOGRAPHY How are the immigrants depicted in the image?

_____

_____

_____

3 **ANALYZING SOURCES** What aspects of the cartoon allow you to draw this conclusion?

_____

_____

_____

4 **INTEGRATING VISUAL INFORMATION** How does the cartoon support the ideas in the Student Edition?

_____

_____

_____

5 **DETERMINING POINT OF VIEW** How do you think the artist felt about immigration?

_____

_____

_____

6 **MAKING CONNECTIONS** How do the ideas in the image pertain to modern-day immigration?

_____

_____

_____

Helper, Hinton R. The Land of Gold: Reality Versus Fiction. Baltimore: Henry Taylor, 1855.

ESSENTIAL QUESTION

How did the United States become an industrialized society after the Civil War?

VOCABULARY

enact: pass

liberal: free-thinking, broad-minded

intercourse: association, dealings

Hinton Rowan Helper on Chinese Immigration

DIRECTIONS: Read the following excerpt, written by North Carolina author and lecturer Hinton Rowan Helper. Then respond to the questions that follow.

EXPLORE THE CONTEXT: Southern antislavery advocate Hinton Rowan Helper had strong opinions on Chinese immigration. In his book *The Land of Gold* (1855), he presents his perspective.

PRIMARY SOURCE: BOOK

66 The general government, though it has sacrificed so much blood and treasure in acquiring California, is now so **liberal** that it refuses to **enact** a law imposing a tax upon foreign miners; and as a matter of course, it receives no revenue whatever from this source. But the Chinese are more objectionable than other foreigners, because they refuse to have dealing or **intercourse** with us; consequently, there is no chance of making any thing of them, either in the way of trade or labor. They are ready to take all they can get from us, but are not willing to give any thing in return. They did not aid in the acquisition or settlement of California, and they do not intend to make it their future home. 99

—from *The Land of Gold*, by Hinton Rowan Helper, 1855

1 **DETERMINING CENTRAL IDEAS** What is Helper's viewpoint on Chinese immigration?

_____

_____

_____

_____

2 CIVICS How does Helper feel about government intervention in Chinese immigration?

_____

_____

_____

_____

3 **DESCRIBING** Describe the mood of the excerpt.

_____

_____

_____

4 **DETERMINING POINT OF VIEW** Why does Helper consider Chinese immigrants to be "more objectionable than other foreigners"?

_____

_____

_____

_____

5 **COMPARING** Compare this excerpt to the political cartoon on the previous pages. What determination can you make about the public's sentiments on immigration during this era?

_____

_____

_____

_____

6 **MAKING CONNECTIONS** Are Helper's opinions in line with his antislavery stance? Why or why not?

_____

_____

_____

_____

_____

Urbanization and Social Reform

DIRECTIONS Search for evidence in Chapter 3, Lesson 4 to help you answer the following questions.

1A **EXPLAINING** How did businessmen respond to challenges caused by growing populations and rising land values?

_____

_____

1B **DETERMINING CENTRAL IDEAS** How did Chicago, Boston, and New York City respond to the growing problem of congestion?

_____

_____

_____

_____

2A **CONTRASTING** What were the lives of middle-class women like compared to the lives of immigrant women?

_____

_____

_____

_____

_____

2B **CONTRASTING** Were all working class people treated the same? If not, why?

_____

_____

_____

ESSENTIAL QUESTION

How did the United States become an industrialized society after the Civil War?

As you gather evidence to answer the Essential Question, think about:

- the downside to urbanization.
- the solutions to overcrowding in cities.
- the differences between social classes.
- the function of political machines.

My Notes

_____

_____

_____

_____

_____

_____

_____

3 UNDERSTANDING CHRONOLOGY Complete the graphic organizer below to explain the negative effects of urbanization.

| More people move to cities to find work. | > | | > | | > | |

4A EXPLAINING How was Darwin's theory of evolution adapted to social views?

_____

_____

_____

_____

4B ANALYZING IDEAS Why did Henry George's ideas spur reformers to challenge Social Darwinism?

_____

_____

_____

_____

5 DIFFERENTIATING How did writers and artists depict their fellow humans at the time? Complete the chart to answer the question.

Writers	Artists

ESSENTIAL QUESTION

How did the United States become an industrialized society after the Civil War?

Sweatshop Conditions

DIRECTIONS: Study the image and answer the accompanying questions.

EXPLORE THE CONTEXT: Factories were a critical part of the industrialization of the United States. Many people labored in what were called sweatshops, doing work by hand. The conditions were appalling, the hours were long, and the pay was low. However, sweatshop laborers had few options if they wanted to feed themselves and their families.

PRIMARY SOURCE: WOOD ENGRAVING

1 **DESCRIBING** Describe the scene shown in the image.

_____

_____

_____

_____

2 **ANALYZING SOURCES** What is the mood of the image?

_____

_____

_____

_____

3 GEOGRAPHY Based on information in the text, who might the people working in the image be?

_____

_____

_____

_____

4 **DETERMINING POINT OF VIEW** How do you think the artist felt about sweatshops? What leads you to this conclusion?

_____

_____

_____

_____

5 **MAKING CONNECTIONS** How do the conditions in modern-day workplaces differ from those of sweatshops such as the one shown here?

_____

_____

_____

_____

"Work of Carnegie," "The Labor World (Duluth and Superior, MN), Jan. 25, 1902."

ESSENTIAL QUESTION

How did the United States become an industrialized society after the Civil War?

VOCABULARY

Dunfermline: city in Scotland

disposal: use

aplication: (application), request

plea: reason, excuse

rebuff: rejection

The Work of Andrew Carnegie

DIRECTIONS: Read the following excerpt from a newspaper article about Andrew Carnegie. Then respond to the questions that follow.

EXPLORE THE CONTEXT: Born in 1835, Andrew Carnegie is the epitome of the "rags to riches" story. A Scottish immigrant who was part of the U.S. child labor force, Carnegie went on to make a fortune in the burgeoning steel industry. He was devoted to learning and used much of his money for philanthropic purposes. The excerpt below discusses Carnegie's boyhood.

PRIMARY SOURCE: NEWSPAPER ARTICLE

❝ His father was a Scotch Liberal, a weaver of **Dunfermline**, and was one of three men, all weavers, who, 75 years ago, gathered their little handful of books together, and placed them at the **disposal** of their fellow-workmen. . . . Andrew Carnegie made **aplication** for books, and was refused on the **plea** that he was not a 'working boy.' At that time clerks, telegraph operators, and other boys and young men not employed in mills, factories, or workshops were not regarded as 'working boys,' and as he was a telegraph operator young Carnegie was refused the privilege of the library. At this time young Carnegie, as he subsequently confessed, had a burning desire to become a reporter and subsequently the editor of a newspaper. He did not achieve his ambition, but he has always been exceedingly ready with his pen and tongue. Stung by his **rebuff** at the Allegheny library young Carnegie made an attack on that institution in the Pittsburg 'Dispatch,' over the signature 'Working Boy,' with such signal success that he forced the librarian to ask an interview, at which the differences were adjusted and Carnegie was admitted to its privileges on the score of being a 'working boy.' ❞

—from "Life of Carnegie," *The Labor World*, January 25, 1902

1 **ANALYZING STRUCTURE** Why does the author include information about Carnegie's father?

_____

_____

_____

2 CIVICS What does this experience tell you about educational opportunities in nineteenth-century society?

_____

_____

_____

_____

3 **ANALYZING POINT OF VIEW** How does the author likely feel about Carnegie?

_____

_____

_____

_____

4 **ANALYZING INDIVIDUALS** How does this incident relate to Carnegie's character in the business world?

_____

_____

_____

_____

5 **MAKING CONNECTIONS** Later in life, Carnegie funded the building of libraries all over the United States. What experience here might have affected his views on opportunity and access to information later in life?

_____

_____

_____

_____

_____

The Segregated Gilded Age

DIRECTIONS Search for evidence in Chapter 3, Lesson 5 to help you answer the following questions.

1A CIVICS What is patronage, and why did many Americans come to disagree with it?

_____

_____

_____

_____

ESSENTIAL QUESTION

How did the United States become an industrialized society after the Civil War?

As you gather evidence to answer the Essential Question, think about:

- the reforms to civil service.
- the workings of the Interstate Commerce Commission.
- how the federal government caused inflation.
- migration of African Americans.

1B CIVICS How did civil service reforms help working Americans?

_____

_____

_____

_____

2A **EXPLAINING** What were the benefits of the Interstate Commerce Commission?

_____

_____

_____

_____

_____

My Notes

_____

_____

_____

_____

_____

_____

2B **DESCRIBING** What were the drawbacks of the Interstate Commerce Commission?

_____

_____

_____

_____

_____

3 `ECONOMICS` Complete the graphic organizer below to explain how inflation occurred and was managed by the federal government.

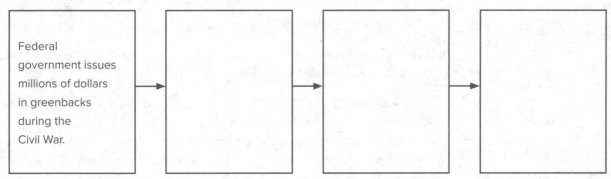

Federal government issues millions of dollars in greenbacks during the Civil War. → | → | → |

4 **DETERMINING CENTRAL IDEAS** Why did the Populist Party appeal to the working class?

_____

_____

_____

_____

5 `GEOGRAPHY` Complete the chart by explaining how each person fought to improve the lives of African Americans.

Benjamin "Pap" Singleton	
Ida B. Wells	
Mary Church Terrell	
Booker T. Washington	
W.E.B. Du Bois	

Cleveland, Grover. Letters and Addresses of Grover Cleveland. Edited by Albert Ellery Bergh. New York: The Unit Book Publishing Co., 1909.

ESSENTIAL QUESTION

How did the United States become an industrialized society after the Civil War?

President Grover Cleveland on "The Principles of True Democracy"

DIRECTIONS: Read the following excerpt from a speech. Then respond to the questions that follow.

EXPLORE THE CONTEXT: Grover Cleveland served as president of the United States from 1885 to 1889 and then again from 1893 to 1897. A reformer, President Cleveland advocated a policy that barred special favors being given to any economic group. He once vetoed a bill to distribute seed grain to Texan farmers whose land was experiencing drought because he did not want people to expect "paternal care on the part of the Government." He also sought to stop fraud by Civil War veterans in regard to pension claims. This speech was presented in 1891 at the Banquet of the Young Men's Democratic Association.

PRIMARY SOURCE: SPEECH

❝It is right that every man should enjoy the result of his labor to the fullest extent consistent with his membership in a civilized community. It is right that the influence of the Government should be known in every humble home as the guardian of frugal comfort and content, and a defense against unjust **exactions**, and the unearned tribute persistently coveted by the selfish and designing. It is right that efficiency and honesty in public service should not be sacrificed to **partisan** greed; and it is right that the **suffrage** of our people should be pure and free. The belief in these **propositions**, as moral truths, is nearly universal among our countrymen. We are mistaken if we suppose the time is distant when the clouds of selfishness and **perversion** will be dispelled and their **conscientious** belief will become the chief motive force in the political action of the people. ❞

—from *Letters and Addresses of Grover Cleveland*, speech by Grover Cleveland, 1891

VOCABULARY

exactions: things gotten or imposed by force

partisan: loyal to a political party

suffrage: the right to vote

propositions: beliefs or ideas

perversion: corruption

conscientious: wanting to do what's right

1 **DETERMINING CENTRAL IDEAS** What is President Cleveland's opinion on labor?

_____

_____

_____

_____

2 CIVICS How does President Cleveland view the government's purpose in the lives of the people it governs?

_____

_____

_____

3 **CITING TEXT EVIDENCE** What evidence can you cite from the excerpt to support your conclusion from Question 2?

_____

_____

_____

4 **ANALYZING TEXT** How does the repetition of the phrase "it is right" affect President Cleveland's speech?

_____

_____

_____

_____

5 **DETERMINING MEANING** What does President Cleveland mean when he says, "We are mistaken if we suppose the time is distant when the clouds of selfishness and perversion will be dispelled and their conscientious belief will become the chief motive force in the political action of the people"?

_____

_____

_____

6 **MAKING CONNECTIONS** In your opinion, how do President Cleveland's statements reflect upon contemporary society?

_____

_____

_____

Plessy v. Ferguson, 163 U.S. 537 (1896) [Transcription courtesy of FindLaw. http://caselaw.findlaw.com/court/us-supreme-court.]

ESSENTIAL QUESTION

How did the United States become an industrialized society after the Civil War?

Associate Justice John Marshall Harlan on *Plessy* v. *Ferguson*

DIRECTIONS: Read the following excerpt from a court case. Then respond to the questions that follow.

EXPLORE THE CONTEXT: In 1896, the U.S. Supreme Court upheld the notion of "separate but equal," which legally segregated people by race in public places. In the following excerpt, Associate Justice John Marshall Harlan, the son of a slaveholding family from Kentucky, gives his opinion on the ruling.

PRIMARY SOURCE: COURT DISSENT

❝I am of the opinion that the statute of Louisiana is inconsistent with the personal liberties of citizens, white and black, in that State, and **hostile** to both the spirit and the letter of the Constitution of the United States. If laws of like character should be enacted in the several States of the Union, the effect would be in the highest degree **mischievous**. Slavery as an **institution** tolerated by law would, it is true, have disappeared from our country, but there would remain a power in the States, by sinister legislation, to interfere with the blessings of freedom; to regulate civil rights common to all citizens, upon the basis of race; and to place in a condition of legal **inferiority** a large body of American citizens, now **constituting** a part of the political community, called the people of the United States, for whom and by whom, through representatives, our government is administrated. Such a system is inconsistent with the guarantee given by the Constitution to each State of a republican form of government. ❞

—from John Marshall Harlan's dissent to *Plessy* v. *Ferguson*, 1896

VOCABULARY

hostile: opposed

mischievous: harmful

institution: tradition

inferiority: a state of being less than something or someone else

constituting: making up

---

1   CIVICS   What is Associate Justice Harlan's view on the court ruling that "separate but equal" laws are constitutional?

_____

_____

_____

_____

2 **CITING TEXT EVIDENCE** What sentence or phrase from the excerpt leads you to your conclusion in Question 1?

_____

_____

_____

_____

3 **DETERMINING MEANING** Why does Associate Justice Harlan use the phrase "by sinister legislation"?

_____

_____

_____

_____

4 **ANALYZING IDEAS** What does Associate Justice Harlan mean when he says, "now constituting a part of the political community, called the people of the United States, for whom and by whom, through representatives, our government is administrated"?

_____

_____

_____

_____

5 **MAKING CONNECTIONS** Do Associate Justice Harlan's opinions seem to be in or out of character? What leads you to this conclusion?

_____

_____

_____

_____

_____

ESSENTIAL QUESTIONS

How did the United States become an industrialized society after the Civil War?

1 Think About It

Review the supporting questions that you developed at the beginning of the chapter. Review the evidence that you gathered in Chapter 3. Were you able to answer each Supporting Question?

If there was not enough evidence to answer your Supporting Questions, what additional evidence do you think you need to consider?

_____

_____

_____

_____

_____

2 Organize Your Evidence

Complete the chart below with information you learned about the industrialization of the United States.

The Industrialization of the United States		
Supporting Question 1 Details:	Supporting Question 2 Details:	Supporting Question 3 Details:

3 Talk About It

Work in small groups. Talk with your group about the information you included in your chart. Did you include the same evidence, or were your classmates' responses different from your responses? Which information is most important to understanding industrialization? Why?

_____

_____

_____

_____

4 Connect to the Essential Question

Work in small groups. On a separate piece of paper or on a computer, create a visual essay that answers the ESSENTIAL QUESTION: _How did the United States become an industrialized society after the Civil War?_ Use the graphic organizer from question two and what you discussed with your group to prepare your essay. Make your notes below. Draw or find photographs online that represent the various people, inventions, and events that helped the country become industrialized. Insert these images into your essay. Alternatively, you can locate pictures in hard copy sources. Be sure to add brief captions for each image that explain its importance.

_____

_____

_____

_____

_____

_____

_____

_____

_____

_____

_____

_____

_____

CITIZENSHIP
TAKE ACTION

MAKE CONNECTIONS The people who lived during the post-Civil War era fought hard to improve their lives as well as the lives of the generations to come. Although the 1950s and '60s are known as the time of the civil rights movement, many people during the post-Civil War era had already laid the groundwork. Because of their hard work, they made it possible for leaders such as Rosa Parks and Martin Luther King, Jr. to fight for equality and basic civil rights.

DIRECTIONS: Working with your teacher, invite a guest speaker to your class to talk about what life was like during times of inequality. For example, the speaker could be an Asian American who had family interred in camps during World War II or who fought alongside Martin Luther King, Jr. during the civil rights movement. The speaker might be a family member, a veteran, or a teacher at your school. He or she might also have immigrated to the United States from a country that did not offer equality to all its citizens. Before the speaker arrives, write a list of questions to help generate memories. Use the space below to draft your questions.

Becoming a World Power

ESSENTIAL QUESTION

How are empires built?

Think about how this question might relate to the United States and its relations with foreign countries. Why did the United States try to increase its influence with other countries? What steps did the country take to spread U.S. doctrine? What disputes arose as a result? How did government leaders and citizens handle those disputes?

TALK ABOUT IT

Discuss with a partner the type of information you would need to know to answer these questions. For example, one question might be: *What did the United States do to expand its influence around the world?*

DIRECTIONS: Now write three additional questions that would help you describe the steps the United States took to increase its influence beyond its borders.

MY RESEARCH QUESTIONS

Supporting Question 1:

_____

_____

_____

Supporting Question 2:

_____

_____

_____

Supporting Question 3:

_____

_____

_____

The Imperialist Vision

DIRECTIONS Search for evidence in Chapter 4, Lesson 1 to help you answer the following questions.

1A **SUMMARIZING** What was the central idea behind imperialism?

_____

_____

_____

_____

1B **IDENTIFYING CAUSES** What factors led to U.S. imperialism?

_____

_____

_____

_____

2A **IDENTIFYING CONNECTIONS** What was the basic premise of Anglo-Saxonism, and how did it relate to imperialism?

_____

_____

_____

_____

2B **DRAWING CONCLUSIONS** In what ways did Christianity support the theory of Anglo-Saxonism?

_____

_____

_____

_____

_____

ESSENTIAL QUESTION

How are empires built?

As you gather evidence to answer the Essential Question, think about:

- the influence of European imperialism on the United States
- U.S. influence around the globe in the nineteenth and early twentieth centuries

My Notes

_____

_____

_____

_____

_____

_____

3 IDENTIFYING CAUSES Use the graphic organizer below to outline some of the reasons Congress authorized the building of a modern navy.

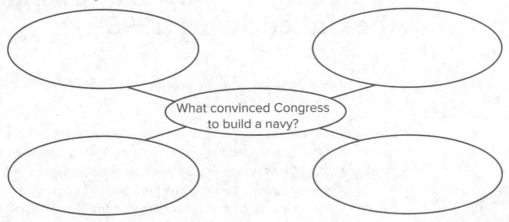

What convinced Congress to build a navy?

4 INFERRING Why did Japan's rulers fear Western influence?

_____

_____

_____

5 SUMMARIZING Complete the flow chart to explain the events leading to the annexation of Hawaii.

_____ grew well in Hawaii, and planters began establishing sugar _____.

↓

In _____, the United States signed a treaty that exempted Hawaiian sugar from _____.

↓

In _____, Sanford _____ and a group of sugar planters forced the Hawaiian king to sign a new _____, thereby limiting the king's authority.

↓

In 1891, Queen _____ tried to regain power but was overthrown by the _____.

↓

In _____, U.S. President _____ approved the annexation of Hawaii.

6 GEOGRAPHY How did geography affect American imperialism?

_____

_____

_____

_____

_____

ESSENTIAL QUESTION
How are empires built?

Joint Resolution to Provide for Annexing the Hawaiian Islands to the United States (1898)

DIRECTIONS: Read the following excerpt from a joint resolution of Congress. Then respond to the questions that follow.

EXPLORE THE CONTEXT: The reach of American imperialism in the mid-nineteenth century extended not only to industrialized countries, but also to nearby islands such as Hawaii and Samoa. The sugar industry in the Hawaiian Islands grew rapidly and attracted a number of white settlers. These settlers placed increasing pressure on the Hawaiian monarchy, eventually leading to the overthrow of Hawaiian Queen Liliuokalani in 1891. In 1898, under the administration of President William McKinley, the United States annexed the Hawaiian Islands.

PRIMARY SOURCE: TRANSCRIPT OF JOINT RESOLUTION

66 Whereas, the Government of the Republic of Hawaii having, in due form, signified its consent, in the manner provided by its constitution, to cede absolutely and without reserve to the United States of America, all rights of **sovereignty** of whatsoever kind in and over the Hawaiian Islands and their dependencies, and also to **cede** and transfer to the United States, the absolute fee and ownership of all public, Government, or Crown lands, public buildings or edifices, ports, harbors, military equipment, and all other public property of every kind and description belonging to the Government of the Hawaiian Islands, together with every right and appurtenance thereunto appertaining. Therefore, resolved by the Senate and House of Representatives of the United States of America in Congress assembled, That said cession is accepted, **ratified**, and confirmed, and that the said Hawaiian Islands and their dependencies be, and they are hereby, annexed as a part of the territory of the United States and are subject to the sovereign dominion thereof, and that all and singular the property and rights hereinbefore mentioned are **vested** in the United States of America. 99

—from the law that annexed the Hawaiian Islands to the United States, 1898

VOCABULARY
cede: to transfer, usually via treaty

sovereignty: self-rule, free of outside control

ratified: formally approved

vested: guaranteed as a legal right or privilege

Hartwell, Alfred S. "The Organization of a Territorial Government for Hawaii." Yale Law Journal 9, no. 3 (1899): 107-113.

1 ANALYZING INFORMATION What benefits did the annexation of Hawaii offer to the United States?

_____

_____

_____

_____

2 INTERPRETING What does "the Government of the Republic of Hawaii . . . signified its consent" mean?

_____

_____

_____

_____

3 CONSTRUCTING HYPOTHESES What did the annexation mean to native Hawaiians?

_____

_____

_____

_____

_____

4 GEOGRAPHY Why was Hawaii a strategic location for the United States?

_____

_____

_____

_____

5 DRAWING CONCLUSIONS In what ways is this transcript an example of American imperialism?

_____

_____

_____

_____

ESSENTIAL QUESTION
How are empires built?

Our Foreign Policy (1900)

DIRECTIONS: Read the following excerpt from a magazine article. Then respond to the questions that follow.

EXPLORE THE CONTEXT: Richard Olney's article, published in *The Atlantic Monthly* in March 1900, discusses the abandonment by the United States of its policy of isolationism at the turn of the century. At the time this article was published, the United States had already annexed Hawaii, built a powerful navy, and generally became a stronger presence on the world stage.

PRIMARY SOURCE: MAGAZINE ARTICLE

66 The substitution of international fellowship—the change from **passive** . . . membership of the society of civilized states to real and active membership—is to be **ascribed** . . . above all to that instinct and impulse in the line of national growth and expansion whose absence would be a sure symptom of our national deterioration. For it is true of states as of individuals—they never stand still, and if not going forward, are surely **retrogressing**. This evolution of the United States as one of the great Powers among the nations has, however, been accompanied by another departure **radical** in character and far-reaching in consequences. The United States has come out of its shell and ceased to be a **hermit** among the nations, naturally and properly. What was not necessary and is certainly of the most doubtful **expediency** is that it should at the same time become a colonizing Power on an immense scale. 99

—from "Our Foreign Policy," published in
The Atlantic Monthly, March 1900

VOCABULARY

passive: not active

ascribed: credited

retrogressing: moving backward

radical: very different

hermit: one who is alone, removed from others

expediency: convenience

---

1 **ANALYZING SOURCES** According to Olney, what is necessary to prevent a nation from deteriorating?

_____

_____

2 **INFERRING** What surprises Olney about the behavior of the U.S. government?

_____

_____

_____

_____

_____

3 **IDENTIFYING BIAS** In general, how does Olney feel about America's foreign policy?

_____

_____

_____

_____

_____

4 **DISTINGUISHING FACT FROM OPINION** In the early twentieth century, could the United States truly be considered a "colonizing power," as Olney claims?

_____

_____

_____

_____

_____

5 **GEOGRAPHY** How does this article relate to the notion of empire building?

_____

_____

_____

_____

_____

The Spanish-American War

DIRECTIONS Search for evidence in Chapter 4, Lesson 2 to help you answer the following questions.

1A **SUMMARIZING** What was the main purpose of "yellow journalism"?

_____

_____

_____

_____

1B **INTERPRETING** How did yellow journalism sway public opinion about conditions in Cuba?

_____

_____

_____

_____

_____

2A **ANALYZING INFORMATION** What were relations like between Spain and the United States a few months before war was declared? What did both countries do?

_____

_____

_____

_____

_____

2B **IDENTIFYING CAUSES** What were some of the reasons the United States went to war with Spain over Cuba?

_____

_____

_____

_____

ESSENTIAL QUESTION

How are empires built?

As you gather evidence to answer the Essential Question, think about:

- what caused the United States to go to war with Spain over Cuba
- U.S. expansion into Asia

My Notes

_____

_____

_____

_____

_____

_____

3 **EXPLAINING CAUSES** Why did the United States get involved in the Philippines when the war was about Cuba?

_____

_____

_____

_____

4 **CONTRASTING** Complete the graphic organizer to answer the following question: What were some of the reasons people supported or opposed the annexation of the Philippines by the United States?

Supported Annexation	Opposed Annexation

5 GEOGRAPHY How did the annexation of the Philippines, Guam, and Puerto Rico contribute to the expansion of the "American empire"?

_____

_____

_____

ESSENTIAL QUESTION
How are empires built?

Proposed Intervention in Cuba (1875)

DIRECTIONS: Read the following excerpt from a letter. Then respond to the questions that follow.

EXPLORE THE CONTEXT: The following excerpt is from a letter written by U.S. Secretary of State Hamilton Fish in 1875, to Caleb Cushing, minister to Spain. In it, Fish relates President Ulysses S. Grant's desire for Spain to end hostilities in Cuba. It would be another 23 years before the United States declared war on Spain in the Spanish-American War.

PRIMARY SOURCE: LETTER

66 The President hopes that Spain may spontaneously adopt measures looking to a **reconciliation**, and to the speedy restoration of peace, and the organization of a stable and satisfactory system of government in the island of Cuba. In the absence of any **prospect** of a termination of the war, or of any change in the manner in which it has been conducted on either side, he feels that the time is at hand when it may be the duty of other governments to **intervene**, solely with the view of bringing to an end a disastrous and destructive conflict, and of restoring peace in the island of Cuba. No government is more deeply interested in the order and peaceful **administration** of this island than is that of the United States, and none has suffered as has the United States from the condition which has obtained there during the past six or seven years. He will, therefore, feel it his duty at an early day to submit the subject in this light, and accompanied by an expression of the views above presented, for the consideration of Congress. 99

—from a letter written by U.S. Secretary of State Hamilton Fish to Caleb Cushing, 1875

VOCABULARY

reconciliation: having good relations restored

intervene: to get involved

prospect: potential; possibility

administration: daily operations

1 **IDENTIFYING PERSPECTIVES** How can you determine from whose perspective this letter was written?

_____

_____

_____

Fish, Hamilton. "Proposed Intervention in Cuba (1875)." House Executive Documents, 44 Cong., I sess., (Washington, 1876), XII, No. 90), 3–11, quoted in American History Told by Contemporaries: Volume IV, Welding of the Nation: 1845–1900, edited by Albert Bushnell Hart, (New York: The Macmillan Company, 1909), 557–561.

2 **ANALYZING SOURCES** What is Secretary Fish referring to when he claims, "no government . . . has suffered as has the United States from the condition which has obtained [in Cuba] during the past six or seven years"?

_____

_____

_____

_____

3 GEOGRAPHY Why was Cuba so important to the United States geographically?

_____

_____

_____

_____

4 **INFERRING** Why was the United States prepared to "intervene" in the conflict in Cuba?

_____

_____

_____

_____

5 **DRAWING CONCLUSIONS** How did the United States use Cuba to further American imperialism?

_____

_____

_____

_____

ESSENTIAL QUESTION
How are empires built?

The Platt Amendment (1901)

DIRECTIONS: Read the following excerpt from legislation. Then answer the questions that follow.

EXPLORE THE CONTEXT: At the gathering of the Fifty-sixth Congress in 1901, The Platt Amendment, written by Secretary of War Elihu Root and submitted by Senator Orville Platt, detailed the terms of Cuba's independence. Although it was considered independent, Cuba was tied to the United States and had to meet certain conditions in order to remain so.

PRIMARY SOURCE: STATUTE

❝ Provided further, that in fulfillment of the declaration contained in the **joint resolution** approved April twentieth, eighteen hundred and ninety-eight, entitled 'For the recognition of the independence of the people of Cuba, demanding that the Government of Spain **relinquish** its authority and government in the island of Cuba, and withdraw its land and naval forces from Cuba and Cuban waters, and directing the President of the United States to use the land and naval forces of the United States to carry these resolutions into effect,' the President is hereby authorized to 'leave the government and control of the island of Cuba to its people' so soon as a government shall have been established in said island under a **constitution** which, either as a part thereof or in an **ordinance** appended thereto, shall define the future relations of the United States with Cuba. ❞

—from the Platt Amendment, 1901

VOCABULARY

joint resolution: an agreement passed by both the Senate and the House of Representatives

relinquish: give up

constitution: set of principles and laws

ordinance: law established by government authority

1 **ANALYZING SOURCES** What does the following phrase say about the status of the United States during this time period: "directing the President of the United States to use the land and naval forces of the United States to carry these resolutions into effect"?

_____

_____

_____

_____

2 ECONOMICS What were the economic benefits of maintaining good relations with Cuba?

_____

_____

_____

_____

_____

3 **INFERRING** What incentive did Cuba have to establish its own form of government?

_____

_____

_____

_____

_____

4 **UNDERSTANDING CONTEXT** Why did the United States impose such strict conditions on Cuba in the Platt Amendment?

_____

_____

_____

_____

_____

_____

5 **DRAWING CONCLUSIONS** Based on this excerpt, do you believe the United States was justified in enforcing the Platt Amendment?

_____

_____

_____

_____

_____

_____

ESSENTIAL QUESTION

How are empires built?

As you gather evidence to answer the Essential Question, think about:

- U.S. foreign policy actions
- U.S. relations with South America

My Notes

_____

_____

_____

_____

_____

_____

_____

New American Diplomacy

DIRECTIONS Search for evidence in Chapter 4, Lesson 3 to help you answer the following questions.

1A **SUMMARIZING** What was the sequence of events that led to the Open Door policy?

_____

_____

_____

_____

_____

_____

_____

1B **IDENTIFYING EFFECTS** What were some of the consequences of the Open Door Policy?

_____

_____

_____

_____

2A **DESCRIBING** How did the building of the Panama Canal spread U.S. influence to other nations?

_____

_____

_____

_____

2B **GEOGRAPHY** In what ways did Panama's geography challenge the builders of the Panama Canal?

_____

_____

_____

_____

3 EVALUATING Complete the graphic organizer to answer this question: How did the Roosevelt Corollary benefit the United States?

How did the Roosevelt Corollary benefit the United States?

4 ECONOMICS What were President Taft's motivations in implementing Dollar Diplomacy?

_____

_____

_____

_____

5 DRAWING CONCLUSIONS How did President Wilson's Mexican policy damage U.S. foreign relations?

_____

_____

_____

_____

ESSENTIAL QUESTION
How are empires built?

"Second Annual Message" by President McKinley

DIRECTIONS: Read the following excerpt from a speech. Then answer the questions that follow.

EXPLORE THE CONTEXT: On December 5, 1898, President William McKinley addressed the Senate and House of Representatives outlining his Open Door policy that would allow the United States and European countries to trade freely with China and in each other's sphere of influence. The Open Door policy was adopted by European countries the following year. The following is an excerpt from that speech.

PRIMARY SOURCE: SPEECH

66 The United States has not been an indifferent spectator of the extraordinary events **transpiring** in the Chinese Empire, whereby portions of its **maritime** provinces are passing under the control of various European powers; but the prospect that the vast commerce which the energy of our citizens and the necessity of our staple productions for Chinese uses has built up in those regions may not be prejudiced through any exclusive treatment by the new occupants has **obviated** the need of our country becoming an actor in the scene. Our position among nations, having a large Pacific coast and a constantly expanding direct trade with the farther Orient, gives us the equitable claim to consideration and friendly treatment in this regard, and it will be my aim to **subserve** our large interests in that quarter by all means appropriate to the constant policy of our Government. The territories of Kiao-chow, of Wei-hai-wei, and of Port Arthur and Talienwan, leased to Germany, Great Britain, and Russia, respectively, for terms of years, will, it is announced, be open to international commerce during such alien occupation; and if no discriminating treatment of American citizens and their trade be found to exist or be hereafter developed, the desire of this Government would appear to be realized. 99

—from a speech given by President William McKinley in 1898

VOCABULARY

transpiring: happening

maritime: bordering the ocean

obviated: prevented

subserve: carry out

McKinley, William. "Second Annual Message." In *A Compilation of the Messages and Papers of the Presidents 1789–1897*, edited by James D. Richardson, 160–201. Washington: Government Printing Office, 1899.

1 **ANALYZING SOURCES** What does President McKinley mean when he says "the United States has not been an indifferent spectator"?

_____

_____

_____

2 **INTERPRETING** What is President McKinley's intent in this excerpt?

_____

_____

_____

_____

3 ECONOMICS How does McKinley's plan promote the idea of American imperialism?

_____

_____

_____

_____

_____

4 **ANALYZING CHANGE** In your opinion, how has trade between the United States and China changed over the last century?

_____

_____

_____

_____

5 GEOGRAPHY According to McKinley, what geographic feature of the United States encourages trade with China?

_____

_____

_____

_____

ESSENTIAL QUESTION
How are empires built?

Dollar Diplomacy and Imperialism

DIRECTIONS: Read the following excerpt of a speech. Then answer the questions that follow.

EXPLORE THE CONTEXT: On June 1, 1917, Commissioner of Immigration Frederic C. Howe delivered the following address at the National Conference on Foreign Relations of the United States in New York City. In this excerpt, Howe questions the aim of U.S. foreign policy in the second decade of the twentieth century.

PRIMARY SOURCE: SPEECH

66 Should not democracy establish the **doctrine** that the flag is a symbol of liberty rather than of **subjection**; that it will safeguard liberty rather than destroy it; and that other peoples—no matter what their stage of development may be—have equal right with ourselves to establish and maintain their governments free from outside interference? . . . Briefly, it seems to me this country should reaffirm the principles laid down by President Wilson . . . The United States, it should be stated, is not a collection agency; we are not in the insurance business. Moreover, our declarations and efforts should be toward establishing and securing freedom for all nations, be they in Europe or elsewhere; and especially for those nations which have lost their freedom through the activities of individuals and corporations engaged in overseas finance. Political freedom is as priceless to the yellow race or the black race as it is to the white. And the subjection of nations and countries in the interest of **exploitation** has less to defend it than any other claim of imperialism thus far put forth. 99

—from a speech given by Frederic C. Howe

VOCABULARY

doctrine: principle

subjection: a state of being under control

exploitation: the act of taking advantage

1 **CIVICS** What is Howe suggesting in this excerpt?

_____

_____

_____

_____

Howe, Frederic C. "Dollar Diplomacy and Imperialism." In Proceedings of the Academy of Political Science in the City of New York July, 1917: Part I, edited by Henry Raymond Mussey and Stephen Pierce Duggan, (597)-(603). New York: Columbia University, 1917. The Foreign Relations of the United States

2 INTERPRETING What does Howe mean when he claims "the United States . . . is not a collection agency"?

_____

_____

_____

_____

3 IDENTIFYING CONNECTIONS What is the connection between Dollar Diplomacy and imperialism in this excerpt?

_____

_____

_____

_____

4 CONTRASTING In what fundamental way does Howe's version of diplomacy under President Wilson differ from President Taft's earlier version of Dollar Diplomacy?

_____

_____

_____

_____

5 CITING TEXT EVIDENCE What is Howe's belief regarding other races? Cite text evidence in your response.

_____

_____

_____

_____

ESSENTIAL QUESTIONS
How are empires built?

① Think About It

Review the Supporting Questions you developed at the beginning of the chapter. Review the evidence that you gathered in Chapter 4. Were you able to answer each Supporting Question?

If there was not enough evidence to answer your Supporting Questions, what additional evidence do you think you need to consider?

_____

_____

_____

_____

② Organize Your Evidence

Use a chart such as the one below to organize the evidence you will use to support your findings about how empires are built.

Method of Imperialism	What steps were taken to implement this method?	Was it successful?	Cite evidence from the text

3 Talk About It

Work in small groups. Talk with your group about the different types of imperialism you noted in your chart. Specifically, discuss: *Which method of imperialism was the most effective? Which one was the least effective?* On the lines below, take notes from the group discussion.

_____

_____

_____

_____

_____

_____

4 Connect to the Essential Question

Using a mix of primary and secondary sources and your notes from the group discussion, choose the method of imperialism that you believe worked best for the United States. On a separate piece of paper, write a persuasive essay to explain your position and to help answer the ESSENTIAL QUESTION: *How are empires built?*

1. State the reasons your chosen method is superior to other methods of imperialism.

2. Explain why the method you chose was the most effective way to build an empire and extend the influence of the United States across the globe.

3. Describe the benefits of this method for the United States as well as for the foreign countries that came under its influence.

_____

_____

_____

_____

_____

_____

_____

_____

_____

CITIZENSHIP
TAKING ACTION

MAKE CONNECTIONS Imperialism has taken on many forms since the mid-nineteenth century. The United States and other industrialized nations wielded economic, political and military power to assert their dominance over other countries and to spread their influence across the world. The legacy of imperialism still lingers in the twenty-first century in different forms. Beginning in the 1950s, the rise of consumerism—spearheaded by the United States—ushered in a new form of imperialism based on the purchase of consumer goods and services. Today, McDonalds, Nike, Coca-Cola, and Apple are just a few of the global American brands that have spread American culture and values to every corner of the globe.

DIRECTIONS: Pick one American brand you feel has had a long-lasting positive impact not only on the United States, but also on the world as a whole. For this activity, consider yourself an "ambassador" for this brand. Write a speech that you will address to the class, much in the same way a U.S. president addressed Congress to promote an imperialist agenda. In the speech, outline the benefits of this brand, how it has impacted the world in a positive way, and the ways in which it continues to promote American values and culture.

_____

_____

_____

_____

_____

_____

_____

_____

_____

_____

The Progressive Movement

ESSENTIAL QUESTION

Can politics fix social problems?

Think about how this question might relate to the Progressive movement. What kinds of social problems existed at this time? Who were the progressives, and how did they attempt to fix these problems? Were they successful?

TALK ABOUT IT

Discuss with a partner the type of information you would need to know to answer these questions. For example, one question might be: *Which social problems drew the most attention?*

MY RESEARCH QUESTIONS

Supporting Question 1:

_____

_____

_____

Supporting Question 2:

_____

_____

_____

Supporting Question 3:

_____

_____

_____

The Roots of Progressivism

DIRECTIONS Search for evidence in Chapter 5, Lesson 1 to help you answer the following questions.

1A IDENTIFYING Who were the muckrakers?

1B DETERMINING CONTEXT How did muckrakers get their name?

2A ANALYZING Why did progressives feel that changes were necessary regarding child labor?

2B CIVICS What was the primary effect that progressives hoped to achieve with policies such as a city commission plan, a council manager system, an initiative, or a recall?

ESSENTIAL QUESTION

Can politics fix social problems?

As you gather evidence to answer the Essential Question, think about:

- the main issues with which progressives were concerned
- how they organized themselves to try to solve social problems

My Notes

3 **SUMMARIZING** As you read Lesson 1, fill in the graphic organizer below with society's main problems that progressives wanted addressed.

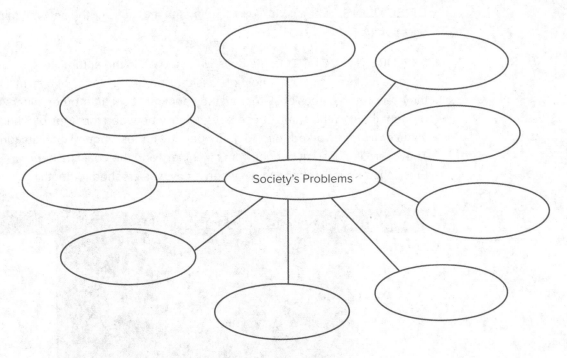

Society's Problems

4 **DETERMINING CENTRAL IDEAS** Fill in the graphic organizer below with details about each of the following leaders of the suffrage movement.

Elizabeth Cady Stanton	Susan B. Anthony	Lucy Stowe
Alice Paul	Rose Winslow	Carrie Chapman Catt

5 **EXPLAINING EFFECTS** How did the actions of the suffragettes fix a social problem?

_____

_____

Detroit Publishing Company, Library of Congress, LC-DIG-det-4a07285   Copyright © McGraw-Hill Education

ESSENTIAL QUESTION

Can politics fix social problems?

Breaker Boys

DIRECTIONS: Examine the following image, and answer the accompanying questions.

EXPLORE THE CONTEXT: The boys who labored in the anthracite coal mines were called breaker boys. Their job was the "breaking stage" of coal mining; they separated pieces of slate from the chunks of coal after other miners had brought it out of the shaft. These boys, usually between the ages of 8 and 12 years old, often worked 14 to 16 hours per day for less money than an adult. They were in constant danger from machinery and the coal crusher. Production never stopped, even when a boy was crushed to death.

PRIMARY SOURCE: PHOTOGRAPH

—from "Breaker boys, Woodward Coal Mines, Kingston, Pa.," 1900

1 **ANALYZING SOURCES** What does the image tell you about the life of these breaker boys?

_____

_____

_____

2 **INFERRING** Why do you think the photographer chose to take and publish this picture?

_____

_____

_____

_____

_____

3 ECONOMICS Why did the owners of the mines employ breaker boys?

_____

_____

_____

4 **PREDICTING** How do you think working in the coal mines affected the breaker boys?

_____

_____

_____

_____

5 **EXPLAINING EFFECTS** How do you think muckrakers had an impact on child labor?

_____

_____

_____

6 **IDENTIFYING CONNECTIONS** What types of roles in today's society compare to the role of muckrakers?

_____

_____

_____

_____

_____

ESSENTIAL QUESTION

Can politics fix social problems?

VOCABULARY

succinctly: briefly

nonpartisan: not aligned with a political party

brazenness: shameless boldness

notoriously: widely viewed in a negative way

Arguments Against Woman Suffrage

DIRECTIONS: Read the following excerpt from a magazine article. Then respond to the questions that follow.

EXPLORE THE CONTEXT: During the Progressive Era, the suffrage movement gained momentum, and women were finally guaranteed the right to vote in 1920. Some of those opposed to suffrage were women themselves. Antisuffragists read an "official paper" explaining their reasoning at New York Senate hearings in 1907. The last paragraph is part of the suffragists response.

PRIMARY SOURCE: MAGAZINE ARTICLE

❝The reasons actuating the protest were put forth **succinctly**, whether convincingly or not, in an "official paper," from which we quote.

1. "Would it not be an impulsive act of the New York legislator, moved by the appeals of a minority, to favor the grave social experiment of giving the suffrage to more than two millions of women whom the suffragists, after sixty years of missionary work, cannot convert into wanting it?" . . .

3. "The suffragists appeal to your chivalry on the ground that women need their rights and cannot get them by acts of Legislature." . . .

7. "We believe that woman's **non-partisan** attitude gives her the opportunity for influence in the community which the suffrage would divert and curtail." . . .

8. "We believe that intelligence and integrity of character are more potent factors in governing woman's wages than the ballot would be." . . .

9. "We believe that more enduring good can be accomplished by training and molding a child's nature than by voting on the tariff, civil service reform, railroad monopoly or any other national or State issue." . . .

10. "This is surely not a man's question; it is a woman's question. Do not act on impulse; let the women of this State decide that they want a vote before you use your official position to help make woman suffrage a law. . . ."

11. "We believe that you can be trusted to defeat this resolution, and we earnestly beg you to protect our interests by your constitutional powers of check, to the end that women may continue active and beneficent in ways with which political duties would conflict." . . .

The mere fact that so many excellent women have the courage—or should we say **brazenness**—to appear before **notoriously** corrupt politicians, even to beg that they be saved from themselves and their sisters, indicates the power for good they might wield if endowed with actual authority. ❞

—from the magazine article "Women's Arguments Against Woman Suffrage," published in *North American Review*, February 25, 1907

Harvey, George. "Woman's Arguments Against Woman Suffrage." North American Review 184, no. 610 (1907): 558-560.

1 CIVICS Why do you think women would fight to deny themselves the vote?

_____

_____

_____

2 **SUMMARIZING** What reasons did the antisuffragists give to support their cause?

_____

_____

_____

_____

_____

_____

_____

3 **ANALYZING STRUCTURE** Why do you think the antisuffragists organized the structure of the article the way they did?

_____

_____

_____

4 **DETERMINING MEANING** What do you think the suffragists would have found contradictory about the following statement: "We believe that you can be trusted to defeat this resolution, and we earnestly beg you to protect our interests by your constitutional powers of check, to the end that women may continue active and beneficent in ways with which political duties would conflict"?

_____

_____

_____

5 **EXPLAINING CAUSE AND EFFECT** How did publishing this article help to fix a problem in society?

_____

_____

_____

Roosevelt and Taft

DIRECTIONS Search for evidence in Chapter 5, Lesson 2 to help you answer the following questions.

1A **IDENTIFYING** What is Social Darwinism?

_____

_____

_____

ESSENTIAL QUESTION

Can politics fix social problems?

As you gather evidence to answer the essential question, think about:

- the issues that were important to Presidents Roosevelt and Taft

- what actions these presidents took toward reform

1B **CONTRASTING** How do you think Roosevelt's international philosophy of Social Darwinism differs from his domestic progressivism?

_____

_____

_____

_____

2A **ANALYZING** What were some of the disadvantages of big business trusts?

_____

_____

_____

My Notes

_____

_____

_____

_____

_____

_____

2B **ECONOMICS** President Roosevelt earned the nickname the "trustbuster." Complete the graphic organizer to describe the actions he took against the following companies and institutions.

Company/Institution	Roosevelt's Actions
Northern Securities	
United Mine Workers	
U.S. Steel	
The railroads	
The meatpacking industry	

3 **SUMMARIZING** What did President Roosevelt do to support conservation and protect the natural resources of the United States?

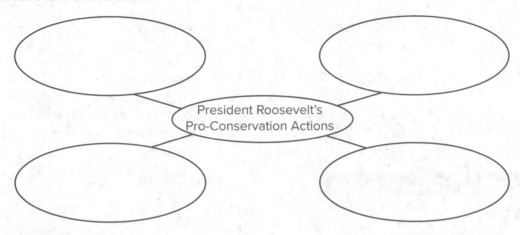

President Roosevelt's Pro-Conservation Actions

4 **EXPLAINING** Why did Democrats and progressive Republicans gain control of Congress halfway through Taft's term?

_____

_____

_____

5 **COMPARING** How did President Taft's achievements compare to Roosevelt's?

_____

_____

_____

_____

_____

_____

ESSENTIAL QUESTION

Can politics fix social problems?

A Nauseating Job, But It Must Be Done

DIRECTIONS: Examine the following political cartoon. Then respond to the questions that follow.

EXPLORE THE CONTEXT: Upton Sinclair became famous for writing *The Jungle,* a book that exposed the hazardous conditions in the meatpacking industry. As a muckraker, he also wrote a series of articles for the *Evening World* newspaper on the subject. This cartoon appeared in the *Utica Saturday Globe* around the time of Sinclair's investigations.

PRIMARY SOURCE: POLITICAL CARTOON

—"A Nauseating Job, But It Must Be Done" in *Utica Saturday Globe*, 1906

1 **INFERRING** How do you think Sinclair's work influenced public opinion about the meatpacking industry?

_____

_____

_____

_____

2 CITING TEXT EVIDENCE What does the artist think about the meatpacking industry? Cite evidence from the cartoon to support your answer.

_____

_____

_____

_____

3 INTERPRETING How did the artist select the imagery in the cartoon?

_____

_____

_____

_____

4 CIVICS How did muckrakers such as Sinclair influence President Roosevelt?

_____

_____

_____

_____

_____

_____

_____

5 ANALYZING SOURCES What does the rake depicted in the cartoon represent?

_____

_____

_____

6 EXPLAINING EFFECTS What reaction do you believe most readers had to this cartoon?

_____

_____

_____

ESSENTIAL QUESTION

Can politics fix social problems?

VOCABULARY

diminution: reduction

denude: to take away

render: to make

zealously: passionately

Letter from John Muir to the Committee on Agriculture

DIRECTIONS: Read the following excerpt from a letter. Then respond to the questions that follow.

EXPLORE THE CONTEXT: John Muir was an American naturalist who believed in preserving wilderness areas and successfully lobbied for the creation of Yosemite National Park. He was the president of the Sierra Club and wrote the following letter to Congress's Committee on Agriculture to protest a bill that would reduce the size of the park.

PRIMARY SOURCE: LETTER

66 Dear Sir,

Whereas at a meeting of the Sierra Club of Saturday, November 5th 1892, said club being a corporation formed for the purposes, to wit: 'To explore, enjoy and **render** accessible the mountain regions of the Pacific Coast; to publish authentic information concerning them; to enlist the support and co-operation of the people and the government in preserving the forests and other natural features of the Sierra Nevada Mountains' . . . The Board of Directors of the Sierra Club . . . do respectfully and emphatically protest against the **diminution** of the Yosemite National Park situated in California as contemplated in Bill HR 5764. . . .

As shown in the accompanying map, all the territory outside of the blue lines is to be taken out of the Yosemite National Park Reservation, which would

First: endanger . . . the headwaters of the San Joaquin River, a river on whose water the irrigation of the whole San Joaquin Valley is dependent.

Secondly: . . . it will **denude** the watersheds between the branches of the Tuolumne River and Merced River of the most valuable timber, destroy forests which in their magnificent growth form an attraction to visitors not only from the State of California, but from all over the United States and from abroad . . .

Thirdly: The taking out of the Reservation . . . will hand over to private ownership most valuable reservoir sites which ought to be **zealously** guarded for the benefit of the state . . .

Fourthly: . . . will endanger the watershed of the tributaries of the Tuolumne River as it passes through the Grand Cañon of the Tuolumne River and finally through Hetch-Hetchy Valley, a valley which in grandeur and uniqueness is in many respects the peer of Yosemite and will in future form one of the principal attractions of the Sierra Nevada. . . .

If . . . Yosemite National Park should be reduced . . . the herds of sheep which now for two seasons have successfully been kept out of the reservation would denude the watersheds of their vegetation, the forest fires following in the wake of the herds would destroy the magnificent forests, and thereafter the reservation itself and the timber of priceless value to the prosperity of the State would become the prey of the speculator.

John Muir, President, Sierra Club 99

—from a letter written by John Muir on January 2, 1893

1 **UNDERSTANDING CONTEXT** According to Muir, what was the purpose of the Sierra Club?

_____

_____

_____

_____

2 **DESCRIBING** How does Muir use maps to persuade his audience?

_____

_____

_____

3 **EXPLAINING EFFECTS** According to Muir, what are some of the dangers of the bill's proposed diminution of the park?

_____

_____

_____

_____

4 **CIVICS** How did Muir help to fix a societal problem?

_____

_____

_____

5 **DISTINGUISHING FACT FROM OPINION** What opinions did Muir express in his letter? If you cite from the text, use quotation marks.

_____

_____

_____

_____

_____

_____

The Wilson Years

DIRECTIONS Search for evidence in Chapter 5, Lesson 3 to help you answer the following questions.

1A **ANALYZING** How did Roosevelt affect the election of 1912?

_____

_____

_____

1B **COMPARING** How would you compare Woodrow Wilson's philosophies to those of Theodore Roosevelt?

_____

_____

_____

_____

2A **CIVICS** What were some of the groups facing discrimination during the Progressive Era, and what organizations emerged to help them?

_____

_____

_____

_____

_____

2B **IDENTIFYING** How did this progressivism activism change the role of government?

_____

_____

_____

_____

_____

_____

ESSENTIAL QUESTION

Can politics fix social problems?

As you gather evidence to answer the essential question, think about:

- how Wilson's philosophies differed from those of Roosevelt
- the limits and failures of the Progressive Era

My Notes

_____

_____

_____

_____

_____

_____

_____

3 CIVICS President Wilson, much like his predecessors, enacted new legislations and reforms. Complete the graphic organizer below to describe the impact each had on the nation's laws.

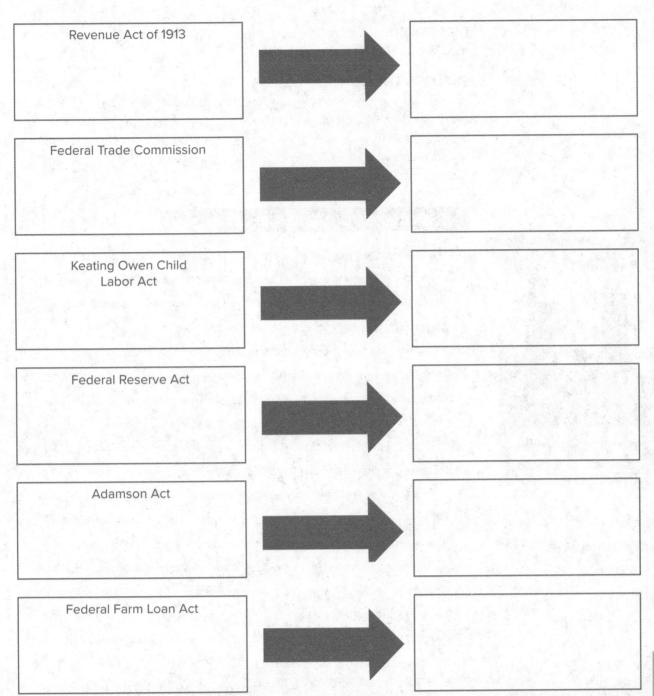

Revenue Act of 1913 →

Federal Trade Commission →

Keating Owen Child Labor Act →

Federal Reserve Act →

Adamson Act →

Federal Farm Loan Act →

ESSENTIAL QUESTION

Can politics fix social problems?

The Keating-Owen Child Labor Act of 1916

DIRECTIONS: Read the following excerpt from an act of Congress. Then respond to the questions that follow.

EXPLORE THE CONTEXT: Woodrow Wilson was the first president to sign into federal law regulations against child labor. The Keating-Owen Child Labor Act, passed in 1916, prohibited employing children under the age of 14 in factories producing goods for interstate commerce. The law was declared unconstitutional by the Supreme Court in 1918, but it was the first effort at curbing child labor.

PRIMARY SOURCE: LEGISLATION

❝ Be it enacted by the Senate and House of Representatives of the United States of America in Congress assembled, That no producer, manufacturer, or dealer shall ship or deliver for shipment in interstate or foreign commerce, any article or **commodity**, the product of any mine or quarry situated in the United States, in which within thirty days prior to the time of the removal of such product therefrom children under the age of sixteen years have been employed or permitted to work, or any article or commodity the product of any mill, cannery, workshop, factory, or manufacturing establishment, situated in the United States, in which within thirty days prior to the removal of such product therefrom children under the age of fourteen years have been employed or permitted to work, or children between the ages of fourteen years and sixteen years have been employed or permitted to work more than eight hours in any day, or more than six days in any week, or after the hour of seven o'clock **postmeridian,** or before the hour of six o'clock **antemeridian:** Provided, That a prosecution and conviction of a defendant for the shipment or delivery for shipment of any article or commodity under the conditions herein prohibited shall be a **bar** to any further prosecution against the same defendant for shipments or deliveries for shipment of any such article or commodity before the beginning of said prosecution. ❞

—from the Keating-Owen Child Labor Act of 1916

VOCABULARY

antemeridian: before noon

commodity: a good for sale

postmeridian: after noon

bar: obstacle

An Act to prevent interstate commerce in the products of child labor, and for other purposes, H.R. 8234, 64th Cong. (1916).

Copyright © McGraw-Hill Education

1 **COMPARING** How do you think this law affected the lives of the breaker boys from Lesson 1?

_____
_____
_____
_____

2 **INFERRING** Based on this law, what can you infer about the working conditions of children at the time?

_____
_____
_____
_____

3 **RELATING EVENTS** Why do you think the law stipulated that it could prosecute manufacturers who dealt in interstate or foreign commerce?

_____
_____
_____
_____

4 **CIVICS** What possible reason could the Supreme Court use to declare this law unconstitutional?

_____
_____
_____

5 **EVALUATING** Why did this legislation help Wilson's reputation with progressives?

_____
_____
_____
_____

ESSENTIAL QUESTION

Can politics fix social problems?

VOCABULARY

disheartened: discouraged

disenfranchisement: the act of depriving one of a legal right or privilege

tacit: implied

The Call

DIRECTIONS: Read the following excerpt from a petition. Then respond to the questions that follow.

EXPLORE THE CONTEXT: The race riots of 1908 in Springfield, Illinois, shocked many people. In 1909, an interracial group gathered in William English Walling's New York apartment to discuss how they could create an organization to advocate for the rights of African Americans. To raise awareness and support, the group issued a call for a national conference. A petition named "The Call" was written by Oswald Garrison Villard and was sent to prominent white and black Americans for endorsement. Many prominent progressives signed it.

PRIMARY SOURCE: ARTICLE

❝ To Discuss Means for Securing Political and Civil Equality for the Negro

. . . Besides a day of rejoicing, Lincoln's birthday in 1909 should be one of taking stock of the nation's progress since 1865. How far has it lived up to the obligations imposed upon it by the Emancipation Proclamation? . . .

If Mr. Lincoln could revisit this country he would be **disheartened** by the nation's failure in this respect. He would learn that on January 1st, 1909, Georgia had rounded out a new oligarchy by disfranchising the negro after the manner of all the other Southern states. He would learn that the Supreme Court of the United States, designed to be a bulwark of American liberties, had failed to meet several opportunities to pass squarely upon this **disfranchisement** of millions by laws avowedly discriminatory and openly enforced in such manner that white men may vote, and black men be without a vote in their government; he would discover, there, that taxation without representation is the lot of millions of wealth-producing American citizens, in whose hands rests the economic progress and welfare of an entire section of the country. He would learn that the Supreme Court, according to the official statement of one of its own judges in the Berea College case, has laid down the principle that if an individual State chooses it may 'make it a crime for white and colored persons to frequent the same marketplace at the same time, or appear in an assemblage of citizens convened to consider questions of a public or political nature in which all citizens, without regard to race, are equally interested.'

In many States Lincoln would find justice enforced, if at all, by judges elected by one element in a community to pass upon the liberties and lives of another. He would see the black men and women, for whose freedom a hundred thousand soldiers gave their lives, sit apart in trains, in which they pay first-class fares for third-class service, in railway stations, and in places of entertainment, while State after State declines to do its elementary duty in preparing the negro through education for the best exercise of citizenship. Added to this, the spread of lawless attacks upon the negro, North, South and West . . .

Silence under these conditions means **tacit** approval. The indifference of the North is already responsible for more than one assault upon democracy, and every such attack reacts as unfavorably upon whites as upon blacks. . . . 'A house divided against itself cannot stand'; this government cannot exist half slave and half free any better today than it could in 1861. Hence we call upon all the believers in democracy to join in a national conference for the discussion of present evils, the voicing of protests, and the renewal of the struggle for civil and political liberty. ❞

—from "The Call," Committee on the Negro "Call" for a National Conference, February 1909

1 CIVICS Did Villard feel that America had made progress in racial equality since the Emancipation Proclamation?

_____

_____

_____

2 **CITING TEXT EVIDENCE** What examples does the author give to prove his point? Cite evidence from the text to support your answer.

_____

_____

_____

3 **ANALYZING STRUCTURE** Why do you think Villard used the image of Abraham Lincoln returning to see what was happening in America?

_____

_____

_____

4 **INFERRING** What do you think Villard meant by the statement, "Silence under these conditions means tacit approval"?

_____

_____

_____

5 **DRAWING CONCLUSIONS** What was the purpose of "The Call"?

_____

_____

_____

ESSENTIAL QUESTION

Can politics fix social problems?

My Notes

① Think About It

Review the Supporting Questions that you developed at the beginning of the chapter. Review the evidence that you gathered in Chapter 5. Were you able to answer each Supporting Question?

If there was not enough evidence to answer your Supporting Questions, what additional evidence do you think you need to consider?

② Organize Your Evidence

Complete the chart below with information you learned about social problems and how politics was used to help or hinder their resolution.

Societal problem	Action taken to fix the problem	Did it succeed?	Evidence to support your claim

③ Write About It

Of all the reforms of the early 1900s, which two do you feel had the most positive effect on people's lives? Write a paragraph describing these reforms, and explain your reasons for choosing them as the most beneficial.

_____

_____

_____

_____

_____

_____

_____

_____

_____

④ Connect to the Essential Question

Think of an issue in today's society that you think needs reform. Conduct an interview with someone who has expertise regarding this issue. It could be a government leader, an industry professional, or a citizen impacted by the issue. On a separate piece of paper, record your interview. You would like your interviewee to help you figure out if politics can help to fix this problem. Prepare for your interview by writing questions that will engage the interviewee and help you draw conclusions. You may want to interview more than one person. Remember to be respectful when asking sensitive questions.

_____

_____

_____

_____

_____

_____

_____

CITIZENSHIP
TAKE ACTION

MAKE CONNECTIONS Now that you have an issue in mind that you feel strongly about, conduct additional research into the difficulties surrounding the issue and possible solutions. Think of the muckrakers of the Progressive Era and how their investigations led to reform. Write an article for your school newspaper detailing your findings and including quotes from your interview(s). Think of your audience. Is there something you feel your fellow students should know about? Could your article make a difference?

DIRECTIONS: Write an article for your school newspaper to share information you have gathered from interviews and your own research about your topic. Outline the difficulties of the issue and the possible solutions. Write your article in such a way that you will inspire others to act on the information. Submit your article to the school newspaper for publication. Volunteers may also wish to share their articles with the class.

_____

_____

_____

_____

_____

_____

_____

_____

_____

_____

World War I and Its Aftermath

ESSENTIAL QUESTION

Why do nations go to war?

Think about how this question might relate to the lead-up to World War I.

TALK ABOUT IT
Discuss with a partner what type of information you would need to know to answer this question. For example, one question might be: What were the conflicts between nations before the war?

DIRECTIONS: Now write three additional questions that would help you explain some of the reasons nations go to war.

MY RESEARCH QUESTIONS

Supporting Question 1:

_____

_____

Supporting Question 2:

_____

_____

Supporting Question 3:

_____

_____

The United States Enters World War I

DIRECTIONS Search for evidence in Chapter 6, Lesson 1 to help you answer the following questions.

ESSENTIAL QUESTION

Why do nations go to war?

As you gather evidence to answer the Essential Question, think about:

- the root causes of the war in Europe.
- the entry of the United States into the war.
- how Americans were drawn into the war.

1A **IDENTIFYING CAUSES AND EFFECTS** What event from the 1860s contributed to the tensions that led to World War I?

_____

_____

1B GEOGRAPHY When Europe erupted into war, what nations lined up to fight alongside one another?

_____

_____

_____

2A **DETERMINING CENTRAL IDEAS** What factors pushed the United States to stay out of the conflict in Europe?

_____

_____

_____

2B **ANALYZING INDIVIDUALS** Who pushed to break with neutrality and why?

_____

_____

3 **SEQUENCING** In the graphic organizer below, describe the sequence of events that led the United States toward entering the war.

My Notes

_____

_____

_____

_____

_____

_____

					United States enters World War I

4 **DRAWING CONCLUSIONS** What was the effect of British propaganda on the U.S. decision to enter World War I? Complete the chart.

Effects of British Propaganda	

5 **ANALYZING EVENTS** Why did Arthur Zimmermann's telegram anger people in the United States, resulting in more Americans wanting to enter the war?

_____

_____

_____

_____

_____

ESSENTIAL QUESTION
Why do nations go to war?

German Embassy Ad with Lusitania Warning

DIRECTIONS: Read the following advertisement written by the German ambassador. Then answer the questions that follow.

INTRODUCTION: In April 1915, the German Embassy printed a warning in *The New York Times* newspaper. But most people believed that the Lusitania was too big and too fast for a submarine to pose a threat. It was against the law for a navy to attack a passenger ship.

PRIMARY SOURCE: ARTICLE

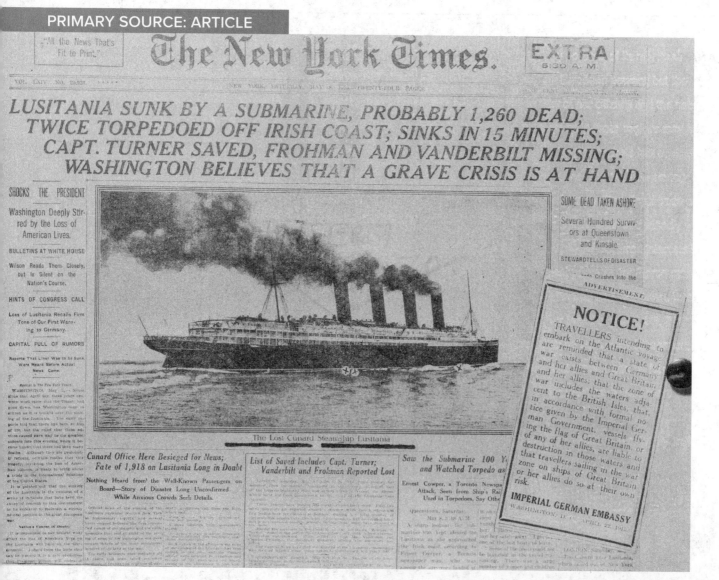

—from *The New York Times*, April 1915

1 **CITING TEXT EVIDENCE** What does the advertisement say? What details in the text are important?

_____

_____

_____

_____

_____

2 GEOGRAPHY What is the "zone of war" that the warning describes?

_____

_____

_____

3 **INFERRING** Look at the date the warning was issued. Why is this important?

_____

_____

_____

4 **DETERMINING CONTEXT** With this warning in the newspaper, what can be said about the United States given that they did not issue their own warning or restrict ships from sailing in the zone?

_____

_____

_____

5 **DRAWING CONCLUSIONS** What can you tell about Germany's posture at this stage of World War I from this advertisement?

_____

_____

_____

President Woodrow Wilson's War Message

ESSENTIAL QUESTION
Why do nations go to war?

VOCABULARY

tragical: sad

grave: serious

belligerent: one party of a war

DIRECTIONS: Read the following excerpt from President Woodrow Wilson's speech. Then answer the questions that follow.

EXPLORE THE CONTEXT: On April 2, 1917, President Woodrow Wilson went to Congress to announce that he had severed diplomatic relations with Germany. He asked Congress to declare war on Germany and its allies. Congress passed the War Resolution Act four days later, which would enter the United States into World War I.

PRIMARY SOURCE: SPEECH

❝With a profound sense of the solemn and even **tragical** character of the step I am taking and of the **grave** responsibilities which it involves, but in unhesitating obedience to what I deem my constitutional duty, I advise that the Congress declare the recent course of the Imperial German Government to be in fact nothing less than war against the Government and people of the United States; that it formally accept the status of **belligerent** which has thus been thrust upon it, and that it take immediate steps not only to put the country in a more thorough state of defense but also to exert all its power and employ all its resources to bring the Government of the German Empire to terms and end the war. ❞

—from "War Message to Congress," by Woodrow Wilson, April 2, 1917

1 **DETERMINING CONTEXT** Who is the author of the speech? What is his occupation? How does this help you understand the speech?

_____

_____

_____

_____

2 **DETERMINING MEANING** What is President Wilson asking of Congress? Use the text to support your answer.

_____

_____

_____

3 **ANALYZING** Look at the date of the speech. What is the historical context in which it was given? Why is this passage important?

_____

_____

_____

_____

4 **INFERRING** What does Wilson mean by "the recent course of the Imperial German Government"?

_____

_____

_____

_____

_____

5 **CIVICS** What principle of the Constitution is supported in this passage?

_____

_____

_____

_____

6 **DESCRIBING** What does Wilson mean by "employ all its resources to bring the Government of the German Empire to terms and end the war"?

_____

_____

_____

The Home Front

DIRECTIONS Search for evidence in Chapter 6, Lesson 2 to help you answer the following questions.

1A IDENTIFYING What systems did the president put in place to prepare the nation for war?

_____

_____

_____

1B DESCRIBING What function did each of these systems serve?

_____

_____

_____

_____

_____

_____

_____

_____

_____

_____

_____

2A EXPLAINING How did women help with the war effort?

_____

_____

_____

_____

_____

ESSENTIAL QUESTION

Why do nations go to war?

As you gather evidence to answer the Essential Question, think about:

- how Americans responded to the declaration of war.
- how the war impacted the American economy.
- how American systems, such as the military and the courts, supported the war effort.

My Notes

_____

_____

_____

_____

_____

_____

2B ECONOMY How did African Americans and Mexicans help with the war effort?

_____

_____

_____

3 RELATING EVENTS How did the Wilson administration help shape public opinion?

_____

_____

_____

4 SUMMARIZING In the graphic organizer below, explain how each act limited free speech.

The Espionage Act of 1917	
The Sedition Act of 1918	

5 DETERMINING CENTRAL IDEAS Fill in the web below with details about how the United States raised a military force to fight in World War I.

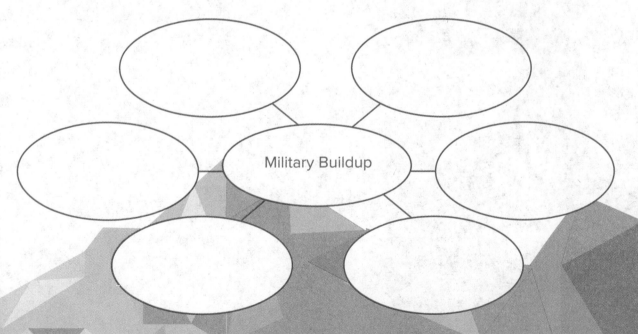

ESSENTIAL QUESTION
Why do nations go to war?

Victory Gardens Poster

DIRECTIONS: Study the following poster encouraging people to grow victory gardens. Then answer the questions that follow.

EXPLORE THE CONTEXT: As the United States moved toward entering the war, Herbert Hoover, the head of the Food Administration, said, "Food will win the war." He encouraged families to help the war effort by growing their own small gardens. He called these gardens "victory gardens" as a way to connect them to the war effort. This program allowed more commercially raised food to be sent abroad for troops.

PRIMARY SOURCE: POSTER

1 ECONOMICS How does the poster connect gardening to the war effort?

_____

_____

_____

2 **INTEGRATING VISUAL INFORMATION** What part of the image gives it a patriotic feel?

_____

_____

3 **EVALUATING EVIDENCE** The poster is a type of government propaganda. What words on the poster reveal the kind of propaganda it is?

_____

_____

_____

4 **INFERRING** For whom was the document written? How does that information help you understand it?

_____

_____

_____

5 **DRAWING CONCLUSIONS** Circle the area of the poster that shows how the government is supporting the effort. What does this tell you about the role government played in mobilizing the nation for war?

_____

_____

_____

_____

An Act To authorize the President to increase temporarily the Military Establishment of the United States. Public Law 12. U.S. Statutes at Large 15 (1917): 76-83.

ESSENTIAL QUESTION

Why do nations go to war?

Selective Service Act of 1917

DIRECTIONS: Read the following excerpt from a law passed by Congress. Then answer the questions that follow.

EXPLORE THE CONTEXT: The Selective Service System is the process that allows a president to increase the size of the military. It is sometimes called the draft. In this process, each eligible person registers with Selective Service and receives a random number. The government then randomly selects a number, and the person who holds that number is called to serve. The government drafts as many citizens as it believes will be needed for the war effort.

PRIMARY SOURCE: ACT

❝No person liable to military service shall hereafter be permitted or allowed to furnish a substitute for such service; nor shall any substitute be received, enlisted, or enrolled in the military service of the United States; and no such person shall be permitted to escape such service or to be discharged therefrom prior to the expiration of his term of service by the payment of money or any other valuable thing whatsoever as consideration his release from military service or liability there to.❞

—from Section 3 of the Selective Service Act of 1917

1 **DETERMINING CENTRAL IDEAS** What is the main idea of the passage? What rule is the passage explaining?

_____

_____

_____

2 EXPLAINING What is the purpose of this act?

_____

_____

3 CITING TEXT EVIDENCE Why do you think this part of the law was necessary? What can you infer about past Selective Service processes?

_____

_____

4 CIVICS If the law worked the way it was intended, how do you think it would affect public perception of the war?

_____

_____

_____

5 INFERRING Look at the date of the act, and consider what it says. What can you conclude was happening at the time?

_____

_____

_____

6 CIVICS Who are the winners and losers if this policy of the Selective Service is strictly enforced?

_____

_____

_____

_____

7 CIVICS What are the civic virtues that are demonstrated in this law?

_____

_____

A Bloody Conflict

DIRECTIONS Search for evidence in Chapter 6, Lesson 3 to help you answer the following questions.

1A **DESCRIBING** One aspect of combat in the early 1900s was life in the trenches. How would you describe the trenches used in World War I?

_____

_____

_____

1B **DRAWING CONCLUSIONS** From the description of new technologies used in World War I, what conclusions can you draw about the combat experience?

_____

_____

_____

2A **IDENTIFYING CAUSES AND EFFECTS** Why did Russia leave the war?

_____

_____

_____

_____

2B **UNDERSTANDING CHRONOLOGY** What trade-off between Germany and Russia occurred that enabled Germany to focus on its western front?

_____

_____

_____

ESSENTIAL QUESTION

Why do nations go to war?

As you gather evidence to answer the Essential Question, think about:

- how technology helps and harms soldiers.

- how the alliances changed throughout the war as some allies entered and others left combat.

- why peace settlements are difficult to reach.

My Notes

_____

_____

_____

_____

_____

_____

3 **IDENTIFYING CAUSES AND EFFECTS** In the graphic organizer below, explain what happened on each date after the United States entered the war.

United States Enters War, 1918	
Late May	
June 1	
July 15	
September 26	
November 11	

4 **IDENTIFYING STEPS** Use the outline below to identify the details of the peace negotiations after World War I.

I. Peace Negotiations

A.

B.

C.

II. The Fourteen Points

A.

B.

C.

D.

III. The Treaty of Versailles

A.

B.

C.

IV. U.S. reaction to the Treaty of Versailles

A.

B.

C.

D.

ESSENTIAL QUESTION

Why do nations go to war?

Diary of World War I

DIRECTIONS: Read the following excerpt from a book written by a soldier in World War I. Then answer the questions that follow.

EXPLORE THE CONTEXT: Some of the most evocative information about World War I comes from personal accounts by soldiers who recorded their experiences in the war. Quiren Groessl grew up in a German American family in Wisconsin. He served in the army from 1914 to 1918.

PRIMARY SOURCE: BOOK

❝We have been under almost constant artillery fire ever since our arrival on this front, and are fast learning from experience to distinguish between incoming and outgoing shells, and whether French or American outgoing. We have learned from the sound of the whine about how close a shell will hit, and also to tell the difference between a high explosive shell and a shrapnel-type shell which explodes in the air and bursts into thousands of steel splinters, any of which can cause a severe wound or death. We can detect the gas shells, which sort of rumble as they come over, and which have frequently been used by the Germans. ❞

—from *"Big Boy": A Diary of World War I,* by Quiren M. Groessl, 1918

1 **DETERMINING CONTEXT** Who wrote this document? How does this information help you understand it?

_____

_____

_____

_____

2 **INFERRING** What does the title of the book that this passage is from tell you about it?

_____

_____

_____

3 INFERRING What can you tell about the author's experience by the level of detail in the passage?

_____

_____

_____

_____

4 ANALYZING SOURCES What details in the document are important to understanding what the author is saying?

_____

_____

_____

_____

5 IDENTIFYING When the United States joined the war, its soldiers were called "doughboys" for lack of experience in combat. Explain whether Quiren Groessl fits this description from what he has written in this passage.

_____

_____

_____

_____

_____

6 CIVICS What conflict might have been at work in Quiren Groessl as he fulfilled his duty to country by serving in the military during World War I?

_____

_____

_____

ESSENTIAL QUESTION

Why do nations go to war?

The Treaty of Versailles

DIRECTIONS: Read the following excerpt from the Treaty of Versailles. Then answer the questions that follow.

EXPLORE THE CONTEXT: The Treaty of Versailles was written at the Paris Peace Conference in 1919. The negotiators were dominated by the four nations who had invested the most resources and suffered the greatest losses in the war: the United Kingdom, France, Italy, and the United States.

VOCABULARY

diminution: making something smaller

PRIMARY SOURCE: TREATY

" GENERAL PROVISIONS.

ARTICLE 231.

The Allied and Associated Governments affirm and Germany accepts the responsibility of Germany and her allies for causing all the loss and damage to which the Allied and Associated Governments and their nationals have been subjected as a consequence of the war imposed upon them by the aggression of Germany and her allies.

ARTICLE: 232.

The Allied and Associated Governments recognise that the resources of Germany are not adequate, after taking into account permanent diminutions of such resources which will result from other provisions of the present Treaty, to make complete reparation for all such loss and damage.

The Allied and Associated Governments, however, require, and Germany undertakes, that she will make compensation for all damage done to the civilian population of the Allied and Associated Powers and to their property during the period of the belligerency of each as an Allied or Associated Power against Germany by such aggression by land, by sea and from the air, and in general all damage as defined in Annex I hereto. "

—from the Treaty of Versailles, 1919

Treaty of Versailles. In Treaties and other international agreements of the United States of America, 1776–1949, compiled under the direction of Charles I. Bevans, 43-240. Washington D.C.: U.S. Govt. Print. Off., 1969.

1 ANALYZING What type of document is this?

_____

_____

2 CITING TEXT EVIDENCE What clues in the passage tell you who wrote the treaty?

_____

_____

_____

_____

3 DETERMINING MEANING Rewrite the message of Article 231 in your own words. What is the historical context for this message?

_____

_____

_____

_____

4 ECONOMICS What are the economic effects of Article 232? What will this policy do to Germany?

_____

_____

_____

5 ANALYZING SOURCES What words from the treaty show that the Allies understand Germany cannot pay what is being required—yet requires it anyway? How might the German people have reacted to this?

_____

_____

_____

_____

_____

The War's Impact

DIRECTIONS Search for evidence in Chapter 6, Lesson 4 to help you answer the following questions.

1A ECONOMICS What were the economic factors that pushed Americans to strike after the war?

_____

_____

_____

1B ECONOMICS What happened to many of the strikers?

_____

_____

_____

2A **IDENTIFYING CAUSES** Explain some of the root causes of the race riots of 1919.

_____

_____

_____

_____

_____

2B **EXPLAINING** What were some of the outcomes of the race riots?

_____

_____

_____

ESSENTIAL QUESTION

Why do nations go to war?

As you gather evidence to answer the Essential Question, think about:

- how Americans reacted to soldiers returning from war.
- how women and minorities reacted to a return to a peacetime economy.
- how communism in Russia affected Americans after the war.

My Notes

_____

_____

_____

_____

_____

_____

3 **DETERMINING CENTRAL IDEAS** Complete the graphic organizer. What events led to the Red Scare?

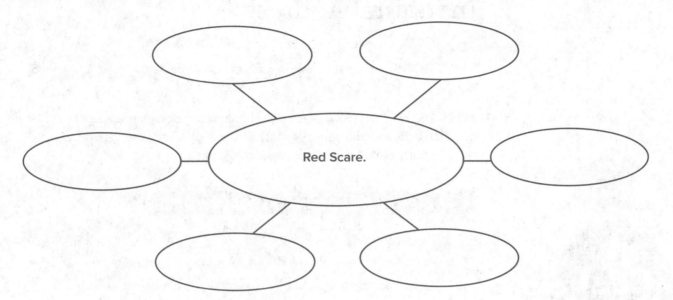

4 **CONTRASTING** Complete the graphic organizer by describing each presidential candidate's position.

Candidate	Position
James M. Cox, Democrat	
Warren G. Harding, Republican	

ESSENTIAL QUESTION

Why do nations go to war?

President Warren G. Harding's Inaugural Address

DIRECTIONS: Read the following excerpt from President Warren G. Harding's inaugural address. Then answer the questions that follow.

EXPLORE THE CONTEXT: Warren G. Harding was elected president in 1920 by a landslide, winning approximately 60 percent of the vote. As president, Harding transformed a war-ready nation to a nation of peace.

PRIMARY SOURCE: INAUGURAL ADDRESS

66 My Countrymen: When one surveys the world about him after the great storm, noting the marks of destruction and yet rejoicing in the ruggedness of the things which withstood it, if he is an American he breathes the clarified atmosphere with a strange mingling of regret and new hope. We have seen a world passion spend its fury, but we **contemplate** our republic unshaken, and hold our civilization secure. Liberty—liberty within the law—and civilization are inseparable, and though both were threatened we find them now secure; and there comes to Americans the profound assurance that our representative government is the highest expression and surest guaranty of both. 99

—from the inaugural address of President Warren G. Harding, March 4, 1921

VOCABULARY

contemplate: think about

1 **CITING TEXT EVIDENCE** What references does the speaker make to World War I?

_____

_____

_____

Inaugural Address of President Warren G. Harding, S. Doc. No. 1, at 3-10 (1921).

2 ANALYZING SOURCES Who is the speaker? What is his background?

_____

_____

_____

3 CIVICS What is the purpose of this speech?

_____

_____

_____

_____

_____

_____

4 EVALUATING EVIDENCE What do you think the speaker means by "a strange mingling of regret and new hope"? How does the context of the speech help you interpret the meaning?

_____

_____

_____

_____

_____

5 INFERRING What does President Harding mean when he says that liberty and civilization are inseparable?

_____

_____

_____

_____

ESSENTIAL QUESTION
Why do nations go to war?

The Boston Police Strike

DIRECTIONS: Read the following excerpt from a speech by Governor Calvin Coolidge. Then answer the questions that follow.

EXPLORE THE CONTEXT: After the end of World War I, the economy went through an adjustment that led to inflation and labor unrest. The Boston Police Strike happened in 1919. In that strike, nearly three-fourths of the police force left their jobs. Calvin Coolidge was governor of Massachusetts at the time.

PRIMARY SOURCE: SPEECH

66 There appears to be a misapprehension as to the position of the police of Boston. In the deliberate intention to intimidate and coerce the government of this Commonwealth a large body of policemen, urging all others to join them, deserted their posts of duty, letting in the enemy. This act of theirs was voluntary, against the advice of their well-wishers, long discussed and premeditated, and with the purpose of obstructing the power of the government to protect its citizens or even to maintain its own existence. Its success meant anarchy. By this act, through the operation of the law they dispossessed themselves. They went out of office. They stand as though they had never been appointed. . . . To place the maintenance of the public security in the hands of a body of men who have attempted to destroy it would be to flout the sovereignty of the laws the people have made. It is my duty to resist any such proposal. 99

—from a speech "Governor's Proclamation Relative to Status of Striking Policemen of City of Boston," by Calvin Coolidge, Governor of Massachusetts, September 14, 1919

1 **ANALYZING POINT OF VIEW** What is Coolidge's position on the strike? Summarize his point of view in your own words.

_____

_____

_____

2 **CITING TEXT EVIDENCE** How does Coolidge view the striking police officers? What parts of the passage reveal this?

_____

_____

_____

_____

_____

3 **IDENTIFYING CAUSES AND EFFECTS** What are the consequences that Coolidge believes are appropriate for the strikers? What part of the passage supports your answer?

_____

_____

_____

_____

_____

4 **DRAWING CONCLUSIONS** How do the events that were taking place in the world when this document was written help reveal the meaning of Coolidge's words?

_____

_____

_____

_____

5 **CIVICS** What is the speaker's background? What are his responsibilities? How does that help you understand what he's saying?

_____

_____

_____

_____

_____

ESSENTIAL QUESTIONS

Why do nations go to war?

My Notes

_____

_____

_____

_____

_____

_____

_____

_____

_____

_____

_____

_____

_____

_____

_____

_____

1 Think About It

Review the supporting questions you developed at the beginning of the chapter. Review the evidence that you gathered in Chapter 6. Were you able to answer each Supporting Question?

If there was not enough evidence to answer your Supporting Questions, what additional evidence do you think you need to consider?

_____

_____

_____

_____

2 Organize Your Evidence

Complete the organizer below with information you learned about the causes and effects of World War I.

Causes		Effects
	World War I	

❸ Talk About It

Work in small groups. Talk with your group about the information you included in your graphic organizer. Did you include the same evidence, or were your classmates' responses different from your responses? Which information is most important to understanding the causes and effects of World War I? Why?

_____

_____

_____

_____

_____

❹ Connect to the Essential Question

Create a scrapbook of people's experiences in World War I. Go to the library or use the Internet to research the experiences of soldiers, nurses, military leaders, and people at home. The scrapbook may include letters or journal entries, copies of photographs, or other materials by people involved in or affected by the war. Compare what you learn from your research to what you have learned from the Student Edition. As you put together your scrapbook, dedicate individual pages to specific people. As you do this, see if you can find evidence to answer the Essential Question: _Why do nations go to war?_

_____

_____

_____

_____

_____

_____

_____

_____

_____

_____

_____

CITIZENSHIP
TAKING ACTION

MAKE CONNECTIONS In modern wars, fighting units often have a journalist traveling with them. These embedded journalists write about what they see and the people fighting in the war. Their stories are often emotionally compelling and powerful. The journalists who report from the battlefront help shape public opinion about how the war is going. Their work is extremely important to balance the information that is filtered by the federal agencies supporting the war.

DIRECTIONS: Use what you have learned in Chapter 6 about the World War I. Imagine you are embedded with American soldiers fighting for the Allied Powers. Write a segment for a newscast that reports on the events of the war and the experiences of the men and women around you. Your news segment can focus on a soldier, a war nurse, an African American soldier from the 93rd infantry fighting with France, or any other person who experienced the war firsthand. Begin your news segment with an interesting hook. Give details about the war experience, and use your segment to answer the question: *Why do nations go to war?* The answers you find should be in the voice of the character through which you are describing the war. Be creative and use details from the Inquiry Journal and the Student Edition to provide background information that makes your segment more realistic.

_____

_____

_____

_____

_____

_____

_____

_____

_____

_____

The Jazz Age

ESSENTIAL QUESTION

How has the cultural identity of the United States changed over time?

Think about how this question might relate to the 1920s. What were the major changes in society during that time? What kinds of changes were they? How did they lead to a new cultural identity in the United States?

TALK ABOUT IT

Discuss with a partner the type of information you would need to know to answer these questions. For example, one question might be: *What components make up the cultural identity of a society?*

MY RESEARCH QUESTIONS

Supporting Question 1:

_____

_____

_____

Supporting Question 2:

_____

_____

_____

Supporting Question 3:

_____

_____

_____

The Politics of the 1920s

DIRECTIONS Search for evidence in Chapter 7, Lesson 1 to help you answer the following questions.

ESSENTIAL QUESTION

How has the cultural identity of the United States changed over time?

As you gather evidence to answer the Essential Question, think about:

- the major shifts in politics and economics.
- the major shifts in the arts.
- how popular culture reflects a society's identity.

1A **RELATING EVENTS** Why did Harding campaign on "a return to normalcy"?

_____

_____

_____

_____

1B **ANALYZING** How did scandal hurt Harding's efforts at "normalcy"? Give examples.

_____

_____

_____

_____

_____

2A **IDENTIFYING** What is isolationism?

_____

_____

_____

_____

2B **INFERRING** Why do you think many Americans favored isolationism during the 1920s?

_____

_____

_____

_____

_____

3 ECONOMICS Use the cause-and-effect graphic organizer below to explain the idea behind supply side economics.

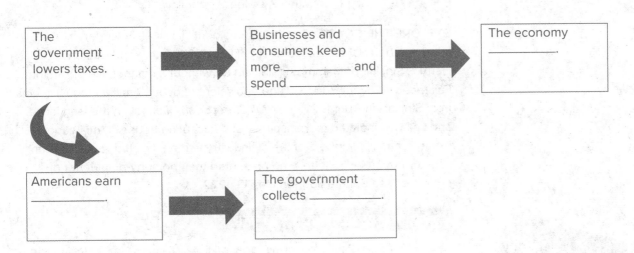

The
government
lowers taxes.

→

Businesses and
consumers keep
more _____ and
spend _____.

→

The economy
_____.

Americans earn
_____.

→

The government
collects _____.

4 DESCRIBING What was the goal of the Washington Conference?

_____

_____

_____

_____

5 RELATING EVENTS How did the Washington Conference lead to the Kellogg-Briand Pact?

_____

_____

A Letter to Senator La Follette

ESSENTIAL QUESTION

How has the cultural identity of the United States changed over time?

DIRECTIONS: Read the following excerpt from the letter to Senator La Follette. Then respond to the questions that follow.

EXPLORE THE CONTEXT: In 1922, President Harding's Secretary of the Interior, Albert B. Fall, leased a plot of land in Wyoming and California to Harry F. Sinclair of Mammoth (Sinclair) Oil without a competitive bid. In turn, Fall received over $300,000 (the equivalent of over $3 million today) in gifts from Sinclair. In April 1922, the *Wall Street Journal* exposed the land lease, and Fall was indicted for conspiracy and accepting bribes in the Teapot Dome scandal. Members of the oil industry wrote this letter to Republican senator Robert La Follette, who presented their point-by-point letter of protest on the Senate floor on May 13, 1922.

PRIMARY SOURCE: LETTER

❝ First. Against the policy of the Secretary of the Interior and the Secretary of the Navy in opening the naval reserves at this time for **exploitation**.

Second. Against the method of **leasing** public lands without competitive bidding, as **exemplified** in the recent contract entered into between Secretary Fall of the Interior and Secretary Denby of the Navy and the Standard Oil-Sinclair-Doheny interest.

Third. Against the policy of any department of the Government of the United States entering into a contract of any character whatsoever, whether competitive or not, which would tend to continue or **perpetuate** a **monopolistic** control of the oil industry of the United States or create a monopoly on the sale of fuel oil or refined oil to the Navy or any other department of the Government. ❞

—from "A Letter to Senator La Follette," *National Petroleum News*, May 10, 1922

VOCABULARY

exploitation: selfish use for personal gain

exemplified: shown

leasing: renting

perpetuate: to make to last

monopolistic: having control over an industry

1 SUMMARIZING What three issues did the oil industry members raise against Albert Fall?

_____

_____

_____

_____

2 INFERRING Why else might oil industry members have been upset about the deal between Albert Fall and Harry Sinclair?

_____

_____

_____

_____

3 ANALYZING How does competitive bidding help to ensure a fair business transaction?

_____

_____

_____

_____

4 EXPLAINING CAUSE AND EFFECT How do you think reading this letter on the Senate floor influenced the scandal?

_____

_____

_____

_____

5 CIVICS What does the Teapot Dome scandal tell you about the cultural identity of the United States at the time?

_____

_____

_____

_____

Treaty for the Renunciation of War (Kellogg-Briand Pact), U.S.-Aus.-Can.-CSR-Ger.-GB-Ind.-Ir.-Ita.-NZL-ZAF-Pol.-Bel.-Fra.-JPN, August 27, 1928, 46 T.S. 2343.

ESSENTIAL QUESTION

How has the cultural identity of the United States changed over time?

The Kellogg-Briand Pact

DIRECTIONS: Read the following excerpt from the Kellogg-Briand Pact. Then respond to the questions that follow.

EXPLORE THE CONTEXT: After World War I and a subsequent costly arms race, the United States began talks with other powerful countries on disarmament and ways to avoid war. U.S. Secretary of State Frank Kellogg and French foreign minister Aristide Briand proposed a treaty to outlaw war altogether. The United States and 14 other countries signed the Kellogg-Briand Pact in 1928. The signing countries agreed to abandon war and to settle all disputes by peaceful means.

PRIMARY SOURCE: PACT

❝The High Contracting Parties **solemnly** declare in the names of their respective peoples that they **condemn** recourse to war for the solution of international controversies, and renounce it, as an instrument of national policy in their relations with one another . . .

The High Contracting Parties agree that the settlement or solution of all disputes or conflicts of whatever nature or of whatever origin they may be, which may arise among them, shall never be sought except by **pacific** means. . . . This Treaty shall, when it has come into effect as prescribed in the preceding paragraph, remain open as long as may be necessary for adherence by all the other Powers of the world. Every instrument evidencing the adherence of a Power shall be deposited at Washington and the Treaty shall immediately upon such deposit become effective as between the Power thus adhering and the other Powers parties hereto.

IN FAITH WHEREOF the respective **Plenipotentiaries** have signed this Treaty in the French and English languages both texts having equal force, and hereunto affix their seals.

DONE at Paris, the twenty seventh day of August in the year one thousand nine hundred and twenty-eight. ❞

—from the Kellogg-Briand Pact, 1928

VOCABULARY

solemnly: seriously

condemn: speak out against

pacific: peaceful

plenipotentiaries: people in power

1 UNDERSTANDING CONTEXT What was the goal of the signers of the Kellogg-Briand Pact?

_____

_____

_____

_____

2 DETERMINING MEANING Why do you think the signers of the treaty used the phrase "solemnly declare"?

_____

_____

_____

_____

3 INFERRING What kinds of solutions do you think the signers had in mind when they said conflicts should be solved by "pacific means"?

_____

_____

_____

_____

4 CIVICS How did the Kellogg-Briand Pact reflect a change in cultural identity of Americans?

_____

_____

_____

_____

5 PREDICTING If all the countries who signed the Kellogg-Briand Pact had honored it, how would history have been different?

_____

_____

_____

_____

ESSENTIAL QUESTION

How has the cultural identity of the United States changed over time?

As you gather evidence to answer the Essential Question, think about:

- the industries that drove the American economy in the 1920s.
- how the economy affected the everyday life of Americans.

My Notes

A Growing Economy

DIRECTIONS Search for evidence in Chapter 7, Lesson 2 to help you answer the following questions.

1A **IDENTIFYING** What is mass production?

1B **ANALYZING** How did mass production bring about change in American society?

2A **ECONOMICS** Why did many new products come on the market during the 1920s?

2B **RELATING EVENTS** How did mass advertising help manufacturers attract consumers for these products?

3 **SUMMARIZING** Fill in the graphic organizer below with information about how the following industries changed life for Americans.

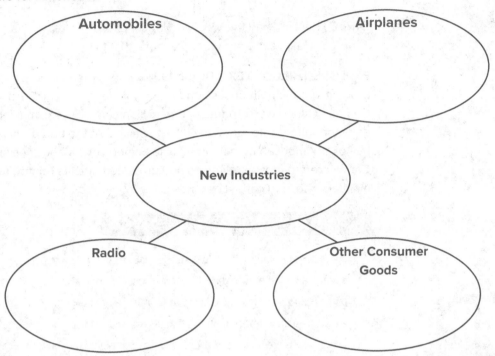

4 **IDENTIFYING CONNECTIONS** What are some examples of consumerism in America today?

_____

_____

5 **INFERRING** Why was the farm crisis also referred to as a "quiet depression"?

_____

_____

_____

Your Car: A Magazine of Romance, Fact and Fiction, May 1 1925, 2. http://memory.loc.gov/cgi-bin/ampage?collId=amrlgs&fileName=yc1page.db&recNum=3   Copyright © McGraw-Hill Education

ESSENTIAL QUESTION

How has the cultural identity of the United States changed over time?

Your Car

DIRECTIONS: Read the following article excerpt from the magazine *Your Car.* Then respond to the questions that follow.

EXPLORE THE CONTEXT: By the 1920s, cars were fast becoming a coveted product and even an obsession for many Americans. The Ford Motor Company alone was producing one million cars per year, making cars cheaper and more affordable for middle class families. At the end of the decade, nearly half of all American homeowners also owned cars. Magazines such as *Your Car* catered to these audiences and produced articles related to driving, car maintenance, and car accessories.

PRIMARY SOURCE: MAGAZINE

" Motoring is the romance of today for millions of kindly Americans, to whom it has opened a door through which they may escape from time and place and the **tyranny** of the **humdrum**. Until the coming of *Your Car*, there never has been an automobile magazine with vision enough to catch the Romantic side of this modern magic carpet. In the June issue readers of *Your Car* will be swept into the thrills and dangers of a great cross-country race, in which hate was a **compelling** factor, but love proves the stronger motivation, as it has since the dawn of humanity. There will be stories of mystery, and romances that will bring the tear of pity to the most unsentimental eye. The humors of travel will not be forgotten and for the practical motorist there will be **enthralling** articles, from which he will learn how to get more of pleasure and of economic use from his car. Dozens of stories and articles, pages of beautiful and interesting pictures in **rotogravure**. Tell your news dealer to have your copy ready for you, or send in your subscription, so that you will not miss a single issue of a magazine that will fill a want you have always felt. "

—from *Your Car*, A Magazine of Romance, *Fact and Fiction*, May 1925

VOCABULARY

tyranny: oppressive condition

humdrum: ordinary, boring

compelling: strong

unsentimental: unfeeling

enthralling: gripping, very interesting

rotogravure: a type of printing

1 CITING TEXT EVIDENCE According to the author, how does a car influence a person's life? Cite evidence from the text to support your answer.

_____

_____

2 COMPARING How was this magazine designed to help adventurous motorists as well as practical ones?

_____

_____

_____

3 CIVICS In what way does the author of the article employ tactics similar to all mass advertisers of the 1920s? Give an example.

_____

_____

_____

_____

4 INFERRING What can you infer from the phrase, "from which he will learn how to get more of pleasure and of economic use from his car"?

_____

_____

_____

_____

5 INTERPRETING What does this article tell you about changes in the cultural identity of the 1920s?

_____

_____

_____

How has the cultural identity of the United States changed over time?

Babe Ruth Eating Quaker Puffed Wheat Cereal

DIRECTIONS: : Examine the following publicity photo for Quaker Puffed Wheat cereal. Then respond to the questions that follow.

EXPLORE THE CONTEXT: Babe Ruth was one of the first baseball players ever to hit 60 home runs in a single season, and he eventually set a record of more than 700 career home runs. He seemed superhuman to fans, and was one of the first athletes to be so famous that he needed a publicity agent to handle his affairs. He was the face on some of the first celebrity-endorsed product marketing and appeared in ads for everything from underwear to chocolate. This publicity photo of Babe Ruth eating Quaker Puffed Wheat cereal was taken in New York in 1930.

PRIMARY SOURCE: PUBLICITY PHOTO

—from Mark Rucker, Trancendental Graphics

1 **UNDERSTANDING CONTEXT** Why do you think the Quaker Company wanted Babe Ruth to appear in a photo eating their Puffed Wheat Cereal?

_____

_____

_____

2 **INFERRING** Do you think Babe Ruth frequently ate Puffed Wheat in his daily life? Why do you think he posed for the publicity photo?

_____

_____

_____

_____

3 **ECONOMICS** Since this photo was taken, how has the way that cereal is packaged changed? What economic reason might underlie this change?

_____

_____

_____

_____

4 **RELATING EVENTS** Why did the 1920s see a rise in both celebrities and consumerism?

_____

_____

_____

_____

5 **IDENTIFYING CONNECTIONS** Who are some celebrities that endorse products today? What products do they endorse?

_____

_____

_____

ESSENTIAL QUESTION

How has the cultural identity of the United States changed over time?

As you gather evidence to answer the Essential Question, think about:

- how the priorities and values of Americans began to change.
- the ways in which different groups of Americans viewed these changes.

My Notes

_____

_____

_____

_____

_____

_____

A Clash of Values

DIRECTIONS Search for evidence in Chapter 7, Lesson 3 to help you answer the following questions.

1A **IDENTIFYING** What is nativism, and how did it relate to immigration policy in the 1920s?

_____

_____

_____

_____

1B **EXPLAINING CAUSES** What led to a rise in nativism during the 1920s?

_____

_____

_____

_____

_____

_____

2A **CIVICS** What was the National Origins Act?

_____

_____

_____

_____

2B **RELATING EVENTS** Which immigrants were favored by the act? Why?

_____

_____

_____

_____

_____

3 **SUMMARIZING** Use the graphic organizer below to list some of the ways beliefs were changing during the 1920s in each of the following areas.

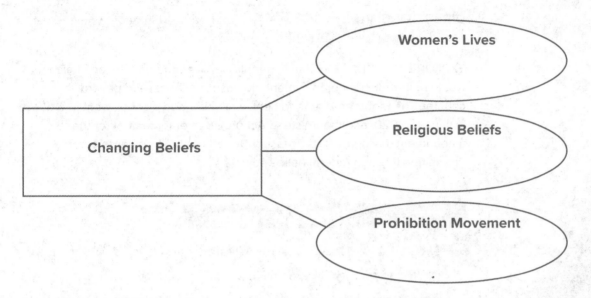

4 **ANALYZING CHANGE** Was the Eighteenth Amendment as effective as prohibitionists had hoped?

_____

_____

_____

5 **DESCRIBING** How long was the Eighteenth Amendment in effect?

_____

_____

_____

U.S. Const. amend. XVIII

ESSENTIAL QUESTION

How has the cultural identity of the United States changed over time?

The Eighteenth Amendment

DIRECTIONS: Read the following excerpt from the Eighteenth Amendment. Then respond to the questions that follow.

EXPLORE THE CONTEXT: Many people believed the prohibition of alcohol would help reduce unemployment, domestic violence, and poverty in the country. The Eighteenth Amendment, which banned alcohol, went into effect in January 1920, and the Volstead Act provided enforcement for the amendment, giving the U.S. Treasury Department the power to enforce Prohibition through federal police powers.

PRIMARY SOURCE: AMENDMENT

" Section 1. After one year from the **ratification** of this article the manufacture, sale, or transportation of **intoxicating** liquors within, the importation thereof into, or the exportation thereof from the United States and all the territory subject to the **jurisdiction** thereof for beverage purposes is hereby prohibited.

Section 2. The Congress and the several States shall have **concurrent** power to enforce this article by appropriate legislation.

Section 3. This article shall be **inoperative** unless it shall have been ratified as an amendment to the Constitution by the legislatures of the several States, as provided in the Constitution, within seven years from the date of the submission hereof to the States by the Congress. "

—"from the Eighteenth Amendment, U.S. Constitution

VOCABULARY

ratification: approval

intoxicating: able to make a person drunk

jurisdiction: authority

concurrent: at the same time

inoperative: without effect

1 **IDENTIFYING** What was the purpose of the Eighteenth Amendment?

_____

_____

_____

_____

2 **ANALYZING** Why do you think lawmakers included a one-year period between the time of the ratification of the amendment and the enforcement of the ban?

_____

_____

_____

_____

3 **SUMMARIZING** What did the supporters of the amendment hope to achieve by banning alcohol?

_____

_____

_____

_____

4 **CIVICS** How did the Eighteenth Amendment allow for enforcement of the ban?

_____

_____

_____

_____

5 **MAKING CONNECTIONS** What is the meaning of the third section?

_____

_____

_____

ESSENTIAL QUESTION

How has the cultural identity of the United States changed over time?

Internal Revenue Service Report on Al Capone

DIRECTIONS: Read the following excerpt from an Internal Revenue Service report. Then respond to the questions that follow.

EXPLORE THE CONTEXT: During the Prohibition Era, many Americans were still able to purchase alcohol from bootleggers and bars known as speakeasies. Al Capone was one of the most successful and well-known gangsters of the era. He was born in Brooklyn, New York, to poor immigrant parents and later settled in Chicago, where his organized crime ring became a multimillion dollar operation based on **bootlegging**, gambling and other **illicit** activities. He was also responsible for many brutal acts of violence. Capone was never convicted of his these crimes, but was finally brought to justice for income-tax evasion in 1931. He spent six and a half years in jail. His life story fascinated the public, and his gangster persona has been immortalized in many movies and books.

PRIMARY SOURCE: GOVERNMENT REPORT

66 The important facts upon which the tax **indictments** were based are as follows: The defendant, during the years 1924 to 1929, inclusive, was a partner in a syndicate or partnership engaged in illicit profitmaking enterprises. The defendant was the leader of the syndicate and received one-sixth of the net profits from its activities . . . The defendant received income in the form of cash, sometimes checks, and, on many occasions, wire transfers of money by Western Union. The defendant, Alphonse Capone, had never filed a (income tax) return for the years covered by the indictment and had never paid any tax on any of the income earned during those years . . .

The income of the taxpayer was derived from gambling . . . and bootlegging. He was referred to by his associates in the newspapers of this country and abroad as the 'Colossus of Racketeers,' the 'King of Gangdom,' and the 'Big Shot.' Although his income was secured wholly through the illegal activities of a large organization of which he was the leader, his activities had not been seriously interfered with by city, county, or state authorities. His **immunity** was explained by statements of members of his organization that all of their activities were protected on account of large graft payments made by them to insure the unmolested conduct of their various businesses. 99

—from "Summary Report" dated December 21, 1933

VOCABULARY

indictments: formal charges

illicit: illegal

bootlegging: selling alcohol illegally

immunity: protection from prosecution

Wilson, Frank J. "Summary Report dated December 21, 1933, prepared at the request of the Chief, Intelligence Unit, Bureau of Internal Revenue, Washington, D.C., in re Alphonse Capone, Lexington Hotel, 2300 Michigan Boulevard, Chicago, Illinois." Treasury Department, Internal Revenue Service, 1933. Copyright © McGraw-Hill Education

1 **SUMMARIZING** How did Al Capone make his money?

_____

_____

_____

2 ECONOMICS Based on the report, in what ways do you think the Eighteenth Amendment did the opposite of what its supporters wanted?

_____

_____

_____

3 **CITING TEXT EVIDENCE** How was Capone viewed by his associates? Cite evidence from the text to support your answer.

_____

_____

_____

4 **DETERMINING MEANING** Based on the text, what do you think a "graft payment" is?

_____

_____

_____

5 **INFERRING** Why do you think Capone was ultimately charged for tax evasion and none of his other crimes?

_____

_____

_____

ESSENTIAL QUESTION

How has the cultural identity of the United States changed over time?

As you gather evidence to answer the Essential Question, think about:

- changes in the arts scene during the 1920s.

- how some of the most famous artists and writers of the 1920s influenced society.

Cultural Innovations

DIRECTIONS Search for evidence in Chapter 7, Lesson 4 to help you answer the following questions..

1A **SUMMARIZING** What were some of the trends that changed popular art during the 1920s?

_____

_____

_____

_____

1B **COMPARING** How did these trends compare to trends in literature?

_____

_____

_____

_____

_____

_____

_____

My Notes

_____

_____

_____

_____

_____

_____

2 **IDENTIFYING CAUSES** Why did so many prominent American writers of the 1920s relocate to Paris?

_____

_____

_____

_____

3 **IDENTIFYING** Fill out the graphic organizer below with the names of the famous artists, authors, and poets of the 1920s.

Artists	Authors	Poets

4A **ANALYZING** How did mass communication lead to the rise of celebrities?

_____

_____

_____

4A **IDENTIFYING CONNECTIONS** How would you compare the goals and methods of mass communication in the 1920s with today?

_____

_____

_____

5 **ECONOMICS** How did changes in the economy affect popular culture during the 1920s?

_____

_____

_____

The Age of Innocence

How has the cultural identity of the United States changed over time?

DIRECTIONS: : Read the following excerpt from the book *The Age of Innocence*. Then respond to the questions that follow.

EXPLORE THE CONTEXT: Edith Wharton was an American writer and the first female to win the Pulitzer Prize. In her prize-winning twelfth novel, *The Age of Innocence*, she criticizes upper-class ignorance and pretensions. The novel depicts the expectations held for upper-class families of New York City. In the story, the characters have to follow society's rules and marry into acceptable families.

PRIMARY SOURCE: BOOK

❝In reality they all lived in a kind of **hieroglyphic** world, where the real thing was never said or done or even thought, but only represented by a set of **arbitrary** signs; as when Mrs. Welland, who knew exactly why Archer had pressed her to announce her daughter's engagement at the Beaufort ball (and had indeed expected him to do no less), yet felt obliged to simulate reluctance, and the air of having had her hand forced, quite as, in the books on Primitive Man that people of advanced culture were beginning to read, the savage bride is dragged with shrieks from her parents' tent. The result, of course, was that the young girl who was the centre of this elaborate system of **mystification** remained the more **inscrutable** for her very frankness and assurance. She was frank, poor darling, because she had nothing to conceal, assured because she knew of nothing to be on her guard against; and with no better preparation than this, she was to be plunged overnight into what people **evasively** called 'the facts of life.'❞

—from *The Age of Innocence*, by Edith Wharton, 1920

VOCABULARY

hieroglyphic: made of pictures to represent words

arbitrary: random

mystification: perplexing; bewildering

inscrutable: hard to understand

evasively: done to avoid

Wharton, Edith. The Age of Innocence. New York: Windsor Editions, 1920.

1 DETERMINING POINT OF VIEW How would you describe the attitude of the narrator toward elite New York society?

_____

_____

_____

2 DETERMINING MEANING Why do you think Wharton uses words such as "pressed," "expected," "obliged," "forced," and "plunged"?

_____

_____

_____

3 CONTRASTING How does the young girl described in the excerpt contrast with those around her?

_____

_____

_____

4 CITING TEXT EVIDENCE How does the author foreshadow that problems will arise for the young girl depicted in the excerpt? Cite evidence from the text to support your answer.

_____

_____

_____

5 GEOGRAPHY How do you think Wharton's novel reflected overall trends in society?

_____

_____

_____

_____

O Russet Witch!

Fitgerald, F. Scott. "O Russett Witch." in Tales from the Jazz Age. New York: Charles Scribner's Sons, 1922.

ESSENTIAL QUESTION

How has the cultural identity of the United States changed over time?

VOCABULARY

desolate: deserted

farce: ridiculous situation

sardonic: mocking

ermine: weasel fur

turbulent: agitated

DIRECTIONS: Read the following excerpt from the short story "O Russet Witch!" Then respond to the questions that follow.

EXPLORE THE CONTEXT: F. Scott Fitzgerald was another famous writer of the 1920s and was known for chronicling the jazz age. He wrote such famous works as *This Side of Paradise* and *The Great Gatsby*. His works often criticized the superficiality of consumerism. "O Russet Witch!" is one of his early short stories printed in a volume entitled *Tales from the Jazz Age*.

PRIMARY SOURCE: SHORT STORY

"It was a dark afternoon, threatening rain and the end of the world, and done in that particularly gloomy gray in which only New York afternoons indulge. A breeze was crying down the streets, whisking along battered newspapers and pieces of things, and little lights were pricking out all the windows—it was so **desolate** that one was sorry for the tops of skyscrapers lost up there in the dark green and gray heaven, and felt that now surely the **farce** was to close, and presently all the buildings would collapse like card houses, and pile up in a dusty, **sardonic** heap upon all the millions who presumed to wind in and out of them.

At least these were the sort of musings that lay heavily upon the soul of Merlin Grainger, as he stood by the window putting a dozen books back in a row after a cyclonic visit by a lady with **ermine** trimmings. He looked out of the window full of the most distressing thoughts—of the early novels of H.G. Wells, of the boot of Genesis, of how Thomas Edison had said that in thirty years there would be no dwelling-houses upon the island, but only a vast and **turbulent** bazaar; and then he set the last book right side up, turned—and Caroline walked coolly into the shop. "

—from "O Russet Witch!" from *Tales of the Jazz Age*, by F. Scott Fitzgerald, 1922

1 **ANALYZING STRUCTURE** How does Fitzgerald use weather to set a tone of despair in this excerpt?

_____

_____

_____

2 **ANALYZING TEXTS** Why do you think Fitzgerald included the detail about a lady with "ermine trimmings"?

_____

_____

_____

3 **CITING TEXT EVIDENCE** How does Fitzgerald show that his main character, Merlin Grainger, was feeling depressed? Cite evidence from the text to support your answer.

_____

_____

_____

4 **ECONOMICS** What does the text tell you about the economy of New York at the time in which the book is set?

_____

_____

_____

_____

_____

5 **PREDICTING** What type of person do you think Caroline will be? Why?

_____

_____

_____

6 **COMPARING AND CONTRASTING TEXTS** In what ways is Fitzgerald's writing similar to Wharton's writing in the previous excerpt?

_____

_____

_____

African American Culture and Politics

DIRECTIONS Search for evidence in Chapter 7, Lesson 5 to help you answer the following questions.

1A **IDENTIFYING** What was the Harlem Renaissance?

_____

_____

_____

1B **RELATING EVENTS** What were some of the major characteristics of writing during the Harlem Renaissance?

_____

_____

2 **ANALYZING** Fill in the graphic organizer below with details about how African American culture was influenced by the arts.

ESSENTIAL QUESTION

How has the cultural identity of the United States changed over time?

As you gather evidence to answer the Essential Question, think about:

- the progress happening and the obstacles still in the way of the rights of African Americans.

- how African American culture was influencing American society.

My Notes

_____

_____

_____

_____

_____

_____

_____

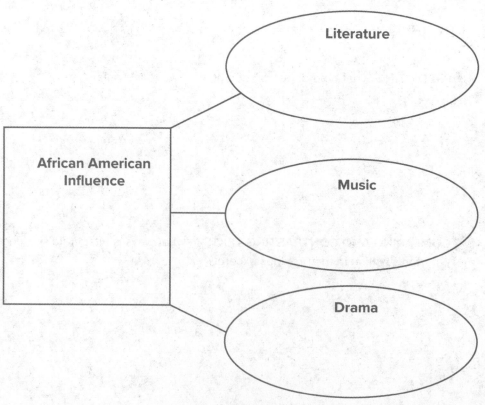

3A `CIVICS` Why did many African Americans move north to cities?

_____

_____

3B **IDENTIFYING EFFECTS** How did this Great Migration influence politics?

_____

_____

4 **UNDERSTANDING CONTEXT** What kinds of injustices did African Americans face at the time, and how did the NAACP fight these injustices?

_____

_____

_____

_____

5 **COMPARING** How would you compare Marcus Garvey's approach to advocating for reform with that of the NAACP?

_____

_____

_____

ESSENTIAL QUESTION

How has the cultural identity of the United States changed over time?

Lift Every Voice and Sing

DIRECTIONS: Read the following poem, "Lift Every Voice and Sing." Then respond to the questions that follow.

EXPLORE THE CONTEXT: James Weldon Johnson was an educator, author, diplomat, lawyer, and early civil rights activist. A leader of the NAACP, he was a key figure in the Harlem Renaissance. Johnson published hundreds of stories and poems during his lifetime. He wrote the poem "Lift Every Voice and Sing" for an event to celebrate Abraham Lincoln's birthday. Later, his brother, J. Rosamond Johnson, set the song to music. The song eventually became the official anthem of the NAACP.

PRIMARY SOURCE: POEM

❝ Lift every voice and sing
Till earth and heaven ring,
Ring with the **harmonies** of Liberty;
Let our rejoicing rise
High as the list'ning skies,
Let it **resound** loud as the rolling seas;
Sing a song full of the faith that the dark past has taught us,
Sing a song full of the hope that the present has brought us;
Facing the rising sun

Of our new day begun,
Let us march on till victory is won.

Stony the road we trod,
Bitter the **chast'ning** rod
Felt in the days when hope had died;
Yet with a steady beat,
Have not our weary feet
Come to the place for which our fathers sighed,
We have come over a way that with tears has been watered,
We have come, treading our path thro' the blood of the **slaughtered,**
Out from the gloomy past,
Till now we stand at last
Where the white gleam of our bright star is cast.

God of our weary years,
God of our silent tears,
Thou who hast brought us thus far on the way;
Thou who hast by Thy might,
Led us into the light,
Keep us forever in the path, we pray,
Lest our feet stray from the places, our God, where we met Thee,
Lest, our hearts drunk with the wine of the world, we forget Thee;
Shadowed beneath Thy hand,
May we forever stand,
True to our God, True to our native land.

—from "Lift Every Voice and Sing," by James Weldon Johnson

VOCABULARY

harmonies: notes that resonate well

resound: echo

chast'ning: punishing

slaughtered: murdered

lest: out of fear that

Johnson, James W. "Lift Every Voice and Sing." In Negro Year Book and Annual Encyclopedia of the Negro 1921-1922, edited by Monroe N. Work. Tuskegee, AL: The Negro Year Book Publishing Company, 1922.

1 **UNDERSTANDING CONTEXT** What role did James Weldon Johnson play in the Harlem Renaissance?

_____

_____

_____

2 **DETERMINING POINT OF VIEW** To what do the phrases "the dark past," the "stony" road, and the "way that with tears has been watered" refer?

_____

_____

_____

3 **INFERRING** What do you think Johnson means by the lines, "Have not our weary feet / Come to the place for which our fathers sighed?"

_____

_____

_____

_____

4 **CIVICS** What does the song tell you about the religious beliefs of some African Americans at the time?

_____

_____

5 **COMPARING AND CONTRASTING TEXTS** How would you compare the tone of Johnson's poem with the works of Wharton and Fitzgerald?

_____

_____

_____

_____

ESSENTIAL QUESTION

How has the cultural identity of the United States changed over time?

Knocking the Color Out of Colored

DIRECTIONS: Read the following excerpt from the Tulsa Star. Then respond to the questions that follow.

EXPLORE THE CONTEXT: The *Tulsa Star* was a weekly newspaper in Oklahoma that published local, state, and national news. The Associated Negro Press, the first national news service for African Americans, was founded in 1919. At the time this article was published, African Americans were still experiencing segregation, discrimination, and violence in many forms.

PRIMARY SOURCE: NEWSPAPER

"In a recent gathering of the civics committee of the Appomattox Club of Chicago, one of the strong points emphasized was the injustice of laboring every criminal story in which a Race man is **implicated** with the 'badge of color.' Evidence was produced which showed that great harm is done, and that constant reference to race in such matters served to increase race feeling and prejudice. It was shown that in many cases such stories were written with '**malice** aforethought' by prejudiced reporters, and frequently without the knowledge and against the policy of the owners of the newspapers. Nahum Daniel Brascher, editor in chief of the Associated Negro Press in his address **dwelt** at length on these facts, and gave concrete examples of two of the greatest **dailies** in the country that have adopted the policy with beneficial results . . . .

As a result of this conference, at least one of the great dailies of Chicago has adopted the policy. *The Chicago American*, which is one of the largest evening newspapers in the country, is the paper. In the recent account of the attempt to lynch three of our men because of the killing of street car conductor, where columns of the first page were made, *The Chicago American* did not at any time refer to race in the stories it carried. "

—from "Knocking the Color out of Colored," the *Tulsa Star*, October 9, 1920

VOCABULARY

implicated: shown to be involved

malice aforethought: plan to harm

dwelt: focused

dailies: newspapers published 365 days a year

1 **INFERRING** What do you think the author means by "the badge of color"?

_____

_____

2 CIVICS Why would references to race increase prejudice?

_____

_____

_____

3 **DETERMINING POINT OF VIEW** Based on the article, how did reporters use "malice aforethought"?

_____

_____

_____

_____

_____

4 **EXPLAINING** What policy did two of the great dailies of the time adopt?

_____

_____

5 **IDENTIFYING CONNECTIONS** How does this article relate to recent events?

_____

_____

_____

_____

ESSENTIAL QUESTIONS

How has the cultural identity of the United States changed over time?

❶ Think About It

Review the Supporting Questions that you developed at the beginning of the chapter. Review the evidence that you gathered in Chapter 7. Were you able to answer each Supporting Question?

If there was not enough evidence to answer your Supporting Questions, what additional evidence do you think you need to consider?

_____

_____

_____

_____

❷ Organize Your Evidence

Use a chart like the one below to organize the evidence you will use to support your findings about changes in the different elements of American culture during the 1920s. Cite evidence from the text.

Cultural Element	How did it affect American culture during the 1920s	Evidence from the text
Politics		
Economics		
Values/morality		
The arts		
African American culture		

③ Write About It

Think about the Essential Question: *How has the cultural identity of the United States changed over time?* Then write a statement that summarizes how the cultural identity of the United States changed during the 1920s. This statement should reflect the evidence you gathered from the chapter

_____

_____

_____

_____

_____

④ Connect to the Essential Question

Create a title, and prepare a visual essay in which you describe how the cultural identity of the United States changed during the 1920s. Include the statement you created in Step 3 in your essay. Add supporting details and examples that relate to the Essential Question. Find photos and art and include them in your essay. Provide captions to connect the illustrations to your written work. Use this creative format to inform your readers about this decade in an interesting way.

_____

_____

_____

_____

_____

_____

_____

_____

_____

_____

CITIZENSHIP
TAKE ACTION

MAKE CONNECTIONS The cultural identity of the United States continues to shift and change today, in large part through immigration. The issues surrounding immigration are just as important and relevant today as they were in the 1920s. Throughout this chapter you read and learned about aspects of isolationism and nativism, the belief that one's native land needs to be protected from immigrants. Think about the incredible diversity of the United States today and the different attitudes toward immigration in our society. Research some of the difficulties and successes of immigration policy. Using your information, initiate an informed conversation with your peers about immigration policy in the United States today. Being aware and able to discuss current issues will help you to meaningfully engage in and improve your community.

DIRECTIONS: To have an informed conversation, you need to know the facts. Begin by arming yourself with information about immigration demographics, policy, and legislation. Take notes as you research to aid you in your conversation. As you research, begin to formulate ideas on proposals that you think would be good immigration policy. Your notes should include current policies, issues, and points that you want to make in the conversation. Next, begin a conversation with your class or a smaller group. Refer to your notes. Ask questions and respectfully listen to each other's ideas. As you finish your conversation, add any notes that may have changed your thinking or new ideas you learned from your classmates.

_____

_____

_____

_____

_____

_____

_____

_____

The Great Depression Begins

ESSENTIAL QUESTION
How do depressions affect societies?

Think about how this question might relate to the economic collapse known in the United States as the Great Depression.

TALK ABOUT IT

Discuss with a partner what type of information you would need to know to answer this question. For example, one question might be: *What caused the Great Depression?*

DIRECTIONS: Now write down three additional questions that would help you explain what caused the Great Depression and how Americans responded to it.

MY RESEARCH QUESTIONS

Supporting Question 1:

_____

_____

_____

Supporting Question 2:

_____

_____

_____

Supporting Question 3:

_____

_____

_____

The Causes of the Great Depression

DIRECTIONS Search for evidence in Chapter 8, Lesson 1 to help you answer the following questions.

1A **DESCRIBING** Why might the stock market have appeared to be a sure way to make money prior to the Great Crash of 1929?

_____

_____

_____

ESSENTIAL QUESTION

How do depressions affect societies?

As you gather evidence to answer the Essential Question, think about:

- the role of the stock market just before the crash.

- what events led to the stock market crash and Black Thursday.

- what other factors helped contribute to the Great Depression in the United States.

1B **IDENTIFYING CAUSES** How did the practice of buying on margin contribute to the stock market crash of 1929?

_____

_____

_____

_____

_____

My Notes

_____

_____

_____

_____

_____

_____

2A **MAKING CONNECTION** What occurred during the Great Crash?

_____

_____

_____

_____

_____

2B **IDENTIFYING EFFECTS** How did the Great Crash contribute to the Great Depression?

_____

_____

_____

_____

_____

3 **EXPLAINING CAUSE AND EFFECT** Complete the graphic organizer to identify what contributed to the weakening of banks as a result of the stock market crash of 1929.

CAUSE	EFFECT

4 **ECONOMICS** Complete the graphic organizer below by explaining the role of the government, banks, manufacturers, and individuals in the Great Depression.

Federal Government	Banks	Manufacturers/ Retailers	Individuals

5 **SUMMARIZING** Based on the information you have collected, could the Great Depression have been avoided? Why or why not?

_____

_____

_____

_____

_____

Smith, Richard Norton and Timothy Walch. The Ordeal of Herbert Hoover. Prologue Magazine, Summer 2004. https://www.archives.gov/publications/prologue/2004/summer/hoover-1.html

ESSENTIAL QUESTION
How do depressions affect societies?

A Modern View of the Great Depression

DIRECTIONS: Read the following excerpt from a modern-day article about the Great Depression. Then answer the accompanying questions.

EXPLORE THE CONTEXT: In this excerpt, written in 2004, authors Richard Norton Smith and Timothy Walch discuss the Great Depression, some of the factors that led to it, and President Herbert Hoover's initial response to the economic crisis.

SECONDARY SOURCE: ARTICLE

❝ Economists are still divided about what caused the Great Depression and what turned a relatively mild downturn into a decade-long nightmare. Hoover himself emphasized the dislocations brought on by World War I, the rickety structure of American banking, excessive stock **[speculation]**, and Congress's refusal to act on many of his proposals. The President's critics argued that in approving the Smoot-Hawley tariff in the spring of 1930, he unintentionally raised barriers around U.S. products, worsened the plight of debtor nations, and set off a round of retaliatory measures that crippled global trade.

Neither claim went far enough. In truth, Hoover's celebration of technology failed to anticipate the end of a postwar building boom, or a glut of twenty-six million new cars and other consumer goods flooding the market. Agriculture, mired in depression for much of the 1920s, was deprived of cash it needed to take part in the consumer revolution. At the same time, the average worker's wages of $1,500 a year failed to keep pace with the spectacular gains in productivity achieved since 1920. By 1929 production was outstripping demand.

The United States had too many banks, and too many of them played the stock market with depositors' funds or speculated in their own stocks. Government had yet to devise insurance for the jobless or income maintenance for the [destitute]. With unemployment, buying power vanished overnight. Together, government and business actually spent more in the first half of 1930 than in all of 1929. Yet such bold action did little to help the economy as frightened consumers cut back their expenditures by 10 percent and a severe drought ravaged the agricultural heartland beginning in the summer of 1930. Foreign banks went under, draining U.S. wealth and destroying world trade. Unemployment soared from five million in 1930 to more than eleven million in 1931. A sharp **[recession]** had become the Great Depression. ❞

—"The Ordeal of Herbert Hoover," by Richard Norton Smith and Timothy Walch, *Prologue Magazine,* 2004

VOCABULARY

speculation: an economic investment

recession: a period in which the economy shrinks

Copyright © McGraw-Hill Education

1 **DISTINGUISHING FACT FROM OPINION** What facts do the authors use to support their argument about what made the Great Depression worse? Provide an example.

_____

_____

_____

2 ECONOMICS What were the consequences of the high tariff policy used by the federal government?

_____

_____

_____

_____

3 **EVALUATING EVIDENCE** According to the authors, what was the role of banks in the Great Depression? What are the authors suggesting about banks?

_____

_____

_____

4 **EVALUATING EVIDENCE** What type of document is this? In what way might this document differ from an account written by an economist who lived during the period?

_____

_____

_____

5 **DRAWING CONCLUSIONS** How aware was President Hoover about the economic problems before the crash of 1929? Who or what did he hold responsible for the downturn?

_____

_____

_____

ESSENTIAL QUESTION

How do depressions affect societies?

Herbert Hoover Addresses the Issue of the Economy

DIRECTIONS: Read the following excerpt from a speech by Herbert Hoover. Then respond to the questions that follow.

EXPLORE THE CONTEXT: In 1928, Herbert Hoover was elected president on a promise to ensure the country's booming prosperity. A little over a year later, the stock market crashed, and the country was plunged into a deep economic depression. In a meeting with railway executives in November 1929, Hoover spoke about the upcoming challenges facing the United States.

PRIMARY SOURCE: SPEECH

"We have also to deal naturally with some unemployment in the semi-necessity trades. But the real problem and the interpretation of it is one of maintenance of employment. This is not a question of bolstering stock markets or stock prices or anything of that kind. We are dealing with the vital question of maintaining employment in the United States and consequently the comfort and standard of living of the people and their ability to buy goods and proceed in the normal course of their lives. So that the purpose of this movement is to disabuse the public mind of the notion that there has been any serious or vital interruption in our economic system, and that it is going to proceed in the ordinary, normal manner, and to get that impression over not by preachment and talks but by definite and positive acts on the part of industry and business and the Government and others. As I said before, I do not believe that words ever convince a discouraged person in these situations. The thing that brings him back is courage and the natural sight of other industries and other men going ahead with their programs and business.

So I wanted you to get that background upon it all, because it seriously concerns the press to give the confidence to the public that the business fabric is now organizing itself, taking steps on its own responsibility to carry on; that it is going to go even farther and stretch itself to meet any possible condition of employment is the thing that will give courage to the public rather than to say to them every day that they should not be alarmed. So that I am trying to get this problem across by action in different industries and other groups rather than by too much talking, and, therefore, I don't want to talk about it. I want the action to speak for itself. These conclusions are not a statement from me. That is the conclusion of those men who were present."

—from "The Economy and Public Confidence," by Herbert Hoover, November 19, 1929

Public Papers of the Presidents of the United States: Herbert Hoover: Containing the Public Messages, Speeches, and Statements of the President: MARCH 4 TO DECEMBER 31, 1929. Washington D.C.: U.S. Government Printing Office, 1974.

1 **DETERMINING MEANING** What is the central message of this speech? What is Hoover asking?

_____

_____

_____

2 **ANALYZING** Why does Hoover believe that maintaining employment will best benefit the American people? Which line of the speech best answers the question?

_____

_____

_____

3 **EVALUATING EVIDENCE** What type of document is this? How does this information help you understand the document?

_____

_____

_____

4 **DETERMINING CONTEXT** How does the setting and audience for the speech help emphasize Hoover's message?

_____

_____

_____

5 **CIVICS** How does this excerpt illustrate President Hoover's attitudes about the limits of the federal government and the U.S. economy?

_____

_____

_____

6 **DETERMINING MEANING** What did President Hoover mean when he said, "I do not believe that words ever convince a discouraged person in these situations. The thing that brings him back is courage and the natural sight of other industries and other men going ahead with their programs and business"? Why might these words have been important?

_____

Life During the Great Depression

DIRECTIONS Search for evidence in Chapter 8, Lesson 2 to help you answer the following questions.

1A **IDENTIFYING EFFECTS** What options were available for people who had lost their jobs during the Great Depression?

_____

_____

1B **DETERMINING CONTEXT** What were Hoovervilles?

_____

_____

_____

_____

2A **MAKING CONNECTIONS** In what ways did modern agricultural production methods and nature contribute to the Dust Bowl?

_____

_____

_____

_____

2B GEOGRAPHY What were the effects of the Dust Bowl on the environment of the Great Plains?

_____

_____

_____

_____

ESSENTIAL QUESTION

How do depressions affect societies?

As you gather evidence to answer the Essential Question, think about:

- how the Great Depression impacted the daily lives of Americans.
- what caused the Dust Bowl and how it impacted the United States.
- how popular culture in the United States reflected the moods of the Great Depression.

My Notes

_____

_____

_____

_____

_____

_____

3 **EXPLAINING** Use the Cornell Notes organizer to answer questions and take notes about popular culture in the United States during the Great Depression.

Main Ideas	Notes
What did people do for entertainment during the Great Depression?	
Why were movies and other forms of entertainment popular?	
What was the importance of entertainment?	
How did artists react to the Great Depression?	

4 **IDENTIFYING CAUSE AND EFFECT** Use the graphic organizer below to take notes about how the Great Depression impacted everyday life for many Americans.

The Effects of the Depression on Everyday Life

CAUSE	EFFECT
Work closings	
Lack of food	
Lack of housing	
Immigrants	

Miscellaneous Items in High Demand, Library of Congress, LC-USZ6-1018 · Copyright © McGraw-Hill Education

ESSENTIAL QUESTION

How do depressions affect societies?

The Dust Bowl Migration

DIRECTIONS: Study the map of migrant camps in California in 1935. Then respond to the questions that follow.

EXPLORE THE CONTEXT: The Dust Bowl displaced thousands of people living in the Great Plains during the Great Depression. Many took everything they owned and headed west to California. Despite their relocation, many migrants had a difficult time; work was scarce, and many people did not want migrants in their cities and towns. To help migrants, the government's Farm Security Administration built 13 camps to provide housing for as many as 300 families in addition to helping them find work. This map from 1935 shows where the initial camps were intended to be placed.

PRIMARY SOURCE: MAP

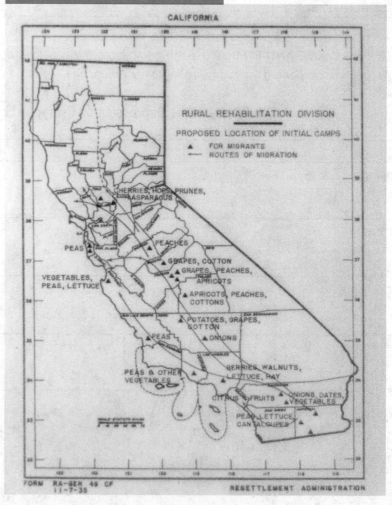

1A **IDENTIFYING PATTERNS** What do the arrows reveal about the movements of migrant workers?

_____

_____

_____

1B **INFERRING** What does this tell you about work in the state of California at the time?

_____

_____

_____

2 GEOGRAPHY What does the placement of migrant camps suggest about the government's attitude toward migrant workers?

_____

_____

_____

3 **USING MAPS** How do you know that the central part of the state had work in the agricultural industry?

_____

_____

_____

4 **DETERMINING CONTEXT** What important things were going on at the time that relate to this document? How does this information help you understand the document?

_____

_____

_____

ESSENTIAL QUESTION

How do depressions affect societies?

Federal Writer's Project

DIRECTIONS: Read the following excerpt from an interview with A.F. Kehr. Then respond to the questions that follow.

EXPLORE THE CONTEXT: From 1936 to 1940, writers, librarians, and teachers traveled throughout the country interviewing Americans from all backgrounds and recording their life histories as part of the Federal Writers Project. The end result is a series of literary snapshots of Americans during the Depression years. This excerpt relates the experiences of a small-town theater owner.

PRIMARY SOURCE: SPEECH

66 In 1914, Mr. A. F. Kehr began his career, by opening the first picture show in Ogallala. He [christened] his [show?] the '[Gem?]' which was located to the building now occupied by Green [Lees?] Clothing Store. For awhile he used bridge planks, nail kegs and 'what have you,' for extra seats, and gave the community the very best pictures available. Mr. Kehr kept up with the moving picture industry by installing the latest equipment available from time to time.

The first two years having been a great success, Mr. Kehr moved one block south, installing new equipment, and also increasing the seating capacity to 150. The name was changed to "The Princess."

In January, 1936, the Kehr family opened the 'Prairie,' a luxurious theatre and one of the finest in the country, with all the very latest and most practical equipment money could buy. We pride Mr. Kehr's theatre as being on an equal with the theatres in the larger cities.

Many of the pictures are shown here before release dates in Omaha and Denver. ...

The 552 comfortable seats are upholstered in black leather and black and rust velour.

The roomy balcony will seat 56. ...

The sound equipment is the new R.C.A. [Victor?] Photophone high fidelity, the same equipment in the two super theaters in Rockefeller Center, New York City. ...

The high fidelity reproduces the human voice without the mechanical tones which are so lacking in character.

The temperature and humidity is maintained by a system of automatic dampers and thermostat. 99

—from an interview with A.F. Kehr, *American Life Histories: Manuscripts from the Federal Writers' Project*

1 RELATING EVENTS This document is an oral history recorded during the Great Depression. How does knowing this help you understand it?

_____

_____

_____

2 CITING TEXT EVIDENCE What line or phrase from the excerpt helps you understand what the theater was like?

_____

_____

_____

3 GEOGRAPHY What does the description of the theater suggest about going to the movies in a Depression-era small town? What does it reveal about the owner?

_____

_____

_____

_____

4 MAKING INFERENCES What can you infer about the technology of the period?

_____

_____

_____

5 DRAWING CONCLUSIONS How does this excerpt demonstrate the idea of movie theaters as "palaces" for people during the Depression?

_____

_____

_____

ESSENTIAL QUESTION

How do depressions affect societies?

As you gather evidence to answer the Essential Question, think about:

- steps President Hoover took to help the country recover from the Great Depression.

- the response of different groups of Americans to the slow economic recovery.

- the long-term impact of Hoover's efforts in trying to turn the economy around.

My Notes

Hoover's Response to the Depression

DIRECTIONS Search for evidence in Chapter 8, Lesson 3 to help you answer the following questions.

1A **DESCRIBING** How did the idea of "rugged individualism" influence President Hoover's approach to the Great Depression?

_____

_____

_____

1B **IDENTIFYING PERSPECTIVES** How did Hoover try to encourage business to do more to help the economy?

_____

_____

_____

_____

_____

2A **RELATING EVENTS** Why were some Americans angry at Hoover?

_____

_____

_____

2B **INFERRING** In what ways might the American Communist Party have benefitted from the poor economy in the United States?

_____

_____

_____

_____

3 CIVICS Use the Cornell Notes organizer to take notes about Hoover's legislation to help the country during the Great Depression.

Main Ideas	Notes
National Credit Corporation (NCC)	
Reconstruction Finance Corporation (RFC)	
Emergency Relief and Construction Act	

4 **ANALYZING** How did Hoover's attitude toward relief change during the Great Depression? What impacted that thinking?

_____

_____

_____

_____

_____

5 **EXPLAINING CAUSE AND EFFECT** In the chart below, explain how farmers and veterans reacted to Hoover's policies during the Depression.

	CAUSE	EFFECT
Farmers		
World War I Veterans		
Unemployed		

ESSENTIAL QUESTION

How do depressions affect societies?

Bonus Army March to Washington

DIRECTIONS: Study the image of the veterans' march to Washington. Then respond to the questions that follow.

EXPLORE THE CONTEXT: In June 1932, a group of between 15,000 and 20,000 World War I veterans marched on Washington, D.C., to ask for early payment of cash bonuses promised to them by the government. Originally, the bonuses were to be paid in 1945, but for countless veterans—many of whom were unemployed—it was too long to wait. By December, the veterans hoped to spur the government to pay the bonuses early.

PRIMARY SOURCE: PHOTO

1 INFERRING Who are the people gathered in this crowd?

_____

_____

_____

2 CITING TEXT EVIDENCE What historical events were happening at the time this photo was taken? What clues in the poster indicate the period?

_____

_____

_____

_____

_____

3 ANALYZING SOURCES What is the purpose of the posters the men are holding?

_____

_____

_____

_____

_____

4 IDENTIFYING CAUSES Why did the Bonus Army march to Washington?

_____

_____

_____

5 CIVICS Can you think of other examples in which groups marched on Washington? Why? What is one thing all marchers on Washington have in common? Explain your answer.

_____

_____

_____

_____

Unemployment Relief: Hearings on S.4632, S.4727, S.4755, and S.4822, Bills Relative to Federal Loans to Aid Unemployment, Before the Committee on Banking and Currency, 72nd Cong. 1st Sess. (1932) (statement of Hon. Odgen L. Mills, Secretary of the Treasury, Washington, D.C.).

ESSENTIAL QUESTION

How do depressions affect societies?

Emergency Relief and Construction Act

DIRECTIONS: Read the following excerpt from a congressional hearing. Then respond to the questions that follow.

EXPLORE THE CONTEXT: In 1932, members of the Senate Committee on Banking met to consider a proposed piece of legislation. That legislation would authorize federal funds to help state and local governments cope with the growing number of people in need of financial relief as a result of the Great Depression.

PRIMARY SOURCE: CONGRESSIONAL HEARING

"Secretary Mills . . . I do not believe there are but very few States in the Union that feel they actually need Federal funds for relief purposes. I say need. That is a very different question, as to whether we want to provide Federal funds directly for relief purposes. That is another issue. But we are dealing this morning with the question whether the States need funds; not whether we will have the Federal Government provide funds for relief purposes. ...

Senator Blaine (interposing). In this national emergency, I assume from what you say that you do not contend that the relief of unemployment and distress is not a national responsibility; or you do contend that it is not a national responsibility, but is a State and local responsibility. ...

Secretary Mills... I think you ought to provide an emergency fund so that under any circumstances none of these local and State relief funds could fail and people be faced with starvation and destitution. There ought to be an emergency fund. Now, my conception of an emergency fund is to create a fund of $300,000,000 and to loan that to States where that emergency exists. And when you loan it you loan it on the credit of that State ... "

—from a hearing held on the Emergency Relief and Construction Act by the U.S. Senate's Committee on Banking, July 1932

1 **CITING EVIDENCE** What appears to be the primary concern of the senators over the proposed legislation? Write the evidence from the hearing on the lines below.

_____

_____

_____

_____

2 **DETERMINING CAUSE AND EFFECT** What brought the issue of emergency relief to the Senate committee?

_____

_____

_____

3 **EVALUATING** What were some of the concerns noted by the senators about the proposed legislation?

_____

_____

_____

_____

4 **DISTINGUISHING FACT FROM OPINION** Cite one example of an opinion stated by Senator Mills in this excerpt.

_____

_____

_____

_____

_____

5 CIVICS What branch of the government is holding the discussions?

_____

_____

_____

ESSENTIAL QUESTION

How do depressions affect societies?

My Notes

① Think About It

Review the supporting questions you developed at the beginning of the chapter. Review the evidence you gathered in Chapter 8. Were you able to answer each of your Supporting Questions?

If there was not enough evidence to answer your Supporting Questions, what additional evidence do you think you need to consider?

② Organize Your Evidence

Complete the web below with information you learned about how the different responses by people and government impacted the Great Depression during the 1930s.

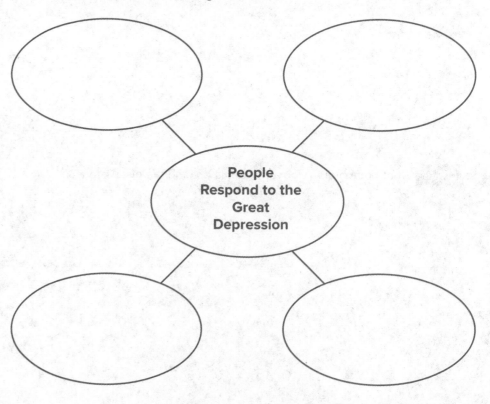

People Respond to the Great Depression

❸ Talk About It

Work in small groups. Talk with your group about the information you included in your web. Were the effects of the Great Depression you listed the same as your classmates', or were they different? Which effects of the Great Depression had the most impact on people's lives? Why?

_____

_____

_____

_____

_____

_____

❹ Connect to the Essential Question

On a separate piece of paper, write out the questions you would like to ask a person who lived during the Great Depression and who was involved in protesting against the government over economic policies. Then interview a person who lived through the Great Depression. If you can't find such a person, then interview a history teacher or librarian, having them answer the questions from their knowledge of the subject. If necessary, use details from the text to help you answer the questions that they could not answer. Your questions should help you answer the ESSENTIAL QUESTION: _How do depressions affect societies?_

_____

_____

_____

_____

_____

_____

TAKE ACTION

MAKE CONNECTIONS One of the biggest challenges people faced during the Great Depression was getting the attention of the federal government to their plight. The Hoover administration did not believe that the government should be involved directly in relief efforts or aid. This caused many different groups to protest because of the Great Depression's impact on their lives.

DIRECTIONS: Use what you have learned in Chapter 8 about the Great Depression and its impact on American society. Then write an editorial about the different ways in which people made their voices heard about President Hoover and his policies. Give details about the different groups. What was similar in each approach? What was different? Then conclude your editorial by discussing how citizens make their voices heard in calling for change today, noting similarities, if any. Your article should be approximately 400 to 500 words. Use details from both the Inquiry Journal and the chapter textbook for your background information.

Roosevelt and the New Deal

ESSENTIAL QUESTION

Can the government fix the economy?

Think about how this question might relate to President Franklin D. Roosevelt's policies. How did Roosevelt address the issues that the country faced after the stock market crashed? Was he able to fix the economy with government programs?

TALK ABOUT IT

Discuss with a partner what type of information you would need to know to answer this question. For example, one question might be: *Did the programs of the New Deal make an important impact on the economy?*

DIRECTIONS: Now write three additional questions that would help you understand the government's role in improving a country's economy.

MY RESEARCH QUESTIONS

Supporting Question 1:

_____

_____

Supporting Question 2:

_____

_____

Supporting Question 3:

_____

_____

The First New Deal

DIRECTIONS Search for evidence in Chapter 9, Lesson 1 to help you answer the following questions.

1A **DESCRIBING** What kind of a person was Roosevelt? What details about his background helped to shape his character?

_____

_____

_____

_____

_____

_____

1B **ANALYZING** How did Roosevelt's disability make him well suited to lead the country out of the Great Depression?

_____

_____

_____

_____

2A **ECONOMICS** What was the state of the economy when FDR took office?

_____

_____

_____

_____

2B **DESCRIBING** What did Roosevelt do to address the banking crisis?

_____

_____

_____

_____

ESSENTIAL QUESTION

Can the government fix the economy?

As you gather evidence to answer the Essential Question, think about

- the state of the economy when Roosevelt became president.
- the causes of the economic trouble in the country.
- how unemployment impacted the nation's economy.

My Notes

_____

_____

_____

_____

_____

_____

_____

3A IDENTIFYING THE MAIN IDEA What were Roosevelt's social policies that brought relief to struggling Americans?

_____

_____

_____

3B COMPARE AND CONTRAST Fill out the Venn diagram to tell how the economic programs were similar to and different from the social programs that FDR enacted in his first one hundred days.

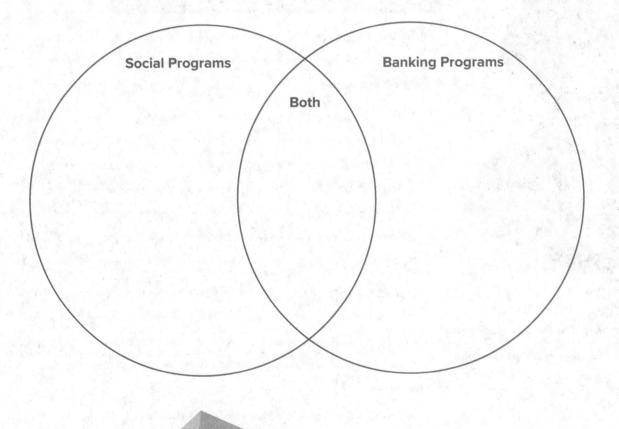

Social Programs

Both

Banking Programs

Beasley, Maurene. "The Press Conferences of Eleanor Roosevelt." Presentation at the Annual Convention of the Association for Education in Journalism and Mass Communication, Corvallis, OR, August 6-9, 1983.

ESSENTIAL QUESTION

Can the government fix the economy?

VOCABULARY

inauguration: ceremonial start to a presidency

press conference: interview given to journalists

newspaperwoman: female journalist

Woman-Only Press Conference

DIRECTIONS: Read the following excerpt from a research paper. Then answer the questions that follow.

INTRODUCTION: In 1983, a researcher named Maurine Beasley discovered 87 transcripts of Eleanor Roosevelt's woman-only **press conferences**. She compiled what she learned from the transcripts and wrote a research paper about the famous figure based on those primary sources.

SECONDARY SOURCE: RESEARCH PAPER

" The first press conference held was on March 6, 1933, just two days after Franklin D. Roosevelt's first **inauguration** as President . . . attended by some 30 **newspaperwomen**. . . .

The idea of the press conference] involved her concept of a newspaperwoman's role, which she defined as 'leading the women in the country to form a general attitude of mind and thought.' The idea is largely to make an understanding between the White House and the general public, she explained, calling the reporters "interpreters to the women of the country as to what goes on politically in the legislative national life, and also what the social and personal life is at the White House. . . .

In her autobiography, [Roosevelt] stated a major reason for the conference was to insure that women reporters, hard-pressed to keep their jobs during the Depression, would be able to get news not available to men competitors, as well as to have an opportunity to report news 'of special interest and value to the women of the country. "

—from *The Press Conferences of Eleanor Roosevelt,* by Maurine Beasley

1 **IDENTIFYING PERSPECTIVES** What was the purpose of Eleanor Roosevelt's woman-only press conferences?

_____

_____

_____

_____

2 INFERRING Why was the first of these woman-only press conferences held just a few days after Roosevelt's husband's inauguration?

_____

_____

_____

3 ECONOMICS How did woman-only press conferences give working women an advantage in the workplace?

_____

_____

_____

_____

_____

4 DETERMINING CONTEXT Using what you know about the historical context of the Great Depression and the 1930s, why was Eleanor Roosevelt's action important?

_____

_____

_____

_____

_____

_____

5 IDENTIFYING CONNECTIONS Eleanor Roosevelt chose how and with whom to share her experience as first lady of the United States. How do we learn about the first lady in the modern era?

_____

_____

_____

ESSENTIAL QUESTION

Can the government fix the economy?

Tennessee Valley Authority

DIRECTIONS: Read the excerpt from legislation. Then answer the questions that follow.

EXPLORE THE CONTEXT: The creation of the Tennessee Valley Authority marked the first time that the federal government took direct action to improve a region of the country.

PRIMARY SOURCE: LEGISLATION

66 May 18, 1933

An Act to Improve the **Navigability** and to Provide for the Flood Control of the Tennessee River:

- to Provide for Reforestation and the Proper Use of **Marginal Lands** in the Tennessee Valley;
- to Provide for the Agricultural and Industrial Development of Said Valley;
- to Provide for the National Defense by the Creation of a Corporation for the Operation of Government Properties at and near Muscle **Shoals** in the State of Alabama, and for Other Purposes

Be it enacted by the Senate and House of Representatives of the United States of America in Congress assembled,

That for the purpose of maintaining and operating the properties now owned by the United States in the vicinity of Muscle Shoals, Alabama, in the interest of the national defense and for agriculture and industrial development, and to improve navigation in the Tennessee River and to control the destructive flood waters in the Tennessee River and Mississippi River Basins, there is hereby created a **body corporate** by the name of the 'Tennessee Valley Authority' . . . The board of directors first appointed shall be deemed the incorporators and the incorporation shall be held to have been effected from the date of the first meeting of the board. **99**

—from the Tennessee Valley Authority Act of 1933

VOCABULARY

navigability: ability to be sailed on

marginal land: poor or dry land areas

shoals: areas of shallow water

body corporate: company

Tennessee Valley Authority Act of 1933, Pub.L. 73-17, 48 Stat. 58 (1933).

1 **ANALYZING SOURCES** How does knowing that this is legislation help you understand the point of view of the authors?

_____

_____

_____

_____

2 **SUMMARIZING** What work was ordered for the Tennessee Valley Authority?

_____

_____

3 **INFERRING** What was happening in the country at that time that explains the creation of the TVA?

_____

_____

_____

4 **ECONOMICS** What were the intended economic effects of the TVA?

_____

_____

_____

5 **PREDICTING** Based on the description of the work that will be undertaken by the TVA, what predictions can you make about the river basins of the Tennessee River and the Mississippi River?

_____

_____

_____

_____

The Second New Deal

DIRECTIONS: Search for evidence in Chapter 9, Lesson 2 to help you answer the following questions.

1A ECONOMICS What is deficit spending?

_____

_____

_____

1B **IDENTIFYING CAUSE AND EFFECT** How did Roosevelt's deficit spending lead to opposition to the New Deal?

_____

_____

_____

2A **ANALYZING** How did Roosevelt use the Supreme Court in his strategy for the Second New Deal?

_____

_____

_____

_____

_____

2B **EXPLAINING EFFECTS** Why did those Supreme Court decisions motivate Congress to act on labor legislation?

_____

_____

_____

ESSENTIAL QUESTION

Can the government fix the economy?

As you gather evidence to answer the Essential Question, think about

- how Roosevelt's opponents pushed back against his programs.
- how the separation of powers put limits on the executive branch of government.
- how the New Deal programs helped seniors and workers.

My Notes

_____

_____

_____

_____

_____

_____

_____

3 **EVALUATING** Complete the graphic organizer with the features of the Wagner Act and Social Security.

Wagner Act	Social Security

4 **ANALYZING POINTS OF VIEW** Why did people object to new labor laws and Social Security?

_____

_____

_____

_____

_____

ESSENTIAL QUESTION

Can the government fix the economy?

Telegram from the Great Sit-Down Strike

DIRECTIONS: Read the telegram. Then answer the questions that follow.

EXPLORE THE CONTEXT: In the 1930s, General Motors was a large automobile manufacturer that provided jobs for many people in Flint, Michigan. However, working conditions were dangerous and the pay was low. Workers unionized in order to increase their power to improve their pay and working conditions. In late 1936 and early 1937, the workers participated in a sit-down strike and sent a telegram to the governor of Michigan.

PRIMARY SOURCE: TELEGRAM

❝We feel it proper to recall to you the **assurance** you have many times given to the public that you would not permit force or violence to be used in **ousting** us from the plants. Unarmed as we are, the introduction of **militia**, sheriff, or police with murderous weapons, will mean a **bloodbath** of unarmed workers. The police of Flint belong to General Motors. The sheriff of Genesee County belongs to General Motors, and the judges of Genesee County belong to General Motors. . . It remains to be seen whether or not the governor of this state also belongs to General Motors. We have decided to stay in the plants. We have no illusions what sacrifices this decision will entail. We fully expect that if violent efforts are used to put us out, many of us will be killed. We take this method to make it known to our wives, our children, and to the people of the state and country, that if this result follows from the attempts to eject us, you are the one who must be held responsible for our death. ❞

—from a telegram to Governor Frank Murphy from the sit-down strike, February 3, 1937

VOCABULARY

assurance: promise

ousting: removing by force

militia: armed military forces

bloodbath: violent slaughter

Weinstone, W. W. The Great Sit-Down Strike. New York: Workers Library Publishers, 1937.

1 **EVALUATING** What is the central message of the telegram?

_____

_____

2 **DETERMINING CONTEXT** What is the background of the authors of the document?

_____

_____

3 **EVALUATING EVIDENCE** What threat do the authors make at the end of the telegram? What is the impact of that threat on the persuasiveness of the telegram?

_____

_____

_____

_____

4 ECONOMICS What legislative actions of the New Deal influenced the sit-down strike and the powers that the authors of the telegram held?

_____

_____

_____

_____

5 **DRAWING CONCLUSIONS** What does this telegram tell you about the role that government played in improving the lives of workers?

_____

_____

_____

_____

_____

Social Security Act, Pub.L. 74-271, 49 Stat. 620 (1935).   Copyright © McGraw-Hill Education

ESSENTIAL QUESTION

Can the government fix the economy?

VOCABULARY

benefits: payments by the state, employer, or insurance company

revenue: annual income

appropriation: money set aside for a specific purpose

Social Security Act of 1935

DIRECTIONS: Read the legislation excerpt. Then answer the questions that follow.

EXPLORE THE CONTEXT: Before the New Deal, most workers worked until they died or could no longer do so. This meant that if they could no longer physically perform work, they often faced a life of poverty. The Great Depression made their situation even worse.

PRIMARY SOURCE: LEGISLATION

❝An act to provide for the general welfare by establishing a system of Federal old-age **benefits,** and by enabling the several States to make more adequate provision for aged persons, blind persons, dependent and crippled children, maternal and child welfare, public health, and the administration of their unemployment compensation laws; to establish a Social Security Board; to raise **revenue;** and for other purposes.

Be it enacted by the Senate and House of Representatives of the United States of America in Congress assembled,

TITLE I—GRANTS TO STATES FOR OLD-AGE ASSISTANCE **APPROPRIATION**

SECTION 1 For the purpose of enabling each State to furnish financial assistance, as far as practicable under the conditions in such State, to aged needy individuals, there is hereby authorized to be appropriated for the fiscal year ended June 30, 1936, the sum of $49,750,000, and there is hereby authorized to be appropriated for each fiscal year thereafter a sum sufficient to carry out the purposes of this title. The sums made available under this section shall be used for making payments to States which have submitted, and had approved by the Social Security Board established by Title VII . . . State plans for old-age assistance.❞

—from Social Security Act of 1935

1 **DESCRIBING** What was the intention of this document?

_____

_____

_____

2 **DETERMINING CONTEXT** What important things were going on in the country at the time the document was written?

_____

_____

_____

3 **CITING TEXT EVIDENCE** Cite text evidence regarding the people whom this legislation aims to help and what assistance is specifically offered?

_____

_____

_____

_____

_____

4 **INFERRING** What can you infer about what legislators of the 1930s believed about the federal government's responsibility towards its citizens?

_____

_____

_____

5 **ECONOMICS** What information does the passage give about the economic arrangement between the federal government and state governments for enacting this legislation?

_____

_____

_____

ESSENTIAL QUESTION

Can the government fix the economy?

As you gather evidence to answer the Essential Question, think about

- how Roosevelt's second term was different from his first term.
- why some of Roosevelt's New Deal programs ended.
- the causes and effects of a recession on a nation.

My Notes

The New Deal Coalition

DIRECTIONS: Search for evidence in Chapter 9, Lesson 3 to help you answer the following questions.

1A **ANALYZING** What problem did Roosevelt hope to solve by his "court-packing" plan?

_____

_____

_____

1B **IDENTIFYING CAUSE AND EFFECT** Why did the plan spark such anger from his opponents?

_____

_____

_____

2A **ECONOMICS** How and when did the New Deal finally end?

_____

_____

_____

2B **ANALYZING INFORMATION** In the web diagram below, write the details that characterize the legacy of the New Deal.

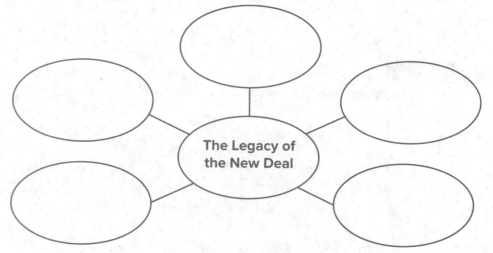

The Legacy of the New Deal

3 **DRAWING CONCLUSIONS** What was it about Roosevelt's policies that gave Americans confidence in the American system?

_____

_____

_____

_____

4 **COMPARING AND CONTRASTING** How did Roosevelt's first and second terms differ? Fill out the Venn diagram to help you answer the question.

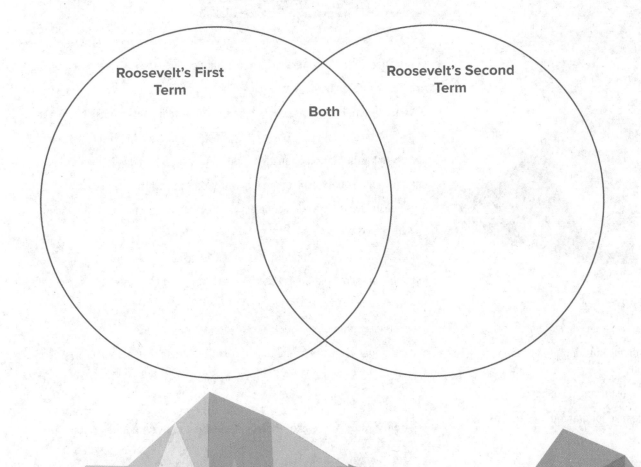

Roosevelt's First Term

Both

Roosevelt's Second Term

ESSENTIAL QUESTION

Can the government fix the economy?

VOCABULARY

express provision: a clear statement

unconstitutional: not supported by the Constitution

limitation: a restriction; a boundary

presume: to take for granted

Reorganization of the Judiciary

DIRECTIONS: Read this excerpt from a radio broadcast delivered by President Franklin D. Roosevelt. Then answer the questions that follow.

EXPLORE THE CONTEXT: After the Supreme Court declared the Agricultural Adjustment Act unconstitutional, President Roosevelt reacted with what became known as the "court-packing plan." Fearing the court's rulings on pending New Deal programs, the president sent a bill to Congress to reorganize the Supreme Court. In this excerpt from one of his fireside chats, President Roosevelt provides us with insight into his rationale.

PRIMARY SOURCE: SPEECH

66 "For nearly twenty years there was no conflict between the Congress and the Court. Then, in 1803, Congress passed a statute which the Court said violated an **express provision** of the Constitution. The Court claimed the power to declare it **unconstitutional** and did so declare it. But a little later the Court itself admitted that it was an extraordinary power to exercise and through Mr. Justice Washington laid down this **limitation** upon it: 'It is but a decent respect due to the wisdom, the integrity and the patriotism of the legislative body, by which any law is passed, to presume in favor of its validity until its violation of the Constitution is proved beyond all reasonable doubt.'

But since the rise of the modern movement for social and economic progress through legislation, the Court has more and more often and more and more boldly asserted a power to veto laws passed by the Congress and State Legislatures in complete disregard of this original limitation.

In the last four years the sound rule of giving statutes the benefit of all reasonable doubt has been cast aside. The Court has been acting not as a judicial body, but as a policy-making body. 99

—from a radio address of Franklin Roosevelt to the American public, 1937

1 `CIVICS` In this broadcast President Roosevelt references *Marbury* v. *Madison*, the 1803 case in which Chief Justice John Marshall struck down an act of Congress. This case established the power of judicial review. What does this power consist of?

_____

_____

_____

2 **CITING TEXT EVIDENCE** What action by the Court has led Roosevelt to announce his intention to reorganize the judiciary?

_____

_____

_____

3 **EVALUATING EVIDENCE** Why do you think President Roosevelt used his radio broadcast to explain his dissatisfaction with the court and his plan for reorganization?

_____

_____

_____

4 **DRAWING CONCLUSIONS** Why do you think the bill to reorganize the judiciary proposed by the president was "killed"?

_____

_____

5 **MAKING CONNECTIONS** Some people have criticized current Supreme Court justices of "legislating from the bench." What do you think is meant by this criticism?

_____

_____

_____

_____

ESSENTIAL QUESTION

Can the government fix the economy?

Fair Labor Standards

DIRECTIONS: Read the excerpt from a piece of legislation. Then answer the questions that follow.

EXPLORE THE CONTEXT: The New Deal had many important legacies. Some legislation from the period changed labor laws to address the problem of child labor, including the Fair Labor Standards Act of 1938. During the industrial era, children as young as 10 years old earned money doing piecework at home and at jobs in factories, farms, and stores. They only rarely could attend school.

PRIMARY SOURCE: LEGISLATION

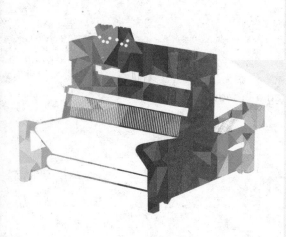

"Title 29 – LABOR; CHAPTER 8 - FAIR LABOR STANDARDS;

§212 Child labor provisions . . .

(b) Investigations and inspections. The Secretary of Labor or any of his authorized representatives, shall make all investigations and inspections under section 211(a) of this **title** with respect to the employment of minors, and, subject to the direction and control of the Attorney General, shall bring all actions under section 217 of this title to enjoin any act or practice which is unlawful by reason of the existence of **oppressive** child labor, and shall administer all other **provisions** of this chapter relating to oppressive child labor.

(c) Oppressive child labor; No employer shall employ any oppressive child labor in commerce or in the production of goods for commerce or in any enterprise engaged in commerce or in the production of goods for commerce.

(d) Proof of age; In order to carry out the objectives of this section, the Secretary may by regulation require employers to obtain from any employee proof of age. "

—from the Fair Labor Standards Act of 1938

VOCABULARY

provisions: conditions

title: law

oppressive: creating a burden

1 **UNDERSTANDING CONTEXT** What events were happening during the Great Depression and the New Deal that created the need for new child labor laws?

_____

_____

_____

_____

2 ECONOMICS What part of the economy was impacted by a change in child labor laws?

_____

_____

_____

_____

3 DRAWING CONCLUSIONS What was the government's long-term goal in creating this law?

_____

_____

_____

_____

4 ANALYZING INFORMATION Who were the beneficiaries of the New Deal child labor laws? Who were the new laws most likely to harm?

_____

_____

_____

_____

5 INFERRING How do the regulations in the source help you understand the society for which it was written?

_____

_____

_____

6 IDENTIFYING CONNECTIONS How does this law impact your life today?

_____

_____

_____

ESSENTIAL QUESTION

Can the government fix the economy?

My Notes

_____

_____

_____

_____

_____

_____

_____

_____

_____

_____

_____

_____

_____

_____

_____

_____

❶ Think About It

Review the supporting questions you developed at the opening of the chapter. Review the evidence you found in Chapter 9. Were you able to answer each of your Supporting Questions?

If you didn't find enough evidence to answer your Supporting Questions, what other evidence do you think you need to consider?

_____

_____

_____

_____

❷ Organize Your Evidence

Use a chart such as the one below to organize the evidence you will use to support your findings about whether the government can fix the economy.

Economic Problem	What kind of action did the government take?	Cite evidence from the text

3 Talk About It

Discuss the evidence you have gathered with a small group or partner. Check your group's understanding of how the government fixed the economy, and consider any additional advice or input they may have. Take notes from the discussion on the lines provided.

_____

_____

_____

_____

_____

_____

_____

4 Connect to the Essential Question

Use a computer and presentation software to create a slideshow. Use images from Roosevelt's first and second terms when he was implementing the New Deal and the Second New Deal. Include captions and headlines for each image to explain how the government impacted people as the country recovered from the economic depression. Your slideshow should answer the Essential Question: _Can the government fix the economy?_

_____

_____

_____

_____

_____

_____

_____

_____

_____

_____

_____

TAKING ACTION

MAKE CONNECTIONS The New Deal created new progressive laws that directly changed the lives of ordinary people. These laws included regulations on child labor, how banks should care for clients' money, the rights of workers to form unions, and the role of government in supporting the disabled and the elderly. Some of these laws still exist today, while others have been repealed. Nonetheless, many politicians and congressional leaders believe that the government still has an important role in improving people's lives. They want to implement laws that will directly help families, children, elderly people, and the disabled.

DIRECTIONS: Think about the role of government in the economy today. What legislation would you support that could improve the lives of ordinary people? Working with a partner, create a modern New Deal. Write two legislative statutes that you could propose to Congress. Your legislation should be intended to improve the economic situation for a group of vulnerable citizens, such as the poor, children, mothers with young children, college students, and so on. Give details to explain how your new law would work. Each legislative statute should be at least 150 words. Be creative with your statute. Use details from the Inquiry Journal and the Student Edition chapter to help you determine how to word your legislation.

A World in Flames

ESSENTIAL QUESTION

Why do some people fail to respond to injustice while others try to prevent injustice?

Think about how this question might relate to the events leading up to and occurring during World War II.

TALK ABOUT IT

Discuss with a partner what type of information you would need to know to answer this question. For example, one question might be: What events were taking place during this time that some considered unjust?

DIRECTIONS: Now write three additional questions that would help you explain why people did or did not respond to injustices before and during World War II.

MY RESEARCH QUESTIONS

Supporting Question 1:

_____

_____

_____

Supporting Question 2:

_____

_____

_____

Supporting Question 3:

_____

_____

_____

The Origins of World War II

DIRECTIONS: Search for evidence in Chapter 10, Lesson 1 to help you answer the following questions.

1A **DESCRIBING** What is fascism? Which dictator in this lesson was associated with this political belief?

_____

_____

_____

_____

1B **DESCRIBING** What shared economic and political factors led to the rise of dictatorships in Germany, Italy, the Soviet Union, and Japan?

_____

_____

_____

_____

2A **DETERMINING CENTRAL IDEAS** How did Adolf Hitler begin preparing for war?

_____

_____

_____

2B **DETERMINING CONTEXT** What was _Anschluss_, and how did it relate to Hitler's vision for Germany?

_____

_____

_____

ESSENTIAL QUESTION

Why do some people fail to respond to injustice while others try to prevent injustice?

As you gather evidence to answer the Essential Question, think about:

- what led to the rise of dictatorships in Germany, Italy, and the Soviet Union.

- what actions governments were willing to take to prevent war in Europe.

- what happened after Germany's invasion of Poland and France.

My Notes

_____

_____

_____

_____

_____

_____

3 **SUMMARIZING** Using the graphic organizer below, fill in the sequence of events as Hitler prepared to go to war.

1937

1938

1939

4 CIVICS Complete the chart by explaining how Hitler's actions affected each nation.

Nation	Action Taken	Outcome
Austria		
Czechoslovakia		
Poland		
Great Britain		
France		

"Agreement signed at Munich Between Germany, the United Kingdom, France, and Italy" (September 29, 1938), in United States Department of State. Documents on German Foreign Policy: From the Archives of the German Foreign Ministry. Washington, DC: United States Government Printing Office, 1957-1964. Series D (1937-1945), Germany and Czechoslovakia, Volume 2: 1937-1938. Document Number 675, pp. 1014-16.

ESSENTIAL QUESTION

Why do some people fail to respond to injustice while others try to prevent injustice?

The Munich Pact

DIRECTIONS: Read the following excerpt from a political pact. Then answer the questions that follow.

EXPLORE THE CONTEXT: In late September 1938, leaders from Germany, Great Britain, France, and Italy met in Munich, Germany. The memory of World War I was still fresh in the leaders' minds. The conference was called in an attempt to prevent another world war and to stop the reach of German leader Adolf Hitler.

PRIMARY SOURCE: PACT EXCERPT

66 GERMANY, the United Kingdom, France and Italy, taking into consideration the agreement, which has been already reached in principle for the [cession] to Germany of the Sudeten German territory, have agreed on the following terms and conditions . . .

(1) The evacuation will begin on 1st October.

(2) The United Kingdom, France and Italy agree that the evacuation of the territory shall be completed by the 10th October, without any existing installations having been destroyed, and that the Czechoslovak Government will be held responsible for carrying out the evacuation without damage to the said installations.

(3) The conditions governing the evacuation will be laid down in detail by an international commission composed of representatives of Germany, the United Kingdom, France, Italy and Czechoslovakia.

(4) The occupation by stages of the predominantly German territory by German troops will begin on 1st October. . . .

(6) The final determination of the frontiers will be carried out by the international commission. The commission will also be entitled to recommend to the four Powers, Germany, the United Kingdom, France and Italy, in certain exceptional cases, minor modifications in the strictly ethnographical determination of the zones which are to be transferred without plebiscite.

(7) There will be a right of option into and out of the transferred territories, the option to be exercised within six months from the date of this agreement. A German-Czechoslovak commission shall determine the details of the option, consider ways of facilitating the transfer of population and settle questions of principle arising out of the said transfer.

(8) The Czechoslovak Government will within a period of four weeks from the date of this agreement release from their military and police forces any Sudeten Germans who may wish to be released, and the Czechoslovak Government will within the same period release Sudeten German prisoners who are serving terms of imprisonment for political offences. 99

—from "Munich Pact," signed by Adolf Hitler, Neville Chamberlain, Edouard Daladier, and Benito Mussolini on September 29, 1938

1 CITING TEXT EVIDENCE What is the area in question ceded in the agreement? Why does Hitler want it?

_____

_____

2 ANALYZING INFORMATION According to the agreement, what is the proposed time line for handover, and how will it be carried out?

_____

_____

_____

_____

3 EVALUATING EVIDENCE What country is noticeably missing from the negotiations? What does this tell you?

_____

_____

_____

_____

4 CIVICS According to the document, what limits have been placed on the Czech government? What does this suggest about the position of the Czech government?

_____

_____

_____

_____

5 DRAWING CONCLUSIONS According to the document, what might the Germans have feared when they stated that no existing military or defensive installations were to be destroyed?

_____

_____

_____

Germany Invades Poland

ESSENTIAL QUESTION

Why do some people fail to respond to injustice while others try to prevent injustice?

DIRECTIONS: Read the following excerpt from a book. Then answer the questions that follow.

EXPLORE THE CONTEXT: In 1939, Clare Hollingworth was a cub reporter living in Poland. She had been on the job only three days when Germany invaded the country. For the next three weeks, Hollingworth, in a series of dispatches, reported the events as they were happening. Her memories of the event were later published in the book *The Three Weeks' War in Poland.*

PRIMARY SOURCE: BOOK EXCERPT

❝Soon after three on the same afternoon, the Provincial Government asked the British and French Consuls to leave, with the last of their nationals. I took a few possessions, knowing this for my last opportunity, and scrambled into the Consul's car. . . . Before we left, we had to call back at our own Consulate. I had a sudden hunch this is going to be bad, this will be a near thing, as the alarms sounded for a raid. Just as we stopped by the Consulate, there was a roar overhead; an anti-aircraft machine-gun crackled on a roof above the car. The racket was tremendous. For the first time the German 'planes were diving and shooting into the streets. We were too fair a mark and ('neutrals' though we still were) we broke out and ran for the building. Then, so soon as the wave was past, we raced out of the town. All along stood the towns-people at their doorways, gas-masks clasped nervously against them, and scared eyes on the heavens. I thought: 'So this is to be the German tactic, the terrorising of civil populations, the machine-gunning of open towns without military objectives. I could not know that not until long after our own entry into the war would Hitler announce his decision in future to attack civilians. . . .

Soon after dawn the sound of heavy artillery was plain and it grew obvious that Cracow would not be secure for long. I took a car out on the Katowice road, but I could not get far, it had become part of the battlefield. This was the only part of my war which looked as war does in books and films and stories. The Poles were concentrated round a cluster of farms by the hamlet of Dolova, and were still busy digging support-trenches in the hard soil. More field-telephones were being erected by small parties of soldiers. Overhead, airplanes—mostly bombers—flew incessantly. Horse-drawn field-kitchens, fodder and supply waggons, wheeled equipment of all sorts was being hurried away over fields and rutted lanes to the north-east. I was surprised to see, as I drove by, that both the large barracks and the temporary flying-field used by the air-force were deserted. Ambulances passed me continually, converted motor-buses with their windows whitewashed to conceal the wounded roughly packed on the ordinary seats. Everything showed me that the army was likely to fall back at any hour. ❞

—from *The Three Weeks' War in Poland*, by Claire Hollingworth, 1940

1 **ANALYZING** Which sentence describes Hollingworth's appraisal of the security in the city she is reporting from?

_____

_____

2 GEOGRAPHY How did the invasion change the landscape of human activity in the area?

_____

_____

_____

3 **EVALUATING EVIDENCE** Is this a primary or secondary source? How does this information help you understand the document?

_____

_____

_____

4 **DETERMINING MEANING** What is the author referring to when she states, "We were too fair a mark and ('neutrals' though we still were) we broke out and ran for the building."

_____

_____

_____

5 **INFERRING** Why might the author have been surprised that the Polish army was willing to sacrifice the Silesian region?

_____

_____

_____

6 **DETERMINING MEANING** What sentence in the excerpt suggests that the rules of war are changing because of Hitler? Why is this important?

_____

_____

_____

ESSENTIAL QUESTION

Why do some people fail to respond to injustice while others try to prevent injustice?

As you gather evidence to answer the Essential Question, think about:

- why Americans chose to stay neutral in the early days of World War II.
- how the United States aided American allies even as a neutral country.
- what events finally forced the United States to enter the war.

My Notes

From Neutrality to War

DIRECTIONS: Search for evidence in Chapter 10, Lesson 2 to help you answer the following question.

1A **DETERMINING CONTEXT** Why were Americans willing to take an isolationist stance as events were unfolding in Europe?

1B **IDENTIFYING PERSPECTIVES** What was the Nye Committee? How did it reflect American attitudes toward Europe?

2A **EXPLAINING CAUSE AND EFFECT** What was the Spanish Civil War about? Which side was supported by Germany and Italy?

2B **SUMMARIZING** What countries were allied with the Axis powers? What was the purpose of the coalition?

3 **RELATING EVENTS** Complete the Cornell Notes organizer about U.S. legislation with regard to neutrality by explaining what each term means.

Main Idea	Notes
Neutrality Act of 1935	
Neutrality Act of 1939	
"cash and carry"	

4 **SUMMARIZING** Complete the graphic organizer below to summarize how American neutrality slowly diminished between 1939 and 1941.

Neutrality Act of 1939

⬇

Lend-Lease Act

⬇

Hemispheric Defense Zone

⬇

The Atlantic Charter

⬇

American Embargo of Japan

⬇

Pearl Harbor Attacked

ESSENTIAL QUESTION

Why do some people fail to respond to injustice while others try to prevent injustice?

The Spanish Civil War

DIRECTIONS: Read the following excerpt from a letter. Then answer the questions that follow.

EXPLORE THE CONTEXT: In 1937, Don Henry was a sophomore at the University of Kansas. Stirred by the plight of the Republican forces fighting against the Fascists in Spain, Henry left college, bound for Europe and Spain. In Spain, he fought as a member of the Abraham Lincoln Brigade, a group of American volunteers helping Republican forces fight fascists. In the following excerpt taken from one of his letters, Henry writes about his experiences.

PRIMARY SOURCE: LETTER EXCERPT

❝I have joined the International Brigade Company three of the MacKenzie Papineau Battalion but over half of the force is composed of U.S. citizens. When training is over I'll expect to be moved—along with the other Americans—into the newly formed Patrick Henry Battalion or the George Washington or Abraham Lincoln . . .

The group I travelled with and am stationed with is composed largely of students. I have five or six particularly good friends here among whom is a man from Harvard, one from Cornell, one from Columbia, one from Michigan, another from K.U. and a professor of physics at Washington U. . . and others ranging from seamen to plumbers.

The people here are a real treat to a radical's eyes. Everywhere is the clenched fist salute of the popular front government and every mans [sic] name is comrade . . . .

We expect to be in training approximately one month and then be shipped to the Madrid front which the American troops defended so valiantly last winter. In the fore part of the war the International troops were shipped with no more than two or three days training directly to the font. Naturally they were slaughtered like flies but had it not been for them Madrid would have fallen and the entire war might possibly have been lost to the fascists. . . .

Now U.S. citizens close their eyes to an assault on a democratic people and in doing that are actually aiding the spread of fascism. You may say that we are suffering from the same delusions that the world war veterans suffered in 1918 but the political line up is entirely different with a threat not to bourgeois government but to a genuine proletariat mass movement. ❞

—from "Letter from Spain" by Don Henry, July 4, 1937

Henry, Don. "Letter from Spain, July 4, 1937." Documents in the case of Don Henry, Exhibits, Evidence and Other Records Related to Various Committee Investigations, Records of the Special House Committee on UnAmerican Activities 1938-45, Records of the U.S. House of Representatives (Record Group 233), Center for Legislative Archives, National Archives, Washington, D.C. 1937.

1 **EVALUATING EVIDENCE** What do the names of the American battalions and brigades suggest?

_____

_____

_____

2 **DETERMINING CONTEXT** How does this document better help you understand the events surrounding the Spanish Civil War?

_____

_____

_____

3 CIVICS In what ways do Don Henry and his fellow Americans exhibit civic virtue?

_____

_____

_____

4 **EVALUATING EVIDENCE** What does this letter tell you about who volunteered to fight in the Spanish Civil War?

_____

_____

_____

5 **ANALYZING SOURCES** What does Henry's statement about the readiness of the international troops fighting near Madrid tell you?

_____

_____

_____

6 **CITING TEXT EVIDENCE** Which sentence in the text suggests that Henry is critical of American isolationism?

_____

_____

Clark, Blake. Remember Pearl Harbor. New York: Modern Age Books, 1942.

Copyright © McGraw-Hill Education

Japanese Americans and Pearl Harbor

ESSENTIAL QUESTION

Why do some people fail to respond to injustice while others try to prevent injustice?

DIRECTIONS: Read the following excerpt from a book. Then answer the questions that follow.

EXPLORE THE CONTEXT: Author Blake Clark was living in Honolulu, Hawaii when Pearl Harbor was attacked on December 7, 1941. Clark was eating breakfast and reading the newspaper when he became aware of planes flying overhead. In the distance, black smoke hung heavily in the air. When a neighbor alerted him that the island was under attack, Clark helped with evacuation efforts. He later wrote a book about the event. In this excerpt, Clark recalls his conversations with Shunzo Sakamaki, an FBI agent overseeing the activities of the Japanese American community.

VOCABULARY

saimin: noodle

PRIMARY SOURCE: BOOK EXCERPT

❝Shunzo felt certain that the intelligence bureaus were not motivated by a feeling of altruism or YMCA good fellowship when they made this pronouncement, nor were they simply up to tricks. They had become aware of a social situation, and were acting upon the knowledge they had gained. "Until they spoke out," he said, "the Japanese in Hawaii were a sad lot, the second generation in particular. We considered ourselves as American as anyone else, yet we met suspicion every time we tried to act. No Japanese could work at Pearl Harbor. We understood the reason, but we still felt the sting of discrimination. Few Japanese were ever admitted to the National Guard. Of those who were let in, none ever reached higher rank than that of sergeant. The rumor spread that Japanese would not be taken into the Army. We really were relieved to find ourselves drafted. At least, induction showed that the Army was not suspicious of our loyalty.

"During this period of distrust and suspicion, the local Japanese had become the victims of petty rackets," Shunzo continued. "Salesmen of I am an American and other patriotic slogans went from house to house in the Japanese communities. If the Japanese woman of the house resisted the sales' talk, the canvasser threatened her with, 'What will your haole [white] friends think when they hear that you refused to have an American emblem in your home?' President Roosevelt's picture hangs in virtually every **saimin** stand in the Territory.❞

—from *Remember Pearl Harbor* by Blake Clark, 1942

1 **DETERMINING CONTEXT** What type of document is this? How does this help you understand the event described?

_____

_____

_____

2 **IDENTIFYING PERSPECTIVES** Based on Shunzo's comments, why might second-generation Japanese Americans have a more difficult time living in the United States?

_____

_____

_____

_____

_____

3 **INFERRING** What does the description of the "I Am an American" sales pitch suggest about the difficulties of being Japanese Americans after Pearl Harbor?

_____

_____

_____

_____

4 **INFERRING** What is Shunzo suggesting when he says, "We considered ourselves as American as anyone else, yet we met suspicion every time we tried to act"?

_____

_____

_____

5 CIVICS In what ways did Japanese Americans exemplify civic virtue after Pearl Harbor?

_____

_____

_____

_____

The Holocaust

DIRECTIONS Search for evidence in Chapter 10, Lesson 3 to help you answer the following questions.

1A **DESCRIBING** What does the term *Shoah* mean, and what is its relationship to the Holocaust?

_____

_____

_____

_____

1B **EXPLAINING ISSUES** Why might the Holocaust be considered a continuation of discrimination against Jewish people in Europe?

_____

_____

_____

_____

2A CIVICS   Why were the Nuremberg Laws so effective in discriminating against German Jews? Why were German Jews so reluctant to leave Germany?

_____

_____

_____

_____

_____

2B **ANALYZING** In what way did the Nazis use the murder of a German diplomat to inflame anti-Semitism? What is the significance of November 9, 1938?

_____

_____

_____

ESSENTIAL QUESTION

Why do some people fail to respond to injustice while others try to prevent injustice?

As you gather evidence to answer the Essential Question, think about:

- how Hitler enacted his program of eradicating the Jewish people of Europe.
- the international response of different countries to the Holocaust.
- what the Final Solution encompassed and its impact.

My Notes

_____

_____

_____

_____

_____

3 **RELATING EVENTS** Complete the Cornell Notes organizer to take notes about the German and international responses to the plight faced by the Jewish people.

Main Idea	Notes
German response to Jewish emigration	
International response to the plight of Jewish people in Germany	
The St. *Louis* affair	

4 **DESCRIBING** Complete the graphic organizer below by describing each event or place in Hitler's Final Solution campaign.

Event	Impact
Wannsee Conference	
Concentration Camps	
Extermination Camps	

ESSENTIAL QUESTION

Why do some people fail to respond to injustice while others try to prevent injustice?

VOCABULARY

pogrom: the organized killing of people or destruction of their property because of their race or religious beliefs

Kristallnacht

DIRECTIONS: Read the following excerpt from a report. Then answer the questions that follow.

EXPLORE THE CONTEXT: In 1938, George Rooby worked for the American Joint Distribution Committee, a Jewish organization dedicated to providing relief for Jewish people living in Eastern and Central Europe. Rooby was sent to Germany where he saw firsthand the violence and persecution directed toward German Jews. During this time, Rooby filed a series of reports documenting what he saw and heard.

PRIMARY SOURCE: REPORT EXCERPT

❝On the night between November 9th and 10th, hundreds of S. A. men in their brown uniforms were assembled on a public square and divided into squads of eight men. Then instructions were given to start the pogrom against Jewish stores, shops, and homes. Each detail of eight men received picks, hammers and shovels and were ordered to start their diabolical work. Each squad was furnished with lists of places to be visited and with large scissors and knives.

At 1 a.m. the **pogrom** started. Windows of Jewish shops were broken and doors forcibly opened. Fixtures were demolished, all merchandise in the stores was either cut into shreds or taken away by the Nails. The synagogue was burned down. Homes were broken into, all men arrested and women forced at the point of guns, either into attics or basements, where they were kept for two hours or longer, in order to avoid interference with the destructive work of the Nazi bands.

Furniture was broken into small splinters, bedding cut up and money and jewelry taken away. It is true that in some rare cases receipts were given for money thus confiscated, but not for jewelry. Suits, linen, shirts, etc. were cut into shreds.

The next day Jewish homes were visited by Aryans offering to buy the 'demolished Jew articles.' Jews were glad to get rid of the splinters in this way, because they themselves were unable to remove the debris, as no truckman would have dared to haul away Jewish property.

In orphanages children were aroused at night and forced to evacuate the buildings in nightshirts and barefeet. ❞

—from "Report on Trip to Germany 1938," by George Rooby

Rooby, George. "Report on Trip to Germany 1938." Paris, December 1, 1938. https://archive.org/details/georgeroobyr001

1 **CITING TEXT EVIDENCE** What were the orders that the S.A. squads were to carry out?

_____

_____

_____

_____

2 **ANALYZING SOURCES** What part of the excerpt suggests that some Germans were frightened to help the Jews affected by _Kristallnacht_?

_____

_____

_____

_____

_____

3 ECONOMICS How were Jews hurt economically by the events of _Kristallnacht_?

_____

_____

_____

_____

4 **DETERMINING CENTRAL IDEAS** What message did the actions of the _Kristallnacht_ send to other Jews?

_____

_____

_____

_____

_____

ESSENTIAL QUESTION

Why do some people fail to respond to injustice while others try to prevent injustice?

The Treatment of Jewish Artifacts

DIRECTIONS: Study the following image. Then answer the questions that follow.

EXPLORE THE CONTENT: The confiscation of Jewish religious and cultural artifacts was one of the many crimes committed by the Nazis. At the end of the World War II, Allied forces faced an enormous task in retrieving and documenting the many stolen Jewish documents, books, manuscripts, and artifacts that had been recovered. In many cases, Jewish chaplains were used to help uncover information about where the sacred manuscripts came from and what they contained.

National Archives (111-SC-209154)

PRIMARY SOURCE: PHOTOGRAPH

1 **EVALUATING EVIDENCE** How does this photograph illustrate German attitudes toward Jewish culture?

_____

_____

_____

_____

2 **COMPARING** What does this photograph tell you about the approach the Allies took with recovered Jewish religious items?

_____

_____

_____

3 **INFERRING** Why do you think this photograph was taken?

_____

_____

_____

4 CIVICS What civic virtues are being practiced here?

_____

_____

5 **PREDICTING** Would this photograph be an effective piece of propaganda? Why or why not?

_____

_____

ESSENTIAL QUESTION

Why do some people fail to respond to injustice while others try to prevent injustice?

My Notes

_____

_____

_____

_____

_____

_____

_____

_____

_____

_____

_____

_____

_____

_____

_____

_____

1 Think About It

Review the supporting questions that you developed at the beginning of the chapter. Review the evidence that you gathered in Chapter 10. Were you able to answer each Supporting Question?

If there was not enough evidence to answer your Supporting Questions, what additional evidence do you think you need to consider?

2 Organize Your Evidence

Complete the chart below with information you learned about the injustices that led to World War II.

EVENT	RESPONSE	OUTCOME

3 Write About It

Choose one of the events from the chart you completed. Write two paragraphs about that event. In the first paragraph, briefly describe how the event actually unfolded. In the second paragraph, consider what steps would have had to have occurred to lead to a different result. Keep in mind the Essential Question: *Why do some people fail to respond to injustice while others try to prevent injustice?*

_____

_____

_____

_____

_____

_____

_____

_____

_____

_____

_____

_____

_____

_____

_____

_____

_____

_____

4 Connect to the Essential Question

Using details from the text, write a magazine article covering the event you wrote about earlier. Your article should detail what the event was about, the response to the event, and what could have been done differently to present a different outcome. Your article should answer the Essential Question: *Why do some people fail to respond to injustice while others try to prevent injustice?*

Read your article to your class, and be prepared to answer questions about the event you have chosen.

CITIZENSHIP
TAKE ACTION

MAKE CONNECTIONS International responses to conflicts and incidents of social injustice vary from country to country. In many cases, people do not wait for an "official" response but volunteer to help as soon as they learn what has happened, just as Don Henry did during the Spanish Civil War. Whether supporting a political cause or a humanitarian one, often individuals will step forward when countries cannot or will not. Think of some of the current events concerning social justice that are happening today. Is there one that you feel strongly about? Do you support the solutions being discussed, or do you have other ideas?

DIRECTIONS: Working in a small group, discuss one current social event that might affect you. Together, write a paper describing the event, its possible outcome, and possible solutions that might help solve the problem. What are some ways that you can help? When you have completed your paper as a group, demonstrate for the rest of your class ways everyone can get involved to support your cause.

America and World War II

ESSENTIAL QUESTION

What kinds of sacrifices does war require?

World War II affected millions of people around the globe. What kinds of sacrifices did the war demand of soldiers? Of civilians living in the war-torn regions? Of civilians whose land was not invaded?

TALK ABOUT IT

With a partner, discuss the sort of information you would need to discover how the events of World War II affected people's lives around the world and the sacrifices it caused those people to make. For example, you might ask: *What new sacrifices did World War II force people to make as compared to previous wars?*

DIRECTIONS: Write down three additional questions that will help you explain the sacrifices that World War II brought about.

MY RESEARCH QUESTIONS

Supporting Question 1:

_____

_____

_____

Supporting Question 2:

_____

_____

_____

Supporting Question 3:

_____

_____

Wartime America

DIRECTIONS: Search for evidence in Chapter 11, Lesson 1 to help you answer the following questions.

1A SUMMARIZING How had Americans viewed the draft before World War II? How did those attitudes change in the early years of the war?

_____

_____

_____

_____

_____

1B EXPLAINING EFFECTS How did the attack on Pearl Harbor affect American attitudes about military service? Was this a change or a continuation of a trend?

_____

_____

_____

_____

_____

_____

2A UNDERSTANDING CONTEXT What does the decision to use cost-plus contracts to produce weapons and equipment tell us about the needs of the government and the importance of American businesses to the war effort?

_____

_____

_____

_____

_____

ESSENTIAL QUESTION

What kinds of sacrifices does war require?

As you gather evidence to answer the Essential Question, think about:

- how and why people volunteered or were drafted for military service in the United States.

- how the move to a wartime economy affected American civilian life.

- how the war affected all of American society.

My Notes

_____

_____

_____

_____

_____

2B EVALUATING Was the policy of converting civilian businesses to wartime production successful? Did this policy meet the government's needs?

_____

_____

3 SUMMARIZING Use the following chart to summarize some of the policies that were instituted to prepare the United States for life during wartime. Analyze these policies in terms of the social changes they caused.

THE UNITED STATES DURING WORLD WAR II

POLICY	SOCIAL CHANGE
Industrial mobilization for war production	
Draft of military-age men	
West Coast designated a military zone.	
Rationing	
Women filled administrative and clerical positions in the armed forces.	

4A `CIVICS` How did the entry of the United States into the war cause the country to compromise some of its values?

_____

_____

_____

_____

4B ANALYZING CHANGE Were these compromises justified? How should rights be balanced against the needs of a war? Explain your answers.

_____

_____

_____

_____

_____

ESSENTIAL QUESTION

What kinds of sacrifices does war require?

VOCABULARY

munitions: weapons and ammunition

fortified: strengthened against attack

creature comforts: things that make life pleasant (adequate food, decent shelter, warm clothing)

complacent: self-satisfied without being aware of potential problems

unprecedented: unheard of; having never occurred before

Fireside Chat

DIRECTIONS: Read the transcript of a fireside chat. Then respond to the questions that follow.

EXPLORE THE CONTEXT: President Franklin D. Roosevelt hosted "fireside chats" during evening radio programming. He used his radio address to explain political issues and clear up rumors. The primary focus of these fireside chats was to allay the fears of the public during the Great Depression and then World War II.

PRIMARY SOURCE: RADIO ADDRESS

❝ Not all of us can have the privilege of working in a **munitions** factory or a shipyard, or on the farms or in oil fields or mines, producing the weapons or the raw materials that are needed by our armed forces. But there is one front and one battle where everyone in the United States—every man, woman, and child—is in action, and will be privileged to remain in action throughout this war. That front is right here at home, in our daily lives, in our daily tasks. Here at home everyone will have the privilege of making whatever self-denial is necessary, not only to supply our fighting men, but to keep the economic structure of our country **fortified** and secure during the war and after the war. This will require, of course, the abandonment not only of luxuries but of many other **creature comforts**.

Every loyal American is aware of his individual responsibility. Whenever I hear anyone saying, 'The American people are **complacent**—they need to be aroused,' I feel like asking him to come to Washington to read the mail that floods into the White House and into all departments of this government. The one question that recurs through all these thousands of letters and messages is, 'What more can I do to help my country in winning this war?'

To build the factories, to buy the materials, to pay the labor, to provide the transportation, to equip and feed and house the soldiers and sailors and marines, and to do all the thousands of things necessary in a war—all cost a lot of money, more money than has ever been spent by any nation at any time in the long history of the world. We are now spending, solely for war purposes, the sum of about $100 million every day in the week. But, before this year is over, that almost unbelievable rate of expenditure will be doubled. All of this money has to be spent—and spent quickly—if we are to produce within the time now available the enormous quantities of weapons of war which we need. But the spending of these tremendous sums presents grave danger of disaster to our national economy. When your government continues to spend these **unprecedented** sums for munitions month by month and year by year, that money goes into the pocketbooks and bank accounts of the people of the United States. At the same time raw materials and many manufactured goods are necessarily taken away from civilian use; and machinery and factories are being converted to war production. You do not have to be a professor of mathematics or economics to see that if people with plenty of cash start bidding against each other for scarce goods, the price of those goods goes up ❞

—from a radio address by President Franklin D. Roosevelt, April 28, 1942

1 **ANALYZING POINT OF VIEW** To whom do you think this radio speech is directed?

_____

_____

2 **SUMMARIZING** What is President Roosevelt trying to convey about the country's economy in this radio address?

_____

_____

_____

_____

3 CIVICS According to President Roosevelt, how did the civilians contribute to the war effort?

_____

_____

_____

4 **UNDERSTANDING CONTEXT** Why do you think this speech was broadcast on the radio rather than in a newspaper?

_____

_____

5 **IDENTIFYING BIAS** Does President Roosevelt reveal any bias in this speech? How can you tell?

_____

_____

_____

_____

6 **DRAWING CONCLUSIONS** How would this radio speech motivate Americans to support (or continue their support) for the war?

_____

_____

_____

ESSENTIAL QUESTION
What kinds of sacrifices does war require?

Grow Your Own, Can Your Own

DIRECTIONS: Study the poster. Then respond to the questions that follow.

EXPLORE THE CONTEXT: Wartime meant shortages of all kinds, as resources and materials were diverted to the war effort and hundreds of thousands (and eventually, millions) of men were called to serve in the armed forces overseas. To keep the population fed and healthy, citizens were encouraged to grow fruits and vegetables in their own garden and to learn to preserve them by canning and pickling. Posters such as the one shown here were distributed to encourage these practices in support of the war effort.

PRIMARY SOURCE: POSTER

—poster created by artist Alfred Parker

1 INTEGRATING INFORMATION What messages were people meant to take from this poster? Explain your answer.

_____

_____

_____

_____

_____

_____

_____

2 UNDERSTANDING CONTEXT Why is this poster considered wartime propaganda?

_____

_____

_____

_____

_____

_____

3 **COMPARING AND CONTRASTING** How are this source and the war bonds referenced in the Student Edition related to one another? What messages do they share? How do they differ?

_____

_____

_____

_____

_____

_____

_____

4 **EVALUATING INFORMATION** What conclusions can you draw about the role of women in wartime from this poster?

_____

_____

_____

5 **ECONOMICS** What might be some economic consequences of people growing and canning their own food?

_____

_____

_____

6 **IDENTIFYING CONNECTIONS** In what ways was World War II different for Americans compared to wars occurring today?

_____

_____

_____

_____

The War in the Pacific

DIRECTIONS Search for evidence in Chapter 11, Lesson 2 to help you answer the following questions.

1A **UNDERSTANDING CONTEXT** What events led to the Bataan Death March?

_____

_____

_____

_____

_____

_____

_____

_____

_____

1B GEOGRAPHY How were the U.S. troops able to last for several months before surrendering to the Japanese?

_____

_____

2A **EXPLAINING EFFECTS** What was one effect of the Bataan Death March on the U.S. troops?

_____

_____

_____

2B **ANALYZING SOURCES** What kind of evidence is given in the Student Edition as proof of the misery of the Bataan Death March?

_____

_____

ESSENTIAL QUESTION

What kinds of sacrifices does war require?

As you gather evidence to answer the Essential Question, think about

- the specific circumstances and requirements of the war in the Pacific.

- the compromises countries made between liberty and security.

- the sacrifices soldiers and civilians made in wartime.

My Notes

_____

_____

_____

_____

_____

_____

3A **DETERMINING MEANING** What is meant by the term *island-hopping*?

_____

_____

3B **USING MAPS** Use the map in Lesson 2 to complete the chart showing the islands "hopped" by Admiral Nimitz and General MacArthur.

Pacific Islands "Hopped" by Battleships

Admiral Chester Nimitz	General Douglas MacArthur

ESSENTIAL QUESTION
What kinds of sacrifices does war require?

VOCABULARY

unintelligible: impossible to understand

intercepted: seized

confer: discuss ideas with another person

Letter to Major Jones

DIRECTIONS: Read the letter. Then respond to the questions that follow.

EXPLORE THE CONTEXT: Philip Johnston was the son of a fluent Navajo speaker and a white missionary to the Navajo. In 1942, he came up with the idea of recruiting Navajo soldiers to use their unique language as a virtually unbreakable code for radio transmissions in the Pacific theater. In fact, the Japanese never broke the code, and it has been credited with being a crucial contribution to the Allies' success in the South Pacific.

PRIMARY SOURCE: LETTER

February 18, 1942

Dear Major Jones:

On my return trip from San Diego, I stopped over at Riverside to **confer** with the superintendent of Sherman Institute with regard to the use of some Navajo students for a demonstration of their native language as a code for the Marine Corps. . . . It is my sincere belief that Navajos, serving in the capacity I have outlined, will make a major contribution to the winning of this war. Therefore, I should like to offer the suggestion that you plan to invite as many officers as possible, connected with Communication, Intelligence, or other branches of the service, who would be interested and qualified to evaluate the project. For your information and theirs, I will summarize the two qualities which make the Navajo language ideal for use as a code in military operation:

1. It is an unwritten language, and completely **unintelligible** to the ear of any person except a Navajo. Therefore, messages sent in this language could not, under any possible conditions, be **intercepted** and translated by the enemy.

2. It is a rich, fluent language—one that is capable of adaptation to the specialized terms employed by the Army, Navy, and Marine Corps.

I await your reply.

Sincerely yours,

Philip Johnston

—from a letter written by Philip Johnston, 1942

1 GEOGRAPHY Why did Johnston believe Navajo would be a highly secure language to use as a code?

_____

_____

_____

2 **DISTINGUISHING FACT AND OPINION** What is one fact contained in Johnston's letter?

_____

3 **DISTINGUISHING FACT AND OPINION** What is one opinion contained in Johnston's letter?

_____

_____

_____

4 **INFERRING** What can you infer from this about U.S. radio transmissions in World War II?

_____

_____

5 **RELATING EVENTS** What might have happened if the United States had not used Navajo soldiers to speak their language on the radio?

_____

_____

_____

6 **EVALUATING** Was it a smart decision to use the Navajo code talkers?

_____

_____

_____

ESSENTIAL QUESTION

What kinds of sacrifices does war require?

Communication from General MacArthur

DIRECTIONS: Read the communication from General MacArthur. Then respond to the questions that follow.

EXPLORE THE CONTEXT: This communication from General MacArthur, commander of the American and Filipino troops defending the Philippines, was written shortly before President Roosevelt ordered MacArthur's evacuation to Australia. In it, he recommends a plan of attack against the Japanese.

VOCABULARY

immemorial: ancient

thrust: attack, offensive

menace: threat, danger

PRIMARY SOURCE: RADIOGRAM

In compliance with your previous directive that from time to time I present my strategic conception of the situation I take this opportunity of presenting what I believe is a fatal mistake on the part of the Democratic Allies. The Japanese are sweeping southward in a great offensive and the Allies are attempting merely to stop them by building up forces in their front. This method, as has almost universally been the case in war, will fail....The lines of weakness from time **immemorial** have been the lines of communication. In this case they are stretched out over two thousand miles of sea with the whole line subject to American sea **thrust**. This line is not defended by enemy bombers but is held by scattered Naval elements.

A sea threat would immediately relieve the pressure on the South and is the only way that pressure can be relieved. A great naval victory on our part is not necessary to accomplish this mission; the threat alone would go far toward the desired end.... You must be prepared to take heavy losses, just so heavy losses are inflicted in return. I wish to reiterate that his bomber strength is practically entirely engaged on his southern front and represents little **menace** to such a naval thrust. With only minor threat from the fleets of Germany and Italy, the American and British Navies can assemble without serious jeopardy the force to make this thrust. I unhesitatingly predict that if this is not done the plan upon which we are now working, based upon the building up of air supremacy in the Southwest Pacific, will fail, the war will be indefinitely prolonged and its final outcome will be jeopardized. ...In submitting these views I may be exceeding the proper scope of my office and therefore do so with great hesitancy. My excuse, if excuse is necessary, is that from my present point of vantage I can see the whole strategy of the Pacific perhaps clearer than anyone else. If agreeable to you I would appreciate greatly the presentation of this view to the highest authority.

—from MacArthur to General Marshall, February 4, 1942

MacArthur, Douglas. "Radiogram From Ft. Mills, P.I. To General Marshall, February 4, 1942." Philippines, Safe Files, 1933 - 1945, President's Secretary's File (Franklin D. Roosevelt Administration), 1933 - 1945, Franklin D. Roosevelt Library 1959.

1 DETERMINING CENTRAL IDEAS What does MacArthur hope to accomplish by writing this communication?

_____

_____

2 CITING TEXT EVIDENCE Why does MacArthur feel that the current plan of defense is flawed?

_____

_____

_____

3 GEOGRAPHY According to MacArthur, how does the geography of the region work to their advantage?

_____

_____

_____

4 DESCRIBING What strategy for countering the Japanese offensive is MacArthur recommending?

_____

_____

_____

5 IDENTIFYING CONNECTIONS Why do you think the Japanese were so interested in attacking the Philippines?

_____

_____

_____

_____

ESSENTIAL QUESTION

What kinds of sacrifices does war require?

As you gather evidence to answer the Essential Question, think about

- the specific circumstances and requirements of the war in Europe.
- the compromises countries made between liberty and security.
- the sacrifices soldiers and civilians made in wartime.

My Notes

_____

_____

_____

_____

_____

_____

_____

The War in Europe

DIRECTIONS Search for evidence in Chapter 11, Lesson 3 to help you answer the following questions.

1A **DETERMINING CONTEXT** Why did Prime Minister Churchill want U.S. troops to attack the periphery of the German Empire instead of directly invading Europe?

_____

_____

_____

_____

_____

2B **SUMMARIZING** What happened when U.S. troops fought the German army for the first time in western Tunisia? What action did General Dwight D. Eisenhower take after the attack?

_____

_____

_____

_____

_____

3 **IDENTIFYING CONNECTIONS** What is a convoy system, and why did the U.S. Navy set one up?

_____

_____

_____

_____

_____

4 **UNDERSTANDING CONTEXT** Use the table below to list the features of the four nighttime strategies discussed for the D-Day invasion. In the right column, write the reasoning for each strategy.

Strategy	Why Use This Strategy?

5A GEOGRAPHY How did the Germans use the Omaha Beach's geography to their advantage?

_____

_____

_____

_____

5B **EVALUATING** What do you think would have been the outcome if the Allies didn't wait for the perfect conditions to execute the D-Day invasion?

_____

_____

U.S. State Department. Plan for the Combined Bomber Offensive From the United Kingdom. Foreign Relations of the United States, Conferences at Washington and Quebec, 1943.[Washington,] 14 May 1943.   Copyright © McGraw-Hill Education

ESSENTIAL QUESTION

What kinds of sacrifices does war require?

Mission Plan

DIRECTIONS: Read the mission plan excerpt. Then respond to the questions that follow.

EXPLORE THE CONTEXT: The United States and Britain formed the Combined Chiefs of Staff with the Allies' top military staff as a way to combine efforts during the war. Below is an excerpt from the plan that was approved at the meeting in 1943.

VOCABULARY

prescribed: authorized; agreed to

offensive: attack

depletion: reduction

synthetic oil: human-made lubricant

PRIMARY SOURCE: MISSION PLAN

The mission of the U.S. and British bomber forces, as **prescribed** by the Combined Chiefs of Staff at Casablanca, is as follows:

To conduct a joint U.S.-British air **offensive** to accomplish the progressive destruction and dislocation of the German Military, industrial, and economic system and the undermining of the morale of the German people to a point where their capacity for armed resistance is fatally weakened. This is constructed as meaning so weakened as to permit initiation of final combined operations on the Continent . . .

Destruction of the submarine building yards selected will reduce present submarine construction by eighty-nine percent (89%) . . .

Depletion of the German Air Force will fatally weaken German capacity to resist our air and surface operations. Complete domination of the air is essential for our ultimate decisive effort . . .

The quantities of petroleum and **synthetic oil** products now available to the Germans is barely adequate to supply the lifeblood which is vital to the German war machine. The oil situation is made more critical by failure of the Germans to secure and retain the Russian supplies.

—from Plan Submitted to the Combined Chiefs of Staff, Conferences at Washington and Quebec, 1943

1 ANALYZING **SOURCES** What is the audience for this mission plan, and what aspects of the passage were targeted specifically for the audience?

_____

_____

_____

_____

2 **DESCRIBING** What is the object of this mission?

_____

_____

_____

3 **INTERPRETING** What does the writer mean when he states, "undermining the morale of the German people to a point where their capacity for armed resistance is fatally weakened?"

_____

_____

_____

4 **COMPARING AND CONTRASTING** How would you compare this mission plan to President Roosevelt's radio speech in Lesson 1?

_____

_____

_____

_____

5 ECONOMICS Why is a lack of petroleum and synthetic oil important to weakening the German army?

_____

_____

_____

ESSENTIAL QUESTION
What kinds of sacrifices does war require?

French Resistance Photograph

DIRECTIONS: Study the image. Then respond to the questions that follow.

EXPLORE THE CONTEXT: This photo shows an American officer and a French partisan crouching behind a car during a street fight in a French city. Members of the French resistance were ordinary people fighting to free their country from German occupation. They did not have uniforms and often lacked military equipment.

VOCABULARY

partisan: foot soldier

PRIMARY SOURCE: PHOTOGRAPH

—taken in France in 1944

1 **EVALUATING** What type of emotion do the men in the photo portray?

_____

_____

2 **INTERPRETING** How would you describe this war scene?

_____

_____

_____

_____

3 **DETERMINING POINT OF VIEW** What was the status of the war in France in 1944?

_____

_____

_____

_____

4 **CIVICS** How could this photo affect the way civilians viewed the war?

_____

_____

_____

5 **UNDERSTANDING CONTEXT** Why doesn't the French partisan have on a uniform in this photo?

_____

_____

_____

_____

6 **EVALUATING** Does this image remind you of modern-day war photos? Why and why not?

_____

_____

The War Ends

DIRECTIONS Search for evidence in Chapter 11, Lesson 4 to help you answer the following questions.

ESSENTIAL QUESTION

What kinds of sacrifices does war require?

As you gather evidence to answer the Essential Question, think about

- the circumstances and consequences of dropping the atomic bomb on Japan.
- the consequences of World War II.

1 **IDENTIFYING CAUSES** Why did President Truman decide to bomb Japan after Germany surrendered?

_____

_____

2 **COMPARING AND CONTRASTING** Use the chart below to list the differences between a firebomb and a nuclear bomb.

Firebomb	Nuclear bomb

3A **UNDERSTANDING CONTEXT** What motivated President Truman to use the nuclear bombs?

_____

_____

_____

_____

3B GEOGRAPHY Where were the nuclear bombs dropped, and why where those cities chosen?

_____

_____

My Notes

_____

_____

_____

_____

_____

_____

_____

4 **EXPLAINING CAUSE AND EFFECT** After Japan surrendered, how did the United States, Britain, France, and the Soviet Union come together to punish German and Japanese leaders for war crimes?

_____

_____

_____

_____

_____

_____

_____

_____

5 **IDENTIFYING CONNECTIONS** How did the end of War World II provoke the Cold War?

_____

_____

_____

_____

ESSENTIAL QUESTION
What kinds of sacrifices does war require?

Indictment for *The United States of America v. Karl Brandt, et al.*

DIRECTIONS: Read this excerpt of the indictment of a German conspirator. Then respond to the questions that follow.

EXPLORE THE CONTEXT: Before the International Military Tribunal, 185 defendants from many sectors of German society were brought to trial known as the "Subsequent Nuremberg Proceedings." The defendants were grouped according to their main area of activity: medical, legal, ethnological, economic, or political. This text below is part of the indictment for the medical case.

VOCABULARY

conspiracy: plan created in secret by two or more people

indictment: formal accusation of a crime

abetted: helped

enterprises: projects undertaken

instigators: people who start action

willfully: on purpose

PRIMARY SOURCE: INDICTMENT

COUNT ONE: THE COMMON DESIGN OR CONSPIRACY

1 Between September 1939 and April 1945 all of the defendants herein, acting pursuant to a common design, unlawfully, **willfully,** and knowingly did conspire and agree together and with each other and with diverse other persons, to commit War Crimes and Crimes against Humanity, as defined in Control Council Law No. 10, Article II.

2 Throughout the period covered by this **Indictment** all of the defendants herein, acting in concert with each other and with others, unlawfully, willfully, and knowingly were principals in, accessories to, ordered, **abetted,** took a consenting part in, and were connected with plans and **enterprises** involving the commission of War Crimes and Crimes against humanity.

3 All of the defendants herein, acting in concert with others for whose acts the defendants are responsible unlawfully, willfully, and knowingly participated as leaders, organizers, **instigators,** and accomplices in the formulation and execution of the said common design, **conspiracy,** plans and enterprises to commit, and which involved the commission of, War Crimes and Crimes against Humanity.

4 It was a part of the said common design, conspiracy, plans and enterprises to perform medical experiments upon concentration camp inmates and other living human subjects, without their consent, in the course of which experiments the defendants committed the murders, brutalities, cruelties, tortures, atrocities, and other inhuman acts, more fully described in Counts II and Three of this Indictment.

5 The said common design, conspiracy, plans and enterprises embraced the commission of War Crimes and Crimes against Humanity, as set forth in Counts Two and Three of this Indictment, in that the defendants unlawfully, willfully, and knowingly encouraged, aided, abetted, and participated in the subjection of thousands of persons, including civilians, and members of the armed forces of nations then at war with the German Reich, to murders, brutalities, cruelties, tortures, atrocities, and other inhumane acts.

—from Nuremberg Military Tribunals Indictment for *The United States of America v. Karl Brandt, et al.,* 1946

1 **SUMMARIZING** Briefly write what the defendant was charged with.

_____

_____

2 **DESCRIBING** What does the indictment say the defendant specifically did?

_____

_____

_____

_____

3 **DETERMINING MEANING** What is the indictment referring to with "common design" or plans"?

_____

_____

4 **RELATING EVENTS** Why did these trials occur?

_____

_____

_____

5 **UNDERSTANDING CHANGE** How would these trials build a better world?

_____

_____

_____

6 CIVICS What verdict do you think a court would reach today in this case?

_____

_____

_____

ESSENTIAL QUESTION

What kinds of sacrifices does war require?

VOCABULARY

ultimatum: demand, requirement

applications: uses, purposes

divulge: make known

Dropping the Atomic Bomb

DIRECTIONS: Read the following excerpt from a press release announcing the decision to drop the atomic bomb on Japan. Then respond to the questions that follow.

EXPLORE THE CONTEXT: The Manhattan Project was a secret program begun by President Roosevelt to build an atomic bomb. Once the bomb became a reality, President Truman considered it a weapon that could be used to save American lives. When Japan ignored the Potsdam Declaration calling for its surrender, President Truman carried out the threat of "prompt and utter destruction" by ordering use of the atomic bomb.

PRIMARY SOURCE: PRESS RELEASE

SIXTEEN HOURS AGO an American airplane dropped one bomb on Hiroshima, an important Japanese Army base. That bomb had more power than 20,000 tons of T.N.T. It had more than two thousand times the blast power of the British "Grand Slam" which is the largest bomb ever yet used in the history of warfare....It is an atomic bomb. It is a harnessing of the basic power of the universe. The force from which the sun draws its power has been loosed against those who brought war to the Far East.

...It was to spare the Japanese people from utter destruction that the **ultimatum** of July 26 was issued at Potsdam. Their leaders promptly rejected that ultimatum. If they do not now accept our terms they may expect a rain of ruin from the air, the like of which has never been seen on this earth. Behind this air attack will follow sea and land forces in such numbers and power as they have not yet seen and with the fighting skill of which they are already well aware.

...It has never been the habit of the scientists of this country or the policy of this Government to withhold from the world scientific knowledge. Normally, therefore, everything about the work with atomic energy would be made public. But under present circumstances it is not intended to **divulge** the technical processes of production or all the military **applications,** pending further examination of possible methods of protecting us and the rest of the world from the danger of sudden destruction.I shall recommend that the Congress of the United States consider promptly the establishment of an appropriate commission to control the production and use of atomic power within the United States. I shall give further consideration and make further recommendations to the Congress as to how atomic power can become a powerful and forceful influence towards the maintenance of world peace.

—a Statement by the President, August 6, 1945

Truman, Harry S. "Press release by the White House, August 6, 1945." Ayers Papers, Subject File, Army U. S., Press releases, the atomic bomb and atomic energy. Harry S. Truman Library & Museum. https://www.trumanlibrary.org/whistlestop/study_collections/bomb/large/documents/index.php?documentid=59&pagenumber=1

1 **CITING TEXT EVIDENCE** Why does Truman feel obligated to break with the tradition of sharing scientific breakthroughs with the world?

_____

_____

_____

2 **DETERMINING POINT OF VIEW** How do you know that President Truman feels strongly about using this new technology responsibly?

_____

_____

_____

_____

3 **GEOGRAPHY** What impact do you think the harnessing of atomic power has on the environment?

_____

_____

_____

4 **UNDERSTANDING CONTEXT** Why do you think the Allies issued an ultimatum (the Potsdam Declaration) to the Japanese?

_____

_____

_____

5 **IDENTIFYING CONNECTIONS** Why does the president say that atomic power and all its potential for massive destruction is a "forceful influence toward the maintenance of world peace"?

_____

_____

ESSENTIAL QUESTIONS

What kinds of sacrifices does war require?

❶ Think About It

Review the supporting questions you developed at the beginning of the chapter. Review the evidence you gathered in Chapter 11. Were you able to answer each Supporting Question? If there was not enough evidence to answer your Supporting Questions, what additional evidence do you think you need to consider?

❷ Organize Your Evidence

Complete the chart below with information you learned about the policies of World War II, how they affected soldiers, how they affected civilians, and how these policies constituted a sacrifice.

Policy	How It Affected Soldiers	How It Affected Civilians	How was This a Sacrifice?
Conscription			
Censorship			
Rationing			

③ Write About It

Work in small groups. With your group, discuss the policies, consequences, and contexts of war sacrifices that you have identified and noted in your charts. Compare your charts. Did each member of the group pick the same policies and sacrifices? Were the sacrifices you identified necessary to help the Allies win World War II? Who made greater sacrifices: civilians or soldiers? Explain your answers.

_____

_____

_____

_____

_____

_____

_____

④ Connect to the Essential Question

Following your work in Step 3, choose the policies that you identified as constituting the greatest and most vital sacrifices in World War II. Then create a multimedia presentation that helps to answer the Essential Question: *What kinds of sacrifices does war require?*

Your presentation should include images, music, or animation. Identify and describe the sacrifices these policies entailed, their effects on soldiers and civilians, and how sacrifices during the war contributed to the Allied victory. Be sure to consider the demands of the war and the specific context of World War II while analyzing these policies and sacrifices. Connect your description to the political, technological, and military situations during the war. Be sure that your presentation is accurate, engaging, and informative.

_____

_____

_____

_____

_____

_____

TAKE ACTION

MAKE CONNECTIONS Throughout its history, the United States has asked men and women to make sacrifices for the good of the country through service in the country's armed forces. Today, over 20 million people are veterans of the armed forces. They have served in conflicts such as World War II, the Korean War, the Vietnam War, and the first Persian Gulf War. The wars in Iraq and Afghanistan are still ongoing, and the United States maintains military bases around the globe. Every one of these servicemen, servicewomen, and their families has direct experience of what it means to make sacrifices for their country, for its citizens, and for people around the globe.

DIRECTIONS: With the help of your teacher identify veterans from your local area to interview about the sacrifices they made in the armed forces. You might identify family members who are veterans or organize a visit to a local veteran's organization. Work in a small group to draft a series of questions you would like to ask your interview subjects. Consider asking them about their background, the circumstances in which they joined the armed forces, where their service took them, and the sacrifices they had to make as a result. Next, decide how you will record your interviews. You might write the answers on a notepad or laptop or record them using a video camera or digital recorder.

After conducting your interviews, create a multimedia presentation from the material you gained from your interviewee(s) in which you will analyze the experiences of your interview subject(s) and draw conclusions about why people serve in the armed forces and the kinds of sacrifices they (and their loved ones) make. Consider the historical context for your conclusions. Has the United States always demanded the same sacrifices of successive generations or across different conflicts? What factors have changed? What could be done to better support the country's veterans?

_____

_____

_____

_____

_____

_____

_____

The Cold War Begins

ESSENTIAL QUESTION

How did Cold War tensions affect American society?

Think about how this question might relate to the postwar period and what it meant for the way people lived. How did they think about their safety and possible threats from foreign countries? What actions did people take to feel safer? What actions did the government take to confront Cold War tensions?

TALK ABOUT IT

Discuss with a partner what type of information you would need to know to answer this question. For example, one question might be: *What fears did Americans have during the Cold War?*

DIRECTIONS: Now write down three additional questions that would help you explain how Americans coped with the Cold War tensions.

MY RESEARCH QUESTIONS

Supporting Question 1:

_____

_____

Supporting Question 2:

_____

_____

Supporting Question 3:

_____

_____

The Origins of the Cold War

DIRECTIONS Search for evidence in Chapter 12, Lesson 1 to help you answer the following questions.

1A **DESCRIBING** What economic decisions were made at the Bretton Woods Conference?

_____

_____

_____

1B **EXPLAINING CAUSE AND EFFECT** How were the policies developed at the Bretton Woods Conference a result of the Great Depression?

_____

_____

_____

_____

2A **EXPLAINING** What **was the purpose of the United Nations?**

_____

_____

_____

2B **INFERRING** How did the United Nations impact Americans?

_____

_____

_____

3 **SUMMARIZING** What was the purpose of the Yalta Conference?

_____

_____

_____

ESSENTIAL QUESTION

How did Cold War tensions affect American society?

As you gather evidence to answer the Essential Question, think about:

- how the Cold War set countries against each other.
- how Americans reacted to the threat from foreign countries.

My Notes

_____

_____

_____

_____

_____

_____

4 **COMPARING AND CONTRASTING** How did U.S. leaders differ from Soviet leaders during the Yalta Conference? Complete the Venn Diagram to organize your answer.

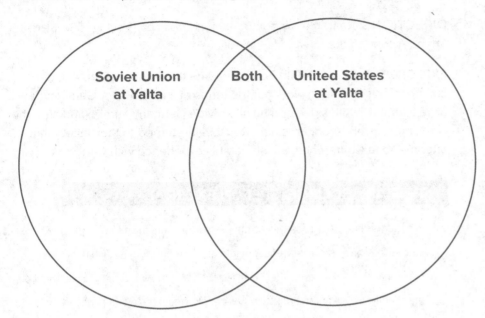

Soviet Union at Yalta **Both** **United States at Yalta**

5 **EXPLAINING** Complete the graphic organizer to explain how the Cold War began.

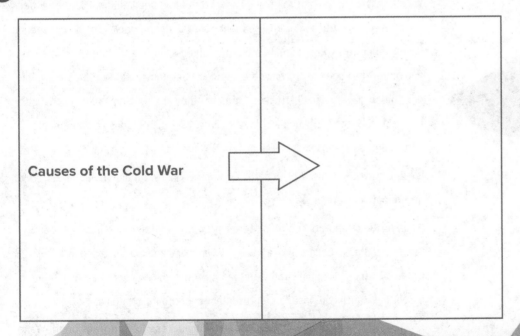

Causes of the Cold War

ESSENTIAL QUESTION

How did Cold War tensions affect American society?

The Yalta Conference

DIRECTIONS: Read the excerpt from an address by President Roosevelt. Then respond to the questions that follow.

EXPLORE THE CONTENT: In February 1945, the leaders of the Allied countries met in Yalta to work out the terms of surrender for Germany. It was at Yalta that the Allies decided how to divide Germany and Poland after the Nazis had surrendered. President Roosevelt returned to the United States after the Yalta Conference and shared his experience with Congress.

PRIMARY SOURCE: SPEECH EXCERPT

" The German people, as well as the German soldiers must realize that the sooner they give up and surrender by groups or as individuals, the sooner their present agony will be over. They must realize that only with complete surrender can they begin to reestablish themselves as people whom the world might accept as decent neighbors.

We made it clear again at Yalta, and I now repeat that unconditional surrender does not mean the destruction or enslavement of the German people. The Nazi leaders have deliberately withheld that part of the Yalta declaration from the German press and radio. They seek to convince the people of Germany that the Yalta declaration does mean slavery and destruction for them—they are working at it day and night for that is how the Nazis hope to save their own skins, and deceive their people into continued and useless resistance.

We did, however, make it clear at the Conference just what unconditional surrender does mean for Germany.

It means the temporary control of Germany by Great Britain, Russia, France, and the United States. Each of these Nations will occupy and control a separate zone of Germany—and the administration of the four zones will be coordinated in Berlin by a Control Council composed of representatives of the four Nations. "

—from Franklin D. Roosevelt's address to Congress on the Yalta Conference, March 1, 1945

Roosevelt, Franklin D. "Message to Congress re the Yalta Conference, March 1, 1945." Franklin D. Roosevelt, Master Speech File, 1898-1945, Franklin D. Roosevelt Presidential Library & Museum. http://www.fdrlibrary.marist.edu/_resources/images/msf/msfb0209

1 IDENTIFYING PERSPECTIVES According to Roosevelt, what is the best response that Germany could have to the decisions of the Yalta Conference?

_____

_____

_____

2 CIVICS What complaint does Roosevelt make about the role of the press in Germany? How does government control of the press put limits on the people of a country?

_____

_____

_____

_____

_____

3 ANALYZING What do you think Roosevelt's purpose was in making this speech to Congress?

_____

_____

_____

4 IDENTIFYING PERSPECTIVES Why would Nazi leaders withhold information about the Yalta declaration from the German people? What is Roosevelt's perspective on the reasons for their policy?

_____

_____

_____

_____

5 ECONOMICS Why was it in Europe's best interest to make Germany into a "decent neighbor"? What are the economic reasons to stabilize Germany?

_____

_____

_____

ESSENTIAL QUESTION
How did Cold War tensions affect American society?

VOCABULARY

inalienable rights: human rights that cannot be taken away by laws

barbarous: cruel; exceedingly brutal

Universal Declaration of Human Rights

DIRECTIONS: Read the following excerpt from a United Nations declaration about human rights. Then respond to the questions that follow.

EXPLORE THE CONTEXT: On December 10, 1948, the UN General Assembly proclaimed a set of standards about human rights. The document was drafted by representatives from all areas of the world and was translated into over 500 languages. It represents a standard against which leaders and nations can be held accountable for the treatment of their own people.

PRIMARY SOURCE: DECLARATION EXCERPT

❝Preamble

Whereas recognition of the inherent dignity and of the equal and **inalienable** rights of all members of the human family is the foundation of freedom, justice and peace in the world,

Whereas disregard and contempt for human rights have resulted in **barbarous** acts which have outraged the conscience of mankind, and the advent of a world in which human beings shall enjoy freedom of speech and belief and freedom from fear and want has been proclaimed as the highest aspiration of the common people. . . .

Whereas it is essential to promote the development of friendly relations between nations,

Whereas the peoples of the United Nations have in the Charter reaffirmed their faith in fundamental human rights, in the dignity and worth of the human person and in the equal rights of men and women and have determined to promote social progress and better standards of life in larger freedom,

Whereas Member States have pledged themselves to achieve, in cooperation with the United Nations, the promotion of universal respect for and observance of human rights and fundamental freedoms. . . .

Now, therefore, The General Assembly, Proclaims this Universal Declaration of Human Rights as a common standard of achievement for all peoples and all nations. ❞

—from "Universal Declaration of Human Rights," the United Nations, 1948

UN General Assembly, "Universal Declaration of Human Rights." 217 (III) A. Paris, 1948.

1 **ANALYZING INFORMATION** What do the authors of the document point to as the reasons for writing the declaration?

_____

_____

_____

_____

2 **ANALYZING** What is the historical context of the statement? What had just happened in the world when this document was written that might have motivated its authors?

_____

_____

_____

3 **CIVICS** The document was created by the United Nations. How does that help you understand how the rules will be enforced?

_____

_____

_____

_____

4 **INFERRING** What do the authors mean by suggesting that the declaration will help "promote the development of friendly relations between nations"?

_____

_____

_____

5 **PREDICTING** How might the language of the document be used in the United States to bring about social change?

_____

_____

ESSENTIAL QUESTION

How did Cold War tensions affect American society?

As you gather evidence to answer the Essential Question, think about:

- how the countries of the world got along with each other during the Cold War.
- why communism seemed like a threat to Americans.
- how Americans showed their commitment to Germany.

My Notes

The Early Cold War Years

DIRECTIONS: Search for evidence in Chapter 12, Lesson 2 to help you answer the following questions.

1A EXPLAINING What was the policy of containment?

1B GEOGRAPHY How did President Truman use the policy of containment in Iran and Turkey?

2A EXPLAINING EFFECTS How was the Marshall Plan designed to harm the Soviet Union?

2B EVALUATING EVIDENCE How did the ideals of the Marshall Plan break down when it came to China?

3 **SUMMARIZING** Use the Cornell Notes organizer to take notes about the developments of the Korean War.

Main Ideas	Notes
Causes for the Korean War	
Escalation of the Korean War	
Armistice	

ESSENTIAL QUESTION

How did Cold War tensions affect American society?

Berlin Airlift

DIRECTIONS: Read the following excerpt from a war memorial. Then respond to the questions that follow.

EXPLORE THE CONTEXT: When the Soviet Union cut off Berlin from the rest of Germany, the Americans knew they needed to get food to Berlin's residents. Colonel Frank Howley was the commander of the U.S. base in Berlin. He agreed with the plan to airlift food into the city and asked for flour to be the first delivery. He wrote about that first delivery in his memoir of the war.

VOCABULARY

apoplexy: speechlessness caused by anger

Tempelhof: name of the airport in Berlin

PRIMARY SOURCE: MEMOIR EXCERPT

66 They wobbled into **Tempelhof,** coming down clumsily through the bomb-shattered buildings around the field, a sight that would have made a spick-and-span air parade officer die of **apoplexy,** but they were the most beautiful things I had ever seen. As the planes touched down, and the bags of flour began to spill out of their bellies, I realized that this was the beginning of something wonderful—a way to crack the blockade. I went back to my office almost breathless with elation, like a man who has made a great discovery and cannot hide his joy. 99

—from *Berlin Command* by Brig. General Frank Howley, 1950

1 **INFERRING** Based on the description of the airplanes, what do you think they looked like?

_____

_____

_____

2 **DRAWING CONCLUSIONS** What did the bags of flour represent for Colonel Howley? Why did they make him so happy?

_____

_____

_____

_____

3 **DETERMINING CONTEXT** What is the "something wonderful" to which Colonel Howley is referring?

_____

_____

_____

4 ECONOMICS What economic impact did the Soviet Union intend from its blockade of Berlin? How do the clumsy planes change the Soviet Union's impact?

_____

_____

_____

_____

5 **DRAWING CONCLUSIONS** What impression does this memoir give you about the role of U.S. military personnel after the war?

_____

_____

_____

_____

The Korean War

Stratemeyer, George E. The Three Wars of Lt. Gen. George E. Stratemeyer: His Korean War Diary, Edited by William T. Y'Blood. Washington: Government Printing Office, 1999.

Copyright © McGraw-Hill Education

ESSENTIAL QUESTION

How did Cold War tensions affect American society?

VOCABULARY

airdrome: airport or military base

38th parallel: the boundary line between North Korea and South Korea

F-51: military fighter aircraft

B-26: twin-engine military aircraft bomber

Yak: short for Yakovlev aircraft, a Soviet military aircraft bomber

CINCFE: Commander in Chief, Far East; in this case, General MacArthur

DIRECTIONS: Read the following excerpt from a journal. Then respond to the questions that follow.

EXPLORE THE CONTEXT: Lieutenant General George Stratemeyer was the Far East Air Forces commander during the Korean War. During his service, he kept a diary of his activities. General MacArthur commanded the operations of the war. The battle line was drawn at the 38th parallel, which is the boundary between the U.S. - and Soviet-occupied zones in Korea.

PRIMARY SOURCE: JOURNAL ENTRY

66 Thursday 29 June 1950.

0600 hours departed with General MacArthur . . . aboard the *Bataan* from Haneda for Suwon Air Field, South Korea. Told **CINCFE** that in order for me to support him full-out, [I] must have authority to attack the enemy (his aircraft and **airdromes**) in North Korea. Permission granted at once and we now cross the **38th Parallel**! [I] wired [General] Partridge re the authority. (With CINCFE's authority to cross the 38th and as a result of my wire to Partridge, General Timberlake got off a **B-26** strike north of the 38th the afternoon of 29 June.) Spent the day interviewing Lt. Colonel McGinn, Brigadier General Kim Chung Yul, General Church and other officers . . . and, in general being 'briefed' on the actual situation. Our liaison officer . . . is a Lt. Colonel McGinn who is doing an outstanding job with the margin of equipment. His needs were many and varied—including 24 shovels with which to dig foxholes around the air strip! Also talked at length with General Kim who commands the South Korean Air Force. Promised him his supply requirements to keep his **F-51s** going. Timing on my escorting fighters for the *Bataan* excellent; CINCFE impressed. A **Yak** attempted to intercept *Bataan*, but was driven off by our escort. Returned to Tokyo and landed Haneda 2205 hours. Came straight to the office where I briefed General Partridge who is now functioning as my vice commander. Left the office after midnight. 99

—from *The Three Wars of Lt. Gen. George E. Stratemeyer: His Korean War Diary*, by George E. Stratemeyer, published in 1999

1 **ANALYZING INFORMATION** How would you describe General Stratemeyer's day? What details help you make that assessment?

_____

_____

2 **EVALUATING EVIDENCE** What are General Stratemeyer's responsibilities in the war?

_____

_____

3 **RELATING EVENTS** What kind of dangers does General Stratemeyer face on the day he writes about in his journal?

_____

_____

_____

_____

4 **EVALUATING EVIDENCE** Based on the details General Stratemeyer includes in his journal, what can you tell about the allies and enemies of the United States? What details help you understand those relationships?

_____

_____

_____

5 GEOGRAPHY Why was it important for General Stratemeyer to get permission from General MacArthur to cross the 38th parallel? What did that permission allow him to do, and what happened as a result of that permission?

_____

_____

_____

_____

_____

6 **INFERRING** What can you infer from the information in the journal about Lt. Colonel McGinn? What is McGinn preparing for in the war?

_____

_____

_____

The Cold War and American Society

ESSENTIAL QUESTION

How did Cold War tensions affect American society?

As you gather evidence to answer the Essential Question, think about:

- the difficulty a person may have in recovering from accusations of disloyalty.

- the power of government officials to instill fear or suspicion.

- what you would do if you faced the threat of nuclear weapons.

My Notes

DIRECTIONS Search for evidence in Chapter 12, Lesson 3 to help you answer the following questions.

1A IDENTIFYING PERSPECTIVES What was the biggest fear for Americans during the Red Scare?

1B EVALUATING EVIDENCE How did President Truman attempt to address those fears?

2A CIVICS What inferences can you make about how effective Truman's loyalty tests were?

2B UNDERSTANDING CHRONOLOGY What was the next step in determining citizens' loyalties?

3 EXPLAINING EFFECTS Complete the cause-and-effect graphic organizer to identify at least four of the effects that fear of communism had on Americans.

4 EVALUATING EVIDENCE What did Americans do to protect themselves from nuclear weapons?

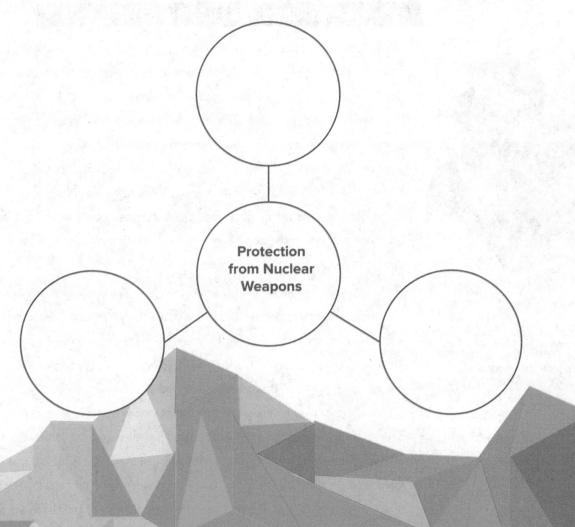

Federal Bureau of Investigations, FBI joint file on Julius and Ethel Rosenberg. New York, 1954. https://archive.org/stream/RosenbergJuliusAndEthel/Rosenberg%2C%20Julius%20and%20Ethel%2001#page/n13/mode/2up

ESSENTIAL QUESTION

How did Cold War tensions affect American society?

Julius and Ethel Rosenberg

DIRECTIONS: Read the following excerpt from an FBI file. Then respond to the questions that follow.

EXPLORE THE CONTEXT: Julius and Ethel Rosenberg were a mild-mannered couple living in upstate New York. They lived normal lives and were similar to many other young couples around them. However, both Julius and Ethel were spies for the Soviet government. Julius worked for the U.S. army, and Ethel's brother was a machinist on the government's project to build the atomic bomb. Both of them used their connections to pass secrets to a Soviet spy. Many believed that the young couple were innocent and that they had come under suspicion because they belonged to the Communist Party. Both of them were convicted and executed for treason.

PRIMARY SOURCE: FBI FILE

❝ On March 19, 1951 **T-1**, of unknown reliability, advised that JULIUS ROSENBERG claimed that he had $7,000 and a **Leica Camera** hidden in his apartment when Special Agents of the FBI visited his apartment on June 16, 1950. ROSENBERG told the informant that on that same day his wife, ETHEL, took the $7,000 and a Leica Camera, placed the money and camera in a brown paper shopping bag, and delivered it to 'friends' who lived in another house in Knickerbocker Village. ROSENBERG described these 'friends' as members of the Communist Party, good friends of his, had two children and at one time considered moving and buying their own home and further that the husband was a member of the American Labor Party (ALP) in the neighborhood of Knickerbocker Village. . . .

Mr. AL GRAY lives at apartment AB-12 at Monroe Street, Knickerbocker Village. . . . He stated that he did not know JULIUS and ETHEL ROSENBERG and knew nothing about them until they were arrested. He stated that he had been a member of the Knickerbocker Village Camera Club from its inception and had been a past president or some other officer. . . . He stated that the camera club was not truly a camera club where people go together and jointly take pictures, discuss their equipment and perform or engage in group activities. He stated that the reason the Camera Club was set up in Knickerbocker Village by the management was due to the fact that many people in the Village were amateur photographers and in the early 1940s did their own development. . . . For this reason the management set aside a room to be used as a camera club. He advised that it is not a social club as is commonly found in many amateur camera clubs. ❞

—from "FBI File on Rosenberg, Julius and Ethel," Federal Bureau of Investigation

VOCABULARY

T-1: source of information

Leica Camera: a popular brand of camera

1 **SUMMARIZING** Summarize the information in the FBI file. Describe the incident captured in the report.

_____

_____

_____

2 **CIVICS** What was going on in the United States at the time that this FBI file was created? Why did the Rosenbergs' connection to the Communist Party create suspicion?

_____

_____

_____

_____

3 **EXPLAINING EFFECTS** What information does Al Gray contribute to the FBI investigation? Does he add to or detract from the suspicion of the Rosenbergs?

_____

_____

_____

4 **INFERRING** Because the Rosenbergs were believed to be spies, what can you infer about the FBI agent's suspicion of Ethel's delivery of the camera and money?

_____

_____

_____

5 **IDENTIFYING PERSPECTIVES** Many Americans believed that the Rosenbergs were victims of overzealous investigators who misinterpreted normal behavior. What assessment would you make about the Rosenbergs based on the information in this part of the FBI file?

_____

_____

_____

Hearings regarding the communist infiltration of the motion picture industry. Hearings before the Committee on Un-American Activities, House of Representatives, Eightieth Congress, first session. Public law 601 (section 121, subsection Q (2)). Washington: Government Printing Office, 1947.

ESSENTIAL QUESTION

How did Cold War tensions affect American society?

The House Un-American Activities Committee

DIRECTIONS: Read the following excerpt from a congressional testimony. Then respond to the questions that follow.

EXPLORE THE CONTEXT: The House Un-American Activities Committee (HUAC) investigated artists and entertainers in the 1940s and 1950s. It was criticized for violating free speech rights. It created a blacklist of individuals who refused to answer their questions. Blacklisted entertainers were often avoided and passed over for work in the industry. Many had to move to other countries to find work.

PRIMARY SOURCE: CONGRESSIONAL TESTIMONY EXCERPT

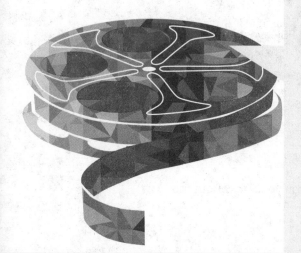

VOCABULARY

subversive: designed to undermine authority

66 October 20, 1947.

Jack L. Warner, vice president of Warner Bros. Studio.

Our American way of life is under attack from without and from within our national borders. I believe it is the duty of each loyal American to resist those attacks and defeat them. . . . If there are Communists in our industry, or any other industry, organization, or society who seek to undermine our free institutions, let's find out about it and know who they are. Let the record be spread clear, for all to read and judge. The public is entitled to know the facts. And the motion-picture industry is entitled to have the public know the facts. . . . Our company is keenly aware of its responsibilities to keep its product free from **subversive** poisons. With all the vision at my command, I scrutinize the planning and production of our motion pictures. It is my firm belief that there is not a Warner Bros. picture that can fairly be judged to be hostile to our country, or communistic in tone or purpose. . . . One of those American principles is the right to gripe and criticize in an effort to improve. That right to gripe is not enjoyed under communistic dictatorships. To surrender that privilege under pressure would betray our American standards. 99

—from "Hearings regarding the communist infiltration of the motion picture industry," held before the Committee on Un-American Activities, House of Representatives, Eightieth Congress, first session, October 20, 1947

1 CIVICS What bedrock civic principle is Jack Warner expressing in his testimony?

_____

_____

_____

2 INFERRING How might citizens react to Jack Warner being called to testify before the House Un-American Activities Committee?

_____

_____

_____

3 EVALUATING EVIDENCE What does Jack Warner mean by "Our American way of life is under attack from without and from within our national borders"?

_____

_____

_____

4 DETERMINING CONTEXT What was going on in the movie industry that makes Jack Warner's testimony particularly relevant?

_____

_____

_____

5 EXPLAINING EFFECTS Does Mr. Warner want something specific to happen as a result of his testimony?

_____

_____

_____

Eisenhower's Cold War Policies

DIRECTIONS: Search for evidence in Chapter 12, Lesson 4 to help you answer the following questions.

1A **INTERPRETING** What is the nuclear triad?

_____

_____

_____

1B **EXPLAINING CAUSE AND EFFECT** How did the nuclear triad lead to ongoing brinkmanship?

_____

_____

_____

_____

2A **COMPARING** How were Eisenhower's policies similarly implemented in the Taiwan Crisis and the Suez Crisis?

_____

_____

_____

2B **IDENTIFYING PERSPECTIVES** How do you think Eisenhower's military background contributed to his response to the threat of communism during his term as President?

_____

_____

_____

_____

_____

ESSENTIAL QUESTION

How did Cold War tensions affect American society?

As you gather evidence to answer the Essential Question, think about:

- how a country's leaders bring change in foreign policy.
- the role of the military during peace time.
- how conflicts in foreign lands can entangle Americans.

My Notes

_____

_____

_____

_____

_____

_____

3 GEOGRAPHY Complete the chart to explain the covert operations President Eisenhower put into place to prevent the spread of communism.

Place	Covert Operation

4 IDENTIFYING CAUSE AND EFFECT Use the graphic organizer below to take notes about Eisenhower's final years as president.

Cause	Effect
The Soviets launch *Sputnik*.	
President Eisenhower asks Congress to authorize military force in the Middle East.	
The Soviet Union shoots down a U.S. spy plane.	

ESSENTIAL QUESTION
How did Cold War tensions affect American society?

The Eisenhower Doctrine

DIRECTIONS: Read the following excerpt from a presidential address. Then respond to the questions that follow.

EXPLORE THE CONTEXT: The Eisenhower Doctrine extends the Truman Doctrine and calls for a policy of containment in the Middle East. President Eisenhower promised to help those nations in the Middle East that needed assistance to resist the spread of communism.

PRIMARY SOURCE: SPEECH EXCERPT

❝ The Middle East has abruptly reached a new and critical stage in its long and important history. In past decades many of the countries in that area were not fully self-governing. Other nations exercised considerable authority in the area and the security of the region was largely built around their power. But since the First World War there has been a steady evolution toward self-government and independence. This development the United States has welcomed and has encouraged. Our country supports without reservation the full **sovereignty** and independence of each and every nation of the Middle East.

The evolution to independence has in the main been a peaceful process. But the area has been often troubled. Persistent **crosscurrents** of distrust and fear with raids back and forth across national boundaries have brought about a high degree of instability in much of the Mid East. Just recently there have been hostilities involving Western European nations that once exercised much influence in the area. Also the relatively large attack by Israel in October has intensified the basic differences between that nation and its Arab neighbors. All this instability has been heightened and, at times, manipulated by International Communism. ❞

—from "Special message to the Congress on the Situation in the Middle East," by President Dwight D. Eisenhower, January 5, 1957

VOCABULARY

sovereignty: right to self-govern

crosscurrents: processes that are in conflict with one another

Eisenhower, Dwight D. "Special Message to the Congress on the Situation in the Middle East, January 5, 1957." In *Public Papers of the Presidents of the United States: Dwight D. Eisenhower, 1957.* Washington: Government Printing Office, 1957.

1 **EVALUATING EVIDENCE** Why might President Eisenhower view the Middle East as important?

_____

_____

_____

2 **DETERMINING CONTEXT** Why does Eisenhower explain this doctrine? Who is listening to it at home or abroad?

_____

_____

_____

_____

3 **ANALYZING INFORMATION** What does Eisenhower expect to happen as a result of this speech?

_____

_____

_____

_____

4 **DETERMINING CONTEXT** What important events were going on when Eisenhower gave his speech?

_____

_____

_____

5 **CIVICS** What principle of the U.S. Constitution is demonstrated in this presidential address to Congress?

_____

_____

_____

ESSENTIAL QUESTION

How did Cold War tensions affect American society?

Censorship Field Manual

DIRECTIONS: Read the following excerpt from a military field manual. Then respond to the questions that follow.

EXPLORE THE CONTEXT: In the tense years of the Cold War, the military developed a standing force of soldiers. It also developed policies to safeguard secrets and to guide soldiers in the conduct of war. Censorship of personal correspondence was a part of those policies to prevent military secrets from getting into the wrong hands.

PRIMARY SOURCE: FIELD MANUAL EXCERPT

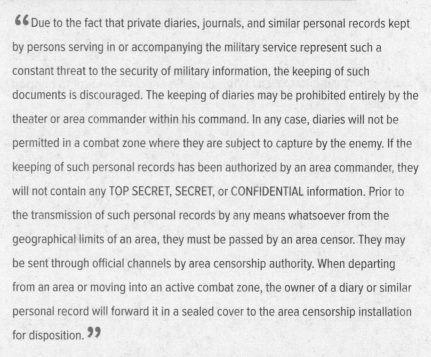

❝Due to the fact that private diaries, journals, and similar personal records kept by persons serving in or accompanying the military service represent such a constant threat to the security of military information, the keeping of such documents is discouraged. The keeping of diaries may be prohibited entirely by the theater or area commander within his command. In any case, diaries will not be permitted in a combat zone where they are subject to capture by the enemy. If the keeping of such personal records has been authorized by an area commander, they will not contain any TOP SECRET, SECRET, or CONFIDENTIAL information. Prior to the transmission of such personal records by any means whatsoever from the geographical limits of an area, they must be passed by an area censor. They may be sent through official channels by area censorship authority. When departing from an area or moving into an active combat zone, the owner of a diary or similar personal record will forward it in a sealed cover to the area censorship installation for disposition.❞

—from "Korean War Field Manuals," *Department of the Army Field Manual*, 1955

Department of the Army Field Manual: Armed Forces Censorship (Army). Washington: Government Printing Office, 1955.   Copyright © McGraw-Hill Education

1. **DETERMINING CONTEXT** Explain the procedures outlined in the field manual. Are they appropriate for the context in which it was written?

_____

_____

_____

_____

2. **ANALYZING** Based on the guidelines described, what kind of information would be permitted in a diary? What information would not be permitted?

_____

_____

_____

3. **RELATING EVENTS** What elements of the culture were present when this document was written that might contribute to its purpose or creation?

_____

_____

_____

4. **EXPLAINING** What must the owner of a diary do if moving into a combat zone?

_____

_____

5. CIVICS What is the government's responsibility for keeping its people safe? What rights can be stripped from soldiers in the spirit of government responsibility?

_____

_____

_____

_____

ESSENTIAL QUESTION

How did Cold War tensions affect American society?

My Notes

_____

_____

_____

_____

_____

_____

_____

_____

_____

_____

_____

_____

_____

1 Think About It

Review the supporting questions that you developed at the beginning of the chapter. Review the evidence that you gathered in Chapter 12. Were you able to answer each Supporting Question?

If there was not enough evidence to answer your Supporting Questions, what additional evidence do you think you need to consider?

_____

_____

_____

_____

2 Organize Your Evidence

Complete the chart below with two examples of how each country contributed to the Cold War.

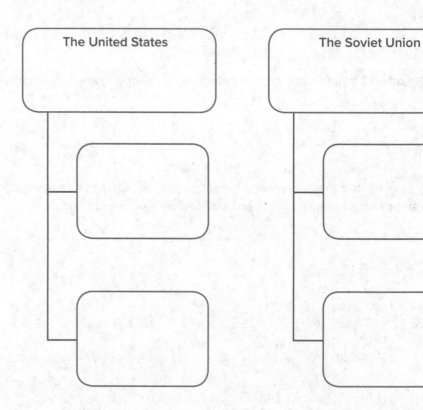

The United States

The Soviet Union

❸ Talk About It

Work in small groups. Talk with your group about the information you included in your chart. Did you include the same evidence, or were your classmates' responses different from your responses? Which information is most important to understanding the Cold War? Why?

_____

_____

_____

_____

_____

❹ Connect to the Essential Question

Work in small groups. Discuss the many ways in which the United States was impacted by the Cold War. Then choose a Cold War issue in which your group is most interested . On a separate piece of paper, write a speech to give before Congress that addresses your issue and the Essential Question: _How did Cold War tensions affect American society?_ Address how Americans can cope with the impact, and offer strength and encouragement for people who feel fearful. Use the elements of a good speech, including an engaging hook, a clear and convincing message, persuasive language, and a call to action at the end. Divide the speech into sections, and have each member of your group deliver his or her section to the class.

_____

_____

_____

_____

_____

_____

_____

_____

_____

CITIZENSHIP
TAKING ACTION

MAKE CONNECTIONS Most presidents of the United States put their thoughts about the world into words. At some point in their presidency, they make a speech that comes to be known as their doctrine. President Truman had a doctrine of containment. Eisenhower's doctrine expanded the containment policy to include the Middle East. The ideas in a doctrine usually are consistent with how the president views the rest of the world.

DIRECTIONS: Use what you have learned in Chapter 12 about the Cold War and the presidential doctrines that helped stoke tensions. Imagine that you have been elected President and must compile your thoughts about the world into a doctrine. Write a presidential speech that conveys your own personal doctrine about how the United States should treat other countries. Your speech can focus on the world as it is today, or your doctrine can be relevant to the 1950s and the Cold War. Begin your speech with an interesting hook. Give details about your idea, and use the speech to urge your audience to change their opinions. Practice delivering your speech to your classmates, and improve it using their suggestions. Finally, perform your revised speech for the class.

Postwar America

ESSENTIAL QUESTION

How does prosperity change the way people live?

Think about how this question might relate to the period of time from the end of World War II until 1960. What led to a more prosperous economy in the United States after World War II? How did the politics and the economy of the time change society? How did different groups of people experience this prosperity?

TALK ABOUT IT

Discuss with a partner the type of information you would need to know to answer these questions. For example, one question might be: *What makes a society prosper?*

MY RESEARCH QUESTIONS

Supporting Question 1:

_____

_____

Supporting Question 2:

_____

_____

_____

Supporting Question 3:

_____

_____

Truman and Eisenhower

DIRECTIONS Search for evidence in Chapter 13, Lesson 1 to help you answer the following questions.

1A **DESCRIBING** What was the Taft-Hartley Act?

_____

_____

_____

_____

_____

_____

1B **ANALYZING** Why was Truman against this bill?

_____

_____

_____

_____

_____

2 **EXPLAINING CAUSES** Who were the Dixiecrats, and why did they abandon the Democratic Party?

_____

_____

_____

_____

3A **SUMMARIZING** What were the main elements of Truman's Fair Deal?

_____

_____

_____

_____

_____

_____

_____

ESSENTIAL QUESTION

How does prosperity change the way people live?

As you gather evidence to answer the Essential Question, think about

- the major accomplishments of the Truman and Eisenhower administrations.
- how new laws and regulations changed American society.

My Notes

_____

_____

_____

_____

_____

_____

3B **DRAWING CONCLUSIONS** Which elements of Truman's Fair Deal were ultimately passed by Congress? Which were not?

_____

_____

_____

_____

4 **CIVICS** Complete the graphic organizer below with some of the major actions taken by Eisenhower's administration.

```
    Reduced Federal                          Expanded Government
       Spending                                   Programs



                        Eisenhower's Administration.



      Infrastructure                               Taxes
```

5 **IDENTIFYING** What was the National Highway Act?

_____

_____

_____

6 **INFERRING** What were some of the positive and negative impacts of developing our country's infrastructure through highways?

Positive Impacts	Negative Impacts

The Fair Deal

ESSENTIAL QUESTION

How does prosperity change the way people live?

DIRECTIONS: Read the following excerpt from President Truman's annual State of the Union address. Then answer the questions that follow.

EXPLORE THE CONTEXT: At the time of the President's address to Congress, the United States was experiencing a "postwar boom," with many people enjoying great prosperity. In his address, President Truman outlined the government's efforts to maintain prosperity and made several recommendations for eliminating economic threats caused by inflation. He urged the cooperation of government and business to keep and increase prosperity.

PRIMARY SOURCE: SPEECH

❝ In this society, we are conservative about the values and principles which we cherish; but we are forward-looking in protecting those values and principles and in extending their benefits. We have rejected the **discredited** theory that the fortunes of the Nation should be in the hands of a privileged few. We have abandoned the **"trickledown"** concept of national prosperity. Instead, we believe that our economic system should rest on a democratic foundation and that wealth should be created for the benefit of all. The recent election shows that the people of the United States are in favor of this kind of society and want to go on improving it.

The American people have decided that poverty is just as wasteful and just as unnecessary as preventable disease. We have pledged our common resources to help one another in the hazards and struggles of individual life. We believe that no unfair prejudice or artificial distinction should bar any citizen of the United States of America from an education, or from good health, or from a job that he is capable of performing. The attainment of this kind of society demands the best efforts of every citizen in every walk of life, and it imposes increasing responsibilities on the Government.

The Government must work with industry, labor, and the farmers in keeping our economy running at full speed. The Government must see that every American has a chance to obtain his fair share of our increasing abundance. These responsibilities go hand in hand. We cannot maintain prosperity unless we have a fair distribution of opportunity and a widespread **consumption** of the products of our factories and farms.

Our Government has **undertaken** to meet these responsibilities. . . . Every segment of our population and every individual has a right to expect from our Government a fair deal.

—from Annual Message to the Congress on the State of the Union,
January 5, 1949

VOCABULARY

discredited: disproved

trickledown: distributed downward from the wealthy

consumption: purchase, use

undertaken: attempted

Truman, Harry S. "Annual Message to the Congress on the State of the Union, January 5, 1949," in Public Papers of the Presidents of the United States: Harry S. Truman, 1949. Washington: U.S. Government Printing Office, 1964.

1 **DETERMINING CENTRAL IDEAS** What kind of society does Truman insist will best serve every American?

_____

_____

2 **ECONOMICS** What two economic systems does Truman describe?

_____

_____

_____

3 **EVALUATING EVIDENCE** Truman places the responsibility for his proposed economic system on both government and the individual? How would you describe the role of each?

_____

_____

_____

_____

_____

_____

4 **SUMMARIZING** How would you summarize Truman's "fair deal"?

_____

_____

_____

5 **MAKING CONNECTIONS** How were Roosevelt's "New Deal" and Truman's "Fair Deal" alike? How were they different?

_____

_____

_____

_____

_____

_____

ESSENTIAL QUESTION

How does prosperity change the way people live?

VOCABULARY

abating: lessening; decreasing

formulation: development

execution: carrying out

disseminate: spread or share

Air Pollution Control Act

DIRECTIONS: Read the following excerpt from the Air Pollution Control Act. Then respond to the questions that follow.

EXPLORE THE CONTEXT: The Air Pollution Control Act was passed in 1955. Its main purpose was to help investigate and control air pollution by providing funds for federal research. The act allocated $5 million over a five-year period for research into the issue, but the primary responsibility of enforcement was left to the states. It was the first federal legislation involving air pollution, and while it did little to actually curb air pollution, it demonstrated the federal government's recognition that air pollution was a growing national problem.

PRIMARY SOURCE: LEGISLATION

❝Be it enacted by the Senate and House of Representatives of the United States of America in Congress assembled, That in recognition of the dangers to the public health and welfare, injury to agricultural crops and livestock, damage to and deterioration of property, and hazards to air and ground transportation, from air pollution, it is hereby declared to be the policy of Congress to preserve and protect the primary responsibilities and rights of the States and local governments in controlling air pollution, to support and aid technical research to devise and develop methods of **abating** such pollution, and to provide Federal technical services and financial aid to State and local government air pollution control agencies and other public or private agencies and institutions in the **formulation** and **execution** of their air pollution abatement research programs . . .

The Surgeon General may (1) encourage cooperative activities by State and local governments for the prevention and abatement of air pollution; (2) collect and **disseminate** information relating to air pollution and the prevention and abatement thereof; (3) conduct in the Public Health Service, and support and aid the conduct by State and local government air pollution control agencies, and other public and private agencies and institutions of, technical research to devise and develop methods of preventing and abating air pollution; and (4) make available to State and local government air pollution control agencies, other public and private agencies and institutions, and industries, the results of surveys, studies, investigations, research, and experiments relating to air pollution and the prevention and abatement thereof. ❞

—from Air Pollution Control Act, July 14, 1955

1 **EXPLAINING EFFECTS** According to the act, what were the main dangers of air pollution?

_____

_____

_____

2 **SUMMARIZING** What four actions did the act propose the federal government do to help the problem?

_____

_____

_____

_____

_____

3 **RELATING EVENTS** What developments of the 1950s may have led to the increased air pollution in the United States?

_____

_____

_____

4 GEOGRAPHY Why do you think air pollution needed to be addressed by federal, state, and local governments?

_____

_____

_____

5 **IDENTIFYING CONNECTIONS** How does air pollution affect modern society? What is being done about it?

_____

_____

_____

_____

_____

The Affluent Society

DIRECTIONS Search for evidence in Chapter 13, Lesson 2 to help you answer the following questions.

1A **EXPLAINING CAUSES** What changes to American society contributed to a prospering economy?

ESSENTIAL QUESTION

How does prosperity change the way people live?

As you gather evidence to answer the Essential Question, think about

- the new technologies, goods, and services that became popular during the postwar era in the United States.

- advances in science and the arts made at the time.

1B **ECONOMICS** Why do you think a prospering economy led to a baby boom?

My Notes

2A **RELATING EVENTS** What was a mass-produced suburb? Give an example.

2B **INFERRING** How did the rise of suburbs affect cities?

3A UNDERSTANDING CHANGE What were some of the ways in which society advanced through technology and science?

_____

_____

_____

3B ANALYZING CHANGE How did these advances change society?

_____

_____

4 SUMMARIZING How did media change during the 1950s? Fill out the graphic organizer below with information about the changes made in movies and television, music, and literature.

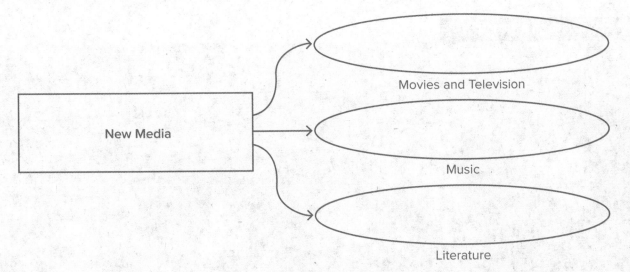

5 UNDERSTANDING CONTEXT Fill out the graphic organizer below with the names of some of the famous scientists, actors, musicians, and writers of the 1950s that influenced society in the United States.

Scientists	Actors	Musicians	Writers

ESSENTIAL QUESTION

How does prosperity change the way people live?

Levittown Sales

DIRECTIONS: Examine the image of a salesman selling homes in Levittown, New York. Then respond to the questions that follow.

EXPLORE THE CONTEXT: Inspired by a postwar housing shortage and using his experience building housing units for defense workers in Virginia, Bill Levitt created Levittown by mass-producing hundreds of simple, similar-looking homes 10 miles east of New York City. Whereas many builders were averaging four houses per year, Levitt aimed for 30 to 40 *per day*. Levittown, New York, was one of the earliest mass-produced suburbs.

Between 1947 and 1951, many families rushed to buy the inexpensive homes and move to the suburbs. Similar suburbs popped up throughout the country. During those years, the suburban population doubled, while the population of cities rose only 10 percent.

PRIMARY SOURCE: PHOTOGRAPH

—Contractor Herbert Richheimer shows a model of Levittown housing development, by Joseph Scherschel/The LIFE Picture Collection

1 **SUMMARIZING** What can you tell about Levittown based on the small-scale model?

_____

_____

_____

_____

2 ECONOMICS Why were homes in communities like Levittown more affordable than homes elsewhere?

_____

_____

_____

_____

3 **INFERRING** What can you infer about American society at the time based on the appearance of the people in the photo?

_____

_____

_____

_____

4 **ANALYZING SOURCES** What do you think a salesman, such as the one in this photo, might say in his salespitch about Levittown?

_____

_____

_____

_____

5 **ANALYZING CHANGES** What do Levittown and other suburbs tell you about changes in American society?

_____

_____

_____

_____

Wilson, Sloan. The Man in the Gray Flannel Suit. Cambridge: Da Cappo Press, 2009.

ESSENTIAL QUESTION
How does prosperity change the way people live?

The Man in the Gray Flannel Suit

DIRECTIONS: Read the following excerpt from *The Man in the Gray Flannel Suit*. Then respond to the questions that follow.

EXPLORE THE CONTEXT: *The Man in the Gray Flannel Suit*, written in 1955, is a novel about a man who had a horrific experience as a soldier in World War II and then comes home and begins to create what is seen as the ideal suburban life. He is a public relations specialist who lives in the suburbs of Connecticut, works for a media company in midtown Manhattan, and worries about money, job security, and educating his children. Written by Sloan Wilson, it was an enormous best seller.

PRIMARY SOURCE: BOOK

66 I really don't know what I was looking for when I got back from the war, but it seemed as though all I could see was a lot of bright young men in gray flannel suits rushing around New York in a **frantic** parade to nowhere. They seemed to me to be **pursuing** neither **ideals** nor happiness—they were pursuing a routine. For a long while I thought I was on the sidelines watching that parade, and it was quite a shock to glance down and see that I too was wearing a gray flannel suit. 99

—from *The Man in the Gray Flannel Suit*, by Sloan Wilson, 1955

VOCABULARY

frantic: hurried and anxious

pursuing: chasing after

ideals: standard principles

1 **INTERPRETING** What does the gray flannel suit represent?

_____

_____

_____

2 **ANALYZING POINTS OF VIEW** Why do you think the narrator was shocked to see he was wearing a gray flannel suit?

_____

_____

_____

_____

3 **ANALYZING CENTRAL IDEAS** What sense does the author evoke by using the image of a parade?

_____

_____

_____

_____

4 **CITING TEXT EVIDENCE** Through what line in the text does Wilson give the reader a sense that the characters' lives lacked meaning?

_____

_____

_____

_____

_____

_____

5 ECONOMICS How was the lifestyle depicted here different from the lifestyle in America during World War II?

_____

_____

_____

_____

_____

_____

The Other Side of American Life

DIRECTIONS Search for evidence in Chapter 13, Lesson 3 to help you answer the following questions.

1A **IDENTIFYING** Which groups of Americans were least likely to enjoy the benefits of the Affluent Society?

_____

_____

_____

_____

ESSENTIAL QUESTION

How does prosperity change the way people live?

As you gather evidence to answer the Essential Question, think about

- the people who were left behind despite a prosperous U.S. economy.

- the ways the U.S. government attempted to improve economic standards and education.

1B **ANALYZING** Why were Native Americans in particular likely to live in poverty?

_____

_____

_____

_____

My Notes

_____

_____

_____

_____

_____

_____

2A **ECONOMICS** How were inner cities hurt by the rise of the suburbs?

_____

_____

_____

2B **RELATING EVENTS** How did the government attempt to help inner cities, and were these actions successful?

_____

_____

_____

_____

_____

3 **SUMMARIZING** Complete the graphic organizer below with reasons why each group did not necessarily experience the prosperity of the 1950s.

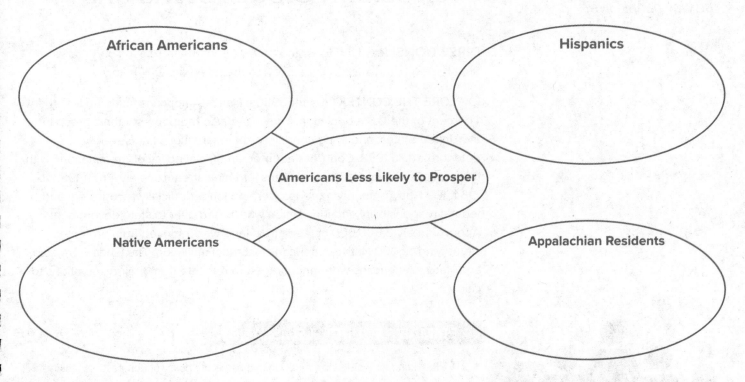

4A **DETERMINING CONTEXT** What were the Sputniks, and what was their significance?

_____

_____

_____

4B **IDENTIFYING CONNECTIONS** Why did the launch of the Sputniks cause panic about education?

_____

_____

_____

5 **EXPLAINING CAUSES** What are the reasons adults pointed to as promoting juvenile delinquency?

_____

_____

_____

Termination of Federal Supervision Over Certain Tribes of Indians; S. 2670 and H.R. 7674, 83rd Cong. (1954).

ESSENTIAL QUESTION

How does prosperity change the way people live?

Termination of Federal Supervision over Certain Groups of Indians

DIRECTIONS: Read the following excerpt from the legislation on Federal Supervision of Indians. Then respond to the questions that follow.

EXPLORE THE CONTEXT: By the 1950s, Native Americans made up less than 1 percent of the U.S. population. They were also the poorest ethnic group in the United States, and living conditions on reservations had severely deteriorated. In 1953, Congress adopted an official policy of "termination," with the goal of bringing Native Americans into mainstream society. From 1953 to 1964, 109 Native American groups were no longer officially recognized, and federal responsibility and jurisdiction was turned over to state governments. Approximately 2,500,000 acres of trust land was removed from protected status, and 12,000 Native Americans lost tribal affiliation. The lands were sold, and Native Americans were encouraged to relocate from their reservations to cities.

PRIMARY SOURCE: LEGISLATION

❝Providing for legislation . . . declaring that it is the policy of Congress, as rapidly as possible, to make the Indians within the territorial limits of the United States subject to the same laws and entitled to the same privileges and responsibilities as are applicable to other citizens of the United States, to end their status as **wards** of the United States, and to grant them all of the rights and **prerogatives** pertaining to American citizenship, and directing the Secretary of the Interior to report to Congress his recommendations as to what legislation, in his judgment, may be necessary to accomplish the purposes of said **resolution**. ❞

—from House Concurrent Resolution 108, 1953

VOCABULARY

wards: people under protection of an authority

prerogatives: privileges; rights

resolution: formal decision to be voted upon

1 **DETERMINING MEANING** Why do you think the government referred to this policy as a "termination" policy?

_____

_____

_____

_____

2 CIVICS How did this policy aim to assimilate Native Americans into society? Cite evidence from the text to support your answer.

_____

_____

_____

_____

_____

_____

_____

3 **EXPLAINING EFFECTS** How did this policy change the lives of Native Americans?

_____

_____

_____

4 **ANALYZING INFORMATION** What was the Secretary of the Interior asked to do by this legislation?

_____

_____

5 **ANALYZING CHANGE** In your opinion, was assimilation a good idea at the time?

_____

_____

ESSENTIAL QUESTION

How does prosperity change the way people live?

Hiya Ike! Still Trying to Muscle In?

DIRECTIONS: Examine the following political cartoon. Then respond to the questions that follow.

EXPLORE THE CONTEXT: In 1957, the Soviet Union launched Sputnik I and Sputnik II, the world's first space satellites. The proud Soviets published news of the event. However, before the news announcement, people across America had already seen a moving point of light in the night sky from their rooftops and backyards. Many Americans were awed, amazed, and frightened. Technological progress by the Soviet Union, led by Nikita Khrushchev, caused Americans to panic about education, with many feeling stunned and disgusted that they had fallen behind an authoritarian communist society. Some blamed what they saw as a lack of technical education, and efforts to improve math and science education began.

PRIMARY SOURCE: POLITICAL CARTOON

"Hiya Ike! Still trying to muscle in?"

—by Franklin, September 27, 1960

1 **INTERPRETING** Who are the two men depicted in the cartoon?

_____

_____

2 **UNDERSTANDING CONTEXT** What do the dumbbells held by the strong man represent?

_____

_____

3 **COMPARING AND CONTRASTING** What is the cartoonist trying to say by how the two men are depicted?

_____

_____

_____

4 **IDENTIFYING PERSPECTIVES** What does the title of the cartoon imply about American sentiment toward the Sputnik launch?

_____

_____

_____

5 **ANALYZING** According to the cartoon, what was holding the United States back from making similar advancements?

_____

_____

_____

6 **ECONOMICS** How did prosperity affect the reaction of Americans to Sputnik?

_____

_____

_____

ESSENTIAL QUESTION

How does prosperity change the way people live?

1 Think About It

Review the Supporting Questions that you developed at the beginning of the chapter. Review the evidence that you gathered in Chapter 13. Were you able to answer each Supporting Question?

If there was not enough evidence to answer your Supporting Questions, what additional evidence do you think you need to consider?

_____

_____

_____

_____

2 Organize Your Evidence

Use a chart such as the one below to organize the evidence you will use to support your findings about how prosperity changes the way people live.

Sign of prosperity	Effect on society	Evidence from the text to support your claim

3 Write About It

Of all the changes that took place from the end of World War II through 1960, which two do you feel had the greatest effect on people's lives in the United States? Write two paragraphs describig these changes, and explain your reasons for choosing them as having the greatest impact.

_____

_____

_____

_____

_____

_____

_____

_____

_____

_____

4 Connect to the Essential Question

Work in small groups to write a play that helps to answer the Essential Question: _How does prosperity change the way people live_? Incorporate some of the political, economic, and cultural changes in American society that occurred during the 1950s as a part of the setting, the characters, or the conflict. Create three to five characters. Your group may choose to include historical figures or ordinary citizens. Think carefully about how you will create a scene that gives people a sense of some of the changes happening at the time. Through your play, the audience should be able to understand the historical context of the era and how people's lives were altered by prosperity.

Perform the play for your class. Through your play, the audience should be able to understand how prosperity changed the way people lived specifically during this time period in American history.

CITIZENSHIP
TAKE ACTION

MAKE CONNECTIONS Just like during the 1950s, many Americans still debate and question the state of public education in our country versus that of other countries. Conduct some research into the positive and negative aspects of an American education and how it ranks around the world. Consider what you think is working and what is not. Are there areas of strength? Are there areas where schools could improve? Do all American children have the same opportunity for education? Are American students adequately prepared to compete in a global economy?

DIRECTIONS: Identify a change that could be made on a local, state, or national level to our system of education. Write a petition outlining a solution to the problem and what you think your local or national government could do to address the issue. Circulate the petition among your peers, and send it to the appropriate representatives. Volunteers may also wish to share their petitions with the class.

The New Frontier and the Great Society

ESSENTIAL QUESTION

How do you think Presidents Kennedy and Johnson changed American society?

Think about how this question might relate to changes that were taking place in society during the 1960s.

TALK ABOUT IT

Discuss with a partner what type of information you would need to know to answer this question. For example, one question might be: *What events were taking place during this time that some considered unjust?*

DIRECTIONS: Write three additional questions that would help you explain the changes that were taking place in the 1960s and how those changes affected society.

MY RESEARCH QUESTIONS

Supporting Question 1:

_____

_____

Supporting Question 2:

_____

_____

Supporting Question 3:

_____

_____

The New Frontier

DIRECTIONS Search for evidence in Chapter 14, Lesson 1 to help you answer the following questions.

1A **DESCRIBING** Why were the candidates for the presidential election of 1960 referred to as "processed"?

_____

_____

_____

_____

1B **DESCRIBING** What qualities did John F. Kennedy possess that helped him win over voters?

_____

_____

_____

_____

2A **DETERMINING CENTRAL IDEAS** What was the New Frontier?

_____

_____

_____

2B **DETERMINING MEANING** Why did Kennedy have a difficult time selling his "New Frontier" agenda?

_____

_____

_____

_____

ESSENTIAL QUESTION

How do you think Presidents Kennedy and Johnson changed American society?

As you gather evidence to answer the Essential Question, think about

- why the 1960 presidential election changed political campaigns.
- what challenges Kennedy faced in his administration.
- why the Warren Court reforms were so important.

My Notes

_____

_____

_____

_____

_____

_____

3 SUMMARIZING Complete the graphic organizer below by describing areas in which Kennedy's administration succeeded.

Women

↓

Disabled

↓

Poor

4 CIVICS Using the chart below, show how the Warren Court decisions impacted American society.

Decision	Court Ruling	What Group Benefits?
Baker v. *Carr* (1962)		
Reynolds v. *Sims* (1964)		
Gideon v. *Wainwright* (1964)		
Miranda v. *Arizona* (1966)		

5 DRAWING CONCLUSIONS In what way was the Fourteenth Amendment used by the U.S. Supreme Court?

_____

_____

_____

_____

How do you think Presidents Kennedy and Johnson changed American society?

Presidential Committee on the Status of Women

DIRECTIONS: Read the following excerpt from a commission report. Then answer the questions that follow.

EXPLORE THE CONTEXT: In 1961, President John F. Kennedy established the Presidential Committee on the Status of Women. The president hoped that the committee would report on the progress of women in the United States while noting areas where changes still needed to be made. In 1963, the committee published its findings. While progress had been made in the preceding years, there were areas where women continued to struggle.

PRIMARY SOURCE: REPORT EXCERPT

❝ With such facts in view, the Commission has considered developments in American institutions which might usefully be coupled to the long series of historic changes that have increased women's opportunities and security. We were directed to review progress and make recommendations as needed for constructive action in six areas:

- Employment policies and practices, including those on wages, under Federal contracts.

- Federal social insurance and tax laws as they affect the . . . income of women.

- Federal and State labor laws dealing with such matters as hours, nightwork, and wages, to determine whether they are accomplishing the purposes for which they were established and whether they should be adapted to changing technological, economic, and social conditions.

- Differences in legal treatment of men and women in regard to political and civil rights, property rights, and family relations.

- New and expanded services that may be required for women as wives, mothers, and workers, including education, counseling, training, home services, and arrangements for care of children during the working day.

- The employment policies and practices of the Government of the United States with reference to additional affirmative steps which should be taken through legislation, executive, or administrative action to assure nondiscrimination on the basis of sex and to enhance constructive employment opportunities for women.

As our work progressed, we became convinced that greater public understanding of the value of continuing education for all mature Americans is perhaps the highest priority item on the American agenda. And it is one of particular importance to women. . . . ❞

—from "Areas of Special Attention," *American Women: Report of the President's Commission on the Status Of Women,* 1963

President's Commission on the Status of Women. "American Women." Report, Washington, D.C., 1963.

1. **DETERMINING MEANING** Which phrase states the purpose of the commission?

_____

_____

2. **ANALYZING INFORMATION** According to the report, why might the commission have studied federal and state labor laws?

_____

_____

3. **EVALUATING EVIDENCE** What is suggested by the fact that the commission was studying the legal treatment of women?

_____

_____

4. **EVALUATING EVIDENCE** How does this report help you to understand the period in which it was written?

_____

_____

_____

5. **ECONOMICS** Based on the document, why do you think the commission paid so much attention to the economic status of women?

_____

_____

_____

6. **DRAWING CONCLUSIONS** Why would the commission address the issue of "new and expanded services"? What does this tell you about the role of women?

_____

_____

7. **DRAWING CONCLUSIONS** According to the commission, what is the most important priority for society, and how does that impact women?

_____

_____

ESSENTIAL QUESTION

How do you think Presidents Kennedy and Johnson changed American society?

VOCABULARY

in custody: in the care of law enforcement officers

interrogation: questioning

informed: told

indigent: poor

fundamental: basic, important

expedient: plan of action; measure

inadmissible: not able to be used in court

Miranda Rights

DIRECTIONS: Read the following excerpt from a court decision. Then answer the questions that follow.

EXPLORE THE CONTEXT: In 1966, the U.S. Supreme Court handed down a decision that reverberated throughout the nation. The case, *Miranda* v. *Arizona*, established certain rights for people who were suspects in a crime or were arrested. The court ruled that every citizen had the right to due process under the Fourteenth Amendment. The decision changed forever the way that law enforcement could interact with suspects.

PRIMARY SOURCE: COURT DECISION EXCERPT

❝(d) In the absence of other effective measures the following procedures to safeguard the Fifth Amendment privilege must be observed: The person **in custody** must, prior to **interrogation,** be clearly **informed** that he has the right to remain silent, and that anything he says will be used against him in court; he must be clearly informed that he has the right to consult with a lawyer and to have the lawyer with him during interrogation, and that, if he is **indigent,** a lawyer will be appointed to represent him. . . .

The Fifth Amendment privilege is so **fundamental** to our system of constitutional rule and the **expedient** of giving an adequate warning as to the availability of the privilege so simple, we will not pause to inquire in individual cases whether the defendant was aware of his rights without a warning being given. Assessments of the knowledge the defendant possessed, based on information as to his age, education, intelligence, or prior contact with authorities, can never be more than speculation; a warning is a clearcut fact. More important, whatever the background of the person interrogated, a warning at the time of the interrogation is indispensable to overcome its pressures and to insure that the individual knows he is free to exercise the privilege at that point in time. The warning of the right to remain silent must be accompanied by the explanation that anything said can and will be used against the individual in court. This warning is needed in order to make him aware not only of the privilege, but also of the consequences of forgoing it. It is only through an awareness of these consequences that there can be any assurance of real understanding and intelligent exercise of the privilege. More over, this warning may serve to make the individual more acutely aware that he is faced with a phase of the adversary system —that he is not in the presence of persons acting solely in his interest. . . . ❞

—from *Miranda* v. *Arizona* No. 759, the Supreme Court of the United States of America, 1966

1 ANALYZING Which phrase describes the issue the court is addressing? Why is this important?

_____

_____

2 CIVICS Based on the decision, what issue was the court addressing?

_____

_____

3 EVALUATING EVIDENCE Is this a primary or secondary resource? What does the information in the decision suggest about law and order prior to 1966?

_____

_____

_____

_____

4 DETERMINING MEANING What is the court referring to when it states, "More over, this warning may serve to make the individual more acutely aware that he is faced with a phase of the adversary system—that he is not in the presence of persons acting solely in his interest. . . ."?

_____

_____

5 INFERRING Why might law enforcement agencies have taken issue with the court's decision in _Miranda_ v. _Arizona_?

_____

_____

_____

6 DETERMINING MEANING What are the rights that a suspect is entitled to according to the court? Why is this important?

_____

_____

_____

JFK and the Cold War

DIRECTIONS Search for evidence in Chapter 14, Lesson 2 to help you answer the following questions.

1A **UNDERSTANDING CONTEXT** Why might communism be seen as a threat at the time President Kennedy took office?

_____

_____

_____

_____

_____

1B **DETERMINING CONTEXT** What did Kennedy mean by a "flexible response" to communism?

_____

_____

_____

_____

2A **DETERMINING MEANING** What was the "missile gap"?

_____

_____

_____

2B **SUMMARIZING** How did Kennedy's approach to the Soviet Union accelerate the arms race?

_____

_____

_____

_____

_____

ESSENTIAL QUESTION

How do you think Presidents Kennedy and Johnson changed American society?

As you gather evidence to answer the Essential Question, think about

- some of the ways President Kennedy addressed the Cold War.

- the Cold War crises faced by the president during his administration.

My Notes

_____

_____

_____

_____

_____

_____

3 **RELATING EVENTS** Complete the Cornell Notes organizer by describing what each term means.

Main Idea	Notes
The Alliance for Progress	
The Peace Corps	

4 **SUMMARIZING** Use the graphic organizer below to show the Cold War crises faced by President Kennedy during his administration.

Event	What Happened	Outcome
Space Race		
Bay of Pigs		
Berlin Wall		
Cuban Missile Crisis		

5 CIVICS What democratic principles guided President Kennedy in facing the various Cold War crises?

_____

_____

_____

ESSENTIAL QUESTION

How do you think Presidents Kennedy and Johnson changed American society?

The Cuban Missile Crisis

DIRECTIONS: Read the following excerpt from a speech. Then answer the questions that follow.

EXPLORE THE CONTEXT: For many Americans, the Cuban missile crisis brought home the reality of a possible nuclear war. The Soviet presence in Cuba and the growing threat of an accelerating arms race were now more immediate. Kennedy and his advisers held a series of meetings to determine how best to deal with the Soviets. Some advisers pushed for an air strike and invasion of Cuba; others suggested a more limited action that would still send a strong message to the Soviets. On Monday, October 22, 1962, President Kennedy, in a televised speech, addressed the American people and discussed the crisis.

PRIMARY SOURCE: POLITICAL SPEECH

❝ To halt this offensive buildup, a strict quarantine on all offensive military equipment under shipment to Cuba is being initiated. All ships of any kind bound for Cuba, from whatever nation or port, will, if found to contain cargoes of offensive weapons, be turned back. . . .

It shall be the policy of this nation to regard any nuclear missile launched from Cuba against any nation in the Western Hemisphere as an attack by the Soviet Union on the United States requiring a full retaliatory response upon the Soviet Union. . . .

I call upon Chairman Khrushchev to halt and eliminate this clandestine, reckless and provocative threat to world peace and to stable relations between our two nations. . . . He has an opportunity now to move the world back from the abyss of destruction. . . .

My fellow citizens: let no one doubt that this is a difficult and dangerous effort on which we have set out. No one can foresee precisely what course it will take or what costs or casualties will be incurred. Many months of sacrifice and self-discipline lie ahead—months in which both our will and our patience will be tested—months in which many threats and denunciations will keep us aware of our danger. But the greatest danger of all would be to do nothing. ❞

—from a speech on the presence of missile sites in Cuba, by John F. Kennedy, October 22, 1962

Kennedy, John F. "Radio and Television Report to the American People on the Soviet Arms Buildup in Cuba." Speech, The White House, October 22, 1962. http://microsites.jfklibrary.org/cmc/oct22/doc5.html i

1. **EVALUATING EVIDENCE** What type of document is this? Why might Kennedy have chosen to deliver it as a televised speech?

_____

_____

_____

_____

2. **DETERMINING CONTEXT** How does this resource better help you understand the events surrounding the Cold War?

_____

_____

_____

_____

3. CIVICS What constitutional authority did President Kennedy have in determining a course of action during the crisis?

_____

_____

_____

_____

4. **EVALUATING EVIDENCE** What does the speech reveal about what might lie ahead for the American people?

_____

_____

_____

_____

5. **DETERMINING MEANING** What does President Kennedy mean when he states, "But the greatest danger of all would be to do nothing"?

_____

_____

ESSENTIAL QUESTION

How do you think Presidents Kennedy and Johnson changed American society?

VOCABULARY

manifestation: expression; demonstration

dichotomy: contrast

formidable: threatening

The Berlin Wall

DIRECTIONS: Read the following excerpt from a report. Then answer the questions that follow.

EXPLORE THE CONTEXT: With the construction of the Berlin Wall in 1961, the sharp division between the forces of Western democracy and Soviet communism took on a dramatic physical presence. For many around the world, images of the wall were a stark reminder of the ongoing Cold War tensions between the world's leading superpowers.

SECONDARY SOURCE: REPORT EXCERPT

❝ At the heart of the city, the Berlin Wall stood as a physical **manifestation** of the Iron Curtain. West of the Wall, Berliners reveled in the growing prosperity of a new, democratic Germany. East of it they labored under the apparatus of a new dictatorship, still overshadowed by the ruins of the old. This **dichotomy** defined life in Berlin. The longer the Cold War lasted, the more concrete that was added to the Wall, the more it seemed that this dichotomy would endure.

Yet, permanent though it appeared, the Wall was impermanent. It was built, not as a demonstration of strength, but as an act of desperation, built to halt the flow of refugees who were fleeing to the West at the rate of 300,000 per year. Throughout the Cold War, it stood as a reminder that here was a regime that lacked the support of its own people and could survive only by walling them in. It was obvious to all that, when the Wall fell, so, too, would the East German regime.

It was also obvious that the fate of East Germany was forever tied to that of the Soviet Union. Despite the **formidable** nature of the Wall's defenses, despite the fact that it was East German guards who patrolled it day and night, there was never any doubt that the Wall was built with the support of Moscow. It and the regime that had built it would vanish as soon as that support was taken away.

No one thought that this would be soon. East Germany was an armed camp, groaning under the weight of tanks, troops and aircraft. The massive military housing projects, the giant statues of Lenin that decorated the landscape, made it clear that the Soviets were there to stay.

Thus, the construction of the Wall brought a kind of enduring stability to the confrontation in Berlin, a recognition of the status quo. This was a shift in Soviet policy. Both Khrushchev and Stalin had pledged to drive out the Western Allies. There is evidence that Khrushchev planned military action to do so, if necessary. The Wall, by putting an end to the steady depopulation of East Germany, seemed to make that unnecessary. East Germans had little choice but to accept the situation and most did so. ❞

—from "The Wall Remained," by Donald P. Steury, 2014

1 DIFFERENTIATING Is this document a primary or secondary resource? How does it help in understanding the period it covers?

_____

_____

_____

_____

2 DETERMINING MEANING What might the author have meant when he wrote, "Yet, permanent though it appeared, the Wall was impermanent"?

_____

_____

_____

3 CITING TEXT EVIDENCE According to the author, how did the building of the Berlin Wall suggest a shift in Soviet policy?

_____

_____

_____

4 INFERRING Which sentences suggest that East Berlin had become a replica of other Soviet cities? What does this tell you about the environment?

_____

_____

_____

_____

5 GEOGRAPHY How did the building of the Berlin Wall change human activity in the city?

_____

_____

_____

ESSENTIAL QUESTION

How do you think Presidents Kennedy and Johnson changed American society?

As you gather evidence to answer the Essential Question, think about:

- ways President Johnson's leadership affected his legislative program.
- the War on Poverty and what it hoped to accomplish.
- the aim of the Great Society and its programs.

My Notes

The Great Society

DIRECTIONS Search for evidence in Chapter 14, Lesson 3 to help you answer the following questions.

1A **DESCRIBING** What was one of the first issues Johnson tackled when he assumed office? Why?

_____

_____

1B **DRAWING CONCLUSIONS** How did Johnson's leadership style help him as President?

_____

_____

_____

_____

_____

2A CIVICS What did President Johnson see as the role of the government in helping the poor?

_____

_____

_____

2B **SUMMARIZING** In what ways was the War on Poverty a continuation of President Kennedy's legislative program?

_____

_____

_____

_____

3 **ANALYZING** Given the state of the Cold War by 1964, why might Americans not be supportive of Barry Goldwater's candidacy as president?

_____

_____

_____

4 **RELATING EVENTS** Complete the Cornell Notes organizer to describe some of the programs established under the Great Society.

Main Ideas	Notes
Health	
Education	
Poverty	
Consumer protection	
Environment	

5 **SUMMARIZING** Complete the graphic organizer below by identifying why a person might support or oppose President Johnson's Great Society programs.

Supporters	Opponents

Johnson, Lyndon B. "Annual Message to the Congress on the State of the Union January 4, 1965." In Public Papers of the Presidents of the United States: Lyndon B. Johnson, 1965. Washington: Government Printing Office, 1965.

ESSENTIAL QUESTION

How do you think Presidents Kennedy and Johnson changed American society?

The Great Society

DIRECTIONS: Read the following excerpt from a State of the Union Address. Then answer the questions that follow.

EXPLORE THE CONTEXT: On January 4, 1965, President Johnson delivered his State of the Union Address to the American people. In his speech, Johnson unveiled his bold new proposal for the country, known as "The Great Society." In his address, Johnson envisioned a society in which all Americans would benefit and prosper.

PRIMARY SOURCE: POLITICAL SPEECH

❝World affairs will continue to call upon our energy and our courage.

But today we can turn increased attention to the character of American life.

We are in the midst of the greatest upward surge of economic well-being in the history of any nation. . . .

We worked for two centuries to climb this peak of prosperity. But we are only at the beginning of the road to the Great Society. Ahead now is a summit where freedom from the wants of the body can help fulfill the needs of the spirit.

We built this Nation to serve its people.

We want to grow and build and create, but we want progress to be the servant and not the master of man.

We do not intend to live in the midst of abundance, isolated from neighbors and nature, confined by blighted cities and bleak suburbs, stunted by a poverty of learning and an emptiness of leisure.

The Great Society asks not how much, but how good; not only how to create wealth but how to use it; not only how fast we are going, but where we are headed.

It proposes as the first test for a nation: the quality of its people.

This kind of society will not flower spontaneously from swelling riches and surging power.

It will not be the gift of government or the creation of presidents. It will require of every American, for many generations, both faith in the destination and the fortitude to make the journey.

And like freedom itself, it will always be challenge and not fulfillment. And tonight we accept that challenge.❞

—from "Toward the Great Society," by President Lyndon Baines Johnson, January 4, 1965

1 **INFERRING** What may have prompted Johnson to call his program "The Great Society"?

_____

_____

_____

_____

2 **PREDICTING** Why was the State of the Union the best place for Johnson to outline his proposals?

_____

_____

_____

_____

3 **CIVICS** What aspect of a civil society is demonstrated in Johnson's speech?

_____

_____

4 **DETERMINING CENTRAL IDEAS** What did Johnson mean when he said, "We built this Nation to serve its people"? How does this support Johnson's view of government responsibility?

_____

_____

_____

_____

5 **EXPLAINING** What did Johnson mean with the statement, "It will not be the gift of government or the creation of presidents"?

_____

_____

_____

_____

ESSENTIAL QUESTION

How do you think Presidents Kennedy and Johnson changed American society?

Highways

DIRECTIONS: Read the following excerpt from a commission report. Then answer the questions that follow.

EXPLORE THE CONTEXT: In 1963, President Kennedy asked for the establishment of an Appalachian Regional Commission to study the problems and challenges faced by that area and to find ways in which to spur economic development. After Kennedy's death, President Johnson directed the commission to continue with their work.

PRIMARY SOURCE: REPORT EXCERPT

66 Developmental activity in Appalachia cannot proceed until the regional isolation has been overcome. Its cities and towns, its areas of natural wealth and its areas of recreation and industrial potential must be penetrated by a transportation network which provides access to and from the rest of the Nation and within the region itself. No analysis of the regional problem has failed to identify the historic and persisting barrier-effect of its mountain-chains as a primary factor in Appalachian underdevelopment. The Commission recommends a mix of investment and timing which give the single problem of access a double priority of emphasis. . . .

The remoteness and isolation of this region, lying directly adjacent to the greatest concentrations of people and wealth in the country, is the very basis of the Appalachian lag. Its penetration by an adequate transportation network is the first requisite of its full participating in industrial America.

The backbone for such a network is the Interstate Highway System. 99

—from "Highways," *Appalachia: A Report*, by the President's Appalachian Regional Commission, 1964

President's Appalachian Regional Commission. "Appalachia." Report. Washington, D.C., 1964.

1 **CITING TEXT EVIDENCE** According to the report, what is the biggest obstacle to overcome in the region?

_____

_____

_____

2 GEOGRAPHY In what ways does the environment of Appalachia connect to its economic development?

_____

_____

_____

3 **EVALUATING EVIDENCE** According to the commission, in what ways would a transportation network help the region?

_____

_____

_____

4 **IDENTIFYING** What would be the "backbone" of the proposed transportation system? Why?

_____

_____

_____

5 **PREDICTING** Based on what you have read in this excerpt, how is the commission an example of the New Frontier and Great Society programs?

_____

_____

_____

_____

How do you think Presidents Kennedy and Johnson changed American society?

1 Think About It

Review the supporting questions that you developed at the beginning of the chapter. Review the evidence that you gathered in Chapter 14. Were you able to answer each Supporting Question?

If there was not enough evidence to answer your Supporting Questions, what additional evidence do you think you need to consider?

_____

_____

_____

2 Organize Your Evidence

Complete the chart below with information you learned about the New Frontier and Great Society programs. Pick one program for each focus, describe it, and explain its outcome.

Focus	Program/Legislation	Outcome
Health		
Education		
Poverty		
Environment		

Social Equality		

❸ Write About It

Choose one of the programs from the chart you completed, and write two paragraphs about it. In the first paragraph, briefly describe how the program worked and what it accomplished. In the second paragraph, consider what steps might have led to a different result. Keep in mind the Essential Question: *How do you think Presidents Kennedy and Johnson changed American society?*

_____

_____

_____

_____

❹ Connect to the Essential Question

Although from very different backgrounds socially, economically, and politically, Presidents Kennedy and Johnson had similar views about the role of government. Using details from the text as well as the primary and secondary resources, write a podcast about Presidents Kennedy and Johnson. Your podcast should focus on some of the programs each president established. Include a conversation with each president about his agenda. What did each see as the greatest need at the time? How did their backgrounds influence their agenda? What might they change now? Your podcast should focus on the Essential Question: *How do you think Presidents Kennedy and Johnson changed American society?*

Practice presenting your podcast, and perform it or record it to share with your class.

TAKE ACTION

MAKE CONNECTIONS   One of the ongoing debates in the United States today is the role of government in people's everyday lives. Does the federal government have a duty to protect the health and well-being of its citizens, especially of those in need? Think of some of the current events that are happening today that are related to this topic. What are your thoughts on the role of the government?

DIRECTIONS: In a small group, discuss one current piece of legislation that demonstrates whether and/or how the government provides assistance to individuals in need. Write a statement paper describing the group's thoughts about whether the piece of legislation is a good or bad idea, as well as how it affects the people. The paper should also describe who most benefits and who most is hurt by the legislation, if anyone. Groups can then share their statement paper with the class.

The Civil Rights Movement

ESSENTIAL QUESTION

What motivates a society to make changes?

Think about how racial segregation motivated people to work for changes in society during the 1950s and 1960s. What specific things did activists do to advocate for change? How did those actions change the country?

TALK ABOUT IT

With a partner, discuss the sort of information you would need to know to answer these questions. For example, one question might be: *What kinds of events can spark a major movement?*

DIRECTIONS: Now write down three additional questions that will help you explain how the civil rights movement emerged in the 1950s and 1960s. For example, you might ask, "What was the current state of politics in the United States at this time? How would this motivate the need for change?"

MY RESEARCH QUESTIONS

Supporting Question 1:

_____

_____

Supporting Question 2:

_____

_____

_____

Supporting Question 3:

_____

_____

The Movement Begins

DIRECTIONS: Search for evidence in Chapter 15, Lesson 1 to help you answer the following questions.

1A **DETERMINING CENTRAL IDEAS** Who was Rosa Parks, and what did she do that challenged segregation?

_____

_____

_____

_____

_____

1B **EVALUATING** What impact did Rosa Parks's action have?

_____

_____

_____

_____

2 **SUMMARIZING** Use this following chart to identify other important events that happened during the civil rights movement.

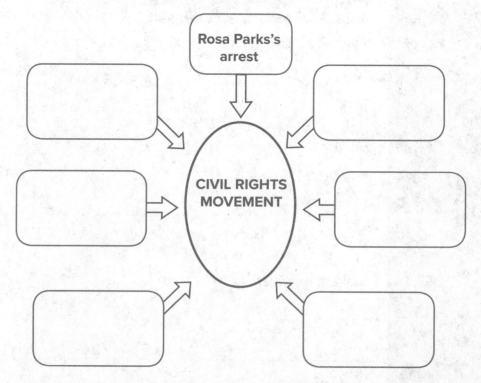

ESSENTIAL QUESTION

What motivates a society to make changes?

As you gather evidence to answer the Essential Question, think about:

- how events may lead to a political movement.

- how political conditions affected the civil rights movement.

- how different ways of thinking can cause division.

My Notes

_____

_____

_____

_____

_____

_____

3 CIVICS How did *Brown v. Board of Education* overturn *Plessy v. Ferguson*?

_____

_____

_____

_____

_____

_____

4A UNDERSTANDING CONTEXT Why did President Eisenhower send troops to Little Rock, Arkansas?

_____

_____

_____

4B IDENTIFYING EFFECTS What happened after the troops arrived?

_____

_____

_____

_____

_____

_____

_____

5 EXPLAINING EFFECTS What led to the Southern Christian Leadership Conference's attempt to register 2 million new African American voters?

_____

_____

_____

_____

ESSENTIAL QUESTION
What motivates a society to make changes?

Executive Order 10730: Desegregation of Central High School

DIRECTIONS: Read the following excerpt from the executive order signed by President Dwight D. Eisenhower that sent the National Guard to Arkansas in 1957. Then respond to the questions that follow.

EXPLORE THE CONTEXT: Nine black students were required to integrate at Central High School in Little Rock, Arkansas, under a court order. After Arkansas Governor Orval Faubus ordered troops from the National Guard to prevent these students from entering the school building, President Dwight D. Eisenhower stepped in to ensure that the federal court's ruling would be followed.

PRIMARY SOURCE: EXECUTIVE ORDER

❝ WHEREAS certain persons in the state of Arkansas, individually and in unlawful **assemblages**, combinations, and conspiracies, have willfully **obstructed** the enforcement of orders of the United States District Court for the Eastern District of Arkansas with respect to matters relating to enrollment and attendance at public schools, particularly at Central High School, located in Little Rock School District, Little Rock, Arkansas; and . . .

WHEREAS such **willful** obstruction of justice hinders the execution of the laws of that State and of the United States, and makes it impracticable to enforce such laws by the ordinary course of judicial proceedings; and

WHEREAS such obstruction of justice constitutes a denial of the equal protection of the laws secured by the Constitution of the United States and **impedes** the course of justice under those laws:

NOW, THEREFORE, I, DWIGHT D. EISENHOWER, President of the United States, under and by virtue of the authority vested in me by the Constitution and Statutes of the United States, . . . do command all persons engaged in such obstruction of justice to **cease and desist** therefrom, and to disperse forthwith; and

WHEREAS the command contained in that Proclamation has not been obeyed and willful obstruction of enforcement of said court orders still exists and threatens to continue:

SECTION 1 I hereby authorize and direct the Secretary of Defense to order into the active military service of the United States as he may deem appropriate to carry out the purposes of this Order, any or all of the units of the National Guard of the United States and of the Air National Guard of the United States within the State of Arkansas to serve in the active military service of the United States for an **indefinite** period and until relieved by appropriate orders. ❞

—from Executive Order 10730, Providing Assistance for the Removal of an Obstruction of Justice Within the State of Arkansas, September 24, 1957

VOCABULARY

assemblages: groups of people

willfully: on purpose

obstructed: blocked

impedes: hinders

cease and desist: stop doing something on a permanent basis

indefinite: without a specific limit

1 **SUMMARIZING** What is the main idea of Eisenhower's executive order?

_____

_____

_____

2 **UNDERSTANDING CONTEXT** How does this executive order show public sentiment about segregation at that time?

_____

_____

_____

_____

3 **RELATING EVENTS** Why did President Eisenhower write this executive order?

_____

_____

_____

_____

_____

4 **CIVICS** How does this excerpt show President Eisenhower applying democratic principles and values?

_____

_____

_____

_____

5 **UNDERSTANDING EFFECTS** How do you think this executive order affected the situation in Little Rock, Arkansas?

_____

_____

6 **INFERRING** Based on the information in the executive order, what can you conclude about Eisenhower's position toward the white Southerners who supported segregation?

_____

_____

_____

ESSENTIAL QUESTION

What motivates a society to make changes?

Rosa Parks's Arrest Record

DIRECTIONS: Read the arrest record. Then respond to the questions that follow.

EXPLORE THE CONTEXT: Rosa Parks was arrested on December 1, 1955, in Montgomery, Alabama, for refusing to give up her seat on the bus when a white man told her to do so. He did this because the designated area for white passengers was full.

VOCABULARY

offense: crime

warrant: court authorization to arrest or search a person

PRIMARY SOURCE: ARREST RECORD

POLICE DEPARTMENT
CITY OF MONTGOMERY

Misc.

Date   12-1-55   19

Complainant   J.F.Blake   (wm)

Address   27 No. Lewis St.   Phone No.

Offense   Misc.   Reported By   Same as above

Address   Phone No.

Date and Time Offense Committed   12-1-55   6:06 pm

Place of Occurrence   In Front of Empire Theatre   (On Montgomery Street)

Person or Property Attacked

How Attacked

Person Wanted

Value of Property Stolen   Value Recovered

Details of Complaint (list, describe and give value of property stolen)

We received a call upon arrival the bus operator said he had a colored female

sitting in the white section of the bus, and would not move back.

We (Day & Mixon) also saw her.

The bus operator signed a warrant for her. Rosa Parks, (cf) 634 Cleveland Court.

Rosa Parks (cf) was charged with chapter 6 section 11 of the Montgomery City Code.

Warrant #14254

THIS OFFENSE IS DECLARED:
UNFOUNDED   □
CLEARED BY ARREST   □
EXCEPTIONALLY CLEARED   □
INACTIVE (NOT CLEARED) □

Officers   F. B. Day
           D. W. Mixon

Division   Patrol   Time 7:00 pm
                                 12-1-55

—arrest record of Rosa Parks, December 1, 1955

1 **SUMMARIZING** What does this arrest record state is the reason that Rosa Parks was arrested?

_____

_____

2 **DETERMINING MEANING** What does this line in the arrest record mean: "The bus operator signed a warrant for her"?

_____

_____

_____

3 **EXPLAINING CAUSES** Why did Rosa Parks get arrested for not moving to the back of the bus?

_____

_____

_____

4 **IDENTIFYING PERSPECTIVES** What is the perspective of the police officer who wrote the arrest record?

_____

_____

_____

_____

5 **IDENTIFYING BIAS** What can one infer about the attitude and ideas of the bus driver?

_____

_____

_____

6 CIVICS Why did Rosa Parks challenge her arrest?

_____

_____

_____

7 **ANALYZING IDEAS** In order to have a segregation law struck down, what had to occur?

_____

Challenging Segregation

DIRECTIONS: Search for evidence in Chapter 15, Lesson 2 to help you answer the following questions.

1 SUMMARIZING Complete the chart below by explaining each of the four movements described in Lesson 2.

ESSENTIAL QUESTION

What motivates a society to make changes?

As you gather evidence to answer the Essential Question, think about:

- what actions African Americans took to end racial segregation.
- who played a key role in these actions.

Movement	Action
Sit-ins	
Freedom Riders	
March in Washington	
Selma march	

2A DESCRIBING How did the people who favored segregation respond to sit-ins?

_____

_____

_____

2B COMPARING How did the reaction to the Freedom Riders compare to that received by those who participated in the sit-ins?

_____

_____

_____

_____

My Notes

_____

_____

_____

_____

_____

_____

3 **EXPLAINING CAUSES** How did President Kennedy finally end segregation on buses?

_____

_____

_____

_____

4 **EXPLAINING EFFECTS** How did the public react to the Sixteenth Street Baptist Church bombing that killed four girls in Birmingham, Alabama?

_____

_____

_____

5A **IDENTIFYING CONNECTIONS** What was the primary goal of the Selma march, and did it succeed?

_____

_____

_____

5B **DIFFERENTIATING** How did the Voting Rights Act of 1965 differ from the Civil Rights Act of 1964?

_____

_____

_____

_____

ESSENTIAL QUESTION

What motivates a society to make changes?

Letter from Robert Kennedy to President Kennedy

DIRECTIONS: Read this excerpt of a letter from Robert Kennedy to President Kennedy. Then respond to the questions that follow.

EXPLORE THE CONTEXT: Attorney General Robert Kennedy wrote a long letter to report to his brother, President John F. Kennedy, on civil rights progress in the country. His letter, written in 1962, has a positive tone regarding the progress being made, particularly in the South.

PRIMARY SOURCE: LETTER

"Dear Mr. President:

For those only interested in headlines, rioting and violence at the University of Mississippi **overshadowed** the civil rights field and painted 1962 as a year of resistance by the south to law and the orders of our courts. The historian, however, will find, on the contrary, that 1962 was a year of great progress in civil rights, in large measure because of the responsibility and respect for law displayed by the great majority of the citizens of the south. In 1962, the United States took major steps toward equal opportunity and equal rights for all our citizens and in every area of civil rights—whether voting, transportation, education, employment, or housing. There were outstanding efforts throughout the Administration on behalf of the full and free exercise of civil rights. Let me take particular note of the successes of the Vice–President and your Committee on Equal Employment Opportunity; the work of the Commission on Civil Rights; the **impetus** provided by the Executive Order against segregation in housing; the 'impact area' school efforts of the Department of Health, Education and Welfare; and improved hiring practices and other activity by all parts of the Executive Branch. . . .

In summary, 1962 was a year of progress for the United States in the field of civil rights. This is not to say the problems are disappearing. They remain, and they remain difficult—not only in the south, with open discrimination, but throughout the country where Negroes are the victims of school 'resegregation,' bias in housing, or employment, or other **facets** of society. Ugly incidents like the Mississippi riot may occur again. But we are accelerating our progress. Again, let me say this acceleration occurs in large measure because of the emerging spirit of the south. In 1962 this spirit was not the brutal one of rioting and violence at the University of Mississippi. The spirit was that exemplified in Georgia last week by Governor Carl E. Sanders, in his inaugural address. 'We **revere** the past,' he said. 'We **adhere to** the values of respectability and responsibility which constitute our tradition.' Then he added, 'We believe in law and order and in the principle that all laws apply equally to all citizens.'
Sincerely,
Robert Kennedy, Attorney General"

—from Attorney General Robert Kennedy to President John F. Kennedy, January 24, 1963

VOCABULARY

overshadowed: dominated; appeared more important than

impetus: push; momentum

facets: features

revere: cherish; value

adhere to: follow

109 Cong. Rec. A401-2 (1963) (report of Robert. F. Kennedy).

1 CIVICS What democratic principle is Robert Kennedy addressing in this letter?

_____

_____

2 **EXPLAINING CAUSES** Why do you think President Kennedy asked his brother to report on the state of civil rights in the South?

_____

_____

_____

_____

3 **SUMMARIZING** What were some of the political events that had already occurred when Robert Kennedy wrote this letter?

_____

_____

_____

4 **IDENTIFYING BIAS** Does Robert Kennedy reveal any bias in this letter?

_____

_____

_____

5 **CITING TEXT EVIDENCE** What examples of support for civil rights does Robert Kennedy mention in his letter?

_____

_____

_____

6 **INFERRING** Consider the obstacles Robert Kennedy mentions as ongoing problems for the civil rights movement. What does he mean by "resegregation" in schools and housing?

_____

_____

Johnson, Lyndon B. "Remarks in the Capitol Rotunda at the Signing of the Voting Rights Act, August 6, 1965." In Public Papers of the Presidents of the United States: Lyndon B. Johnson, 1965. Washington: Government Printing Office, 1965.

ESSENTIAL QUESTION

What motivates a society to make changes?

VOCABULARY

triumph: celebration

shackle: something that binds the arms or legs

subdued: converted land into farm fields

Speech by President Lyndon B. Johnson

DIRECTIONS: Read the excerpt from President Lyndon B. Johnson's remarks in the Capitol Rotunda at the signing of the Voting Rights Act, August 6, 1965. Then respond to the questions that follow.

EXPLORE THE CONTEXT: Although the 1957 legislation had improved opportunities for African Americans to vote, there were still obstacles. In 1965, President Johnson signed new legislation that removed discriminatory voting requirements such as literacy tests. The law also helped register African American voters whose registrations were refused by their local officials.

PRIMARY SOURCE: SPEECH

❝ Today is a **triumph** for freedom as huge as any victory that has ever been won on any battlefield. Yet to seize the meaning of this day, we must recall darker times.

Three and a half centuries ago the first Negroes arrived at Jamestown. They did not arrive in brave ships in search of a home for freedom. They did not mingle fear and joy, in expectation that in this New World anything would be possible to a man strong enough to reach for it.

They came in darkness and they came in chains.

And today we strike away the last major **shackle** of those fierce and ancient bonds. Today the Negro story and the American story fuse and blend.

And let us remember that it was not always so. The stories of our Nation and of the American Negro are like two great rivers. Welling up from that tiny Jamestown spring they flow through the centuries along divided channels.

When pioneers **subdued** a continent to the need of man, they did not tame it for the Negro. When the Liberty Bell rang out in Philadelphia, it did not toll for the Negro. When Andrew Jackson threw open the doors of democracy, they did not open for the Negro.

It was only at Appomattox, a century ago, that an American victory was also a Negro victory. And the two rivers—one shining with promise, the other dark-stained with oppression—began to move toward one another. ❞

—from "Remarks in the Capitol Rotunda at the Signing of the Voting Rights Act," by President Lyndon B. Johnson, August 6, 1965

1 **DETERMINING MEANING** What did President Johnson mean when he said, "The stories of our Nation and of the American Negro are like two great rivers"?

_____

_____

_____

_____

2 **DETERMINING CONTEXT** What important details about the political climate in which this speech was delivered help you understand its message?

_____

_____

_____

_____

3 **INTERPRETING** What does the speech indicate about President Johnson's stance on equal rights?

_____

_____

_____

4 **EVALUATING** Do you think President Johnson was correct in stating that the "two rivers would move towards one another" with this Voting Rights Act?

_____

_____

_____

_____

5 **ECONOMICS** Did improving voting opportunities for African Americans improve their economic opportunities as well?

_____

_____

_____

New Civil Rights Issues

DIRECTIONS: Search for evidence in Chapter 15, Lesson 3 to help you answer the following questions.

1A DETERMINING CONTEXT What was the financial situation for many African Americans in the United States in the1950s and 1960s?

_____
_____
_____
_____
_____
_____
_____

1B ECONOMICS How did Martin Luther King, Jr., bring these economic issues to the public's attention?

_____
_____
_____
_____
_____

2 DESCRIBING How did the Fair Housing Act of 1968 help solve housing discrimination issues?

_____
_____
_____
_____
_____
_____

ESSENTIAL QUESTION

What motivates a society to make changes?

As you gather evidence to answer the Essential Question, think about:

- how economics played a role during the civil rights movement.
- what the rise of Black Power meant to the civil rights movement.

My Notes

_____
_____
_____
_____
_____
_____

3A **SUMMARIZING** Who was the leader of the black power movement, and what was its focus?

_____

_____

_____

_____

3B **COMPARING AND CONTRASTING** Use the Venn diagram below to compare and contrast the leadership skills of Martin Luther King, Jr. and Malcolm X.

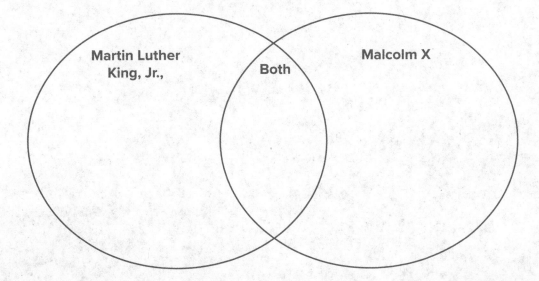

Martin Luther King, Jr.,

Both

Malcolm X

4 **EXPLAINING EFFECTS** How did the death of Martin Luther King, Jr., affect the civil rights movement?

_____

_____

_____

ESSENTIAL QUESTION

What motivates a society to make changes?

Martin Luther King, Jr., Meets Malcolm X

DIRECTIONS: Study the image. Then respond to the questions that follow.

EXPLORE THE CONTEXT: This photo was taken the only time that Martin Luther King, Jr., and Malcolm X met. It was snapped while the men were waiting for a press conference after a Senate hearing about the 1964 Civil Rights Act.

PRIMARY SOURCE: PHOTO

—photograph from the meeting of Malcolm X and Martin Luther King, Jr., March 26, 1964

1 **SUMMARIZING** Why is this photo of these two men important?

_____

_____

_____

2 **INTERPRETING** What does this photo tell you about the meeting between Martin Luther King, Jr., and Malcolm X?

_____

_____

_____

_____

_____

_____

3 **UNDERSTANDING CONTEXT** Why were Martin Luther King, Jr., and Malcolm X at the same event?

_____

_____

_____

4 **ANALYZING POINT OF VIEW** Why did Martin Luther King, Jr., criticize the black power movement led by Malcolm X?

_____

_____

_____

_____

_____

5 **DRAWING CONCLUSIONS** Why might this meeting of the men in the Senate hallway have been tense?

_____

_____

_____

ESSENTIAL QUESTION

What motivates a society to make changes?

Report on the Watts Riots

DIRECTIONS: Read the excerpt of the report from the U.S. Department of Justice about the riot in the Watts neighborhood in Los Angeles, California. Then respond to the questions that follow.

EXPLORE THE CONTEXT: President Johnson signed the Voting Rights Act in 1965, suspending discriminatory voting rules such as literacy tests and allowing federal examiners to register qualified African American voters whose registration had been denied previously by local officials. Five days after the Act was signed, a riot sparked by allegations of police brutality broke out in Watts, an African American neighborhood in Los Angeles.

VOCABULARY

proclamation: announcement

salutary: beneficial; positive

subsides: decreases

looting: stealing goods

hoodlum: thug; young ruffian

PRIMARY SOURCE: GOVERNMENT REPORT

❝ Riot **Subsides,** August 15, 1965

On Saturday, August 14, 1965, Acting Governor Anderson issued a **proclamation** setting an eight o'clock curfew for an area of forty square miles including, of course, the riot area. This had a salutory [**salutary**] effect since it enabled law enforcement officers and National Guardsmen to arrest on sight anyone on the street after the curfew hour. According to National Guard officials, there are now 14,500 National Guardsmen on the scene assisting the local police. On August 15, 1965, Chief Parker stated that local law enforcement officers and the National Guardsmen were then on top of the situation and the violence had subsided, although some shooting by snipers and miscellaneous **looting** by small bands of roving **hoodlums** were continuing.

The riotous activity of the Negroes since the beginning of the violence August 11, 1965, has resulted in more than thirty deaths, including that of a Deputy Sheriff and one Los Angeles fireman. Injuries to approximately 800 persons, including a large number of police officers and city firemen and several National Guardsmen, have been reported. Property damage has been estimated as high as 175 million dollars, and the number of arrests has reached almost 3,000, including over 300 juveniles. ❞

—from the Department of Justice Summary of the Events in Watts, 1965

① **EVALUATING** Why did the Department of Justice write this summary?

_____

_____

_____

DOJ summary of the events in Watts. Case file 144-12-1102, Section 2 (NAID 7987737).

2 CITING TEXT EVIDENCE What were the casualties from the Watts riots? Cite details from the text.

_____

_____

_____

_____

_____

3 DRAWING CONCLUSIONS Why was a curfew enforced?

_____

_____

_____

_____

4 IDENTIFYING BIAS Does the Department of Justice reveal any bias in this excerpt? Explain.

_____

_____

_____

_____

_____

5 INFERRING What does the report tell us about the civil rights movement during this time?

_____

_____

_____

_____

_____

6 RELATING EVENTS Have there been any riots in recent years in the United States? What was their cause and effect?

_____

_____

_____

_____

ESSENTIAL QUESTION

What motivates a society to make changes?

1 Think About It

Review the supporting questions you developed at the beginning of the chapter. Review the evidence you gathered in Chapter 15. Were you able to answer each Supporting Question? If there was not enough evidence to answer your Supporting Questions, what additional evidence do you think you need to consider?

_____

_____

_____

_____

2 Organize Your Evidence

Complete the chart below with information you learned about the civil rights movement, how the political conditions in the United States motivated this movement, and how it affected African Americans.

Cause	Effect
	Rosa Parks and NAACP challenged segregation in court.
Brown v. *Board of Education* rules segregation in public schools is unconstitutional.	
	Segregation in interstate bus travel ends.
the Selma march	
	the Watts Riot
Dr. Martin Luther King, Jr. is assassinated.	

❸ Talk About It

Work in small groups. With your group, discuss the events that occurred during the civil rights movement and how these events led to progress in the United States. Consider each row on your charts as you talk about which events were the most important in motivating Americans to make changes. Take notes about your discussion below.

_____

_____

_____

_____

_____

_____

_____

❹ Connect to the Essential Question

Following your work in step 3, choose two events that you identified that most motivated American society to make changes. Then write an essay describing those two events and why you consider them the most significant in helping the civil rights movement take shape and progress. Be sure to include historical background and facts as well as your reasoning regarding the events' significance.

_____

_____

_____

_____

_____

_____

_____

_____

_____

_____

CITIZENSHIP
TAKE ACTION

MAKE CONNECTIONS The musicians John Legend and Common won a Golden Globe Award, an Academy Award, and a Grammy Award for their song "Glory" from the movie *Selma*. The movie is about Martin Luther King, Jr., and the Selma march for equal voting rights. Common wrote lyrics that reflected the Selma march and the recent Black Lives Matter movement. In doing this, he was able to show how the civil rights movement remains relevant to African Americans in the present day.

DIRECTIONS: Use what you have learned in Chapter 15 to write a song on an issue from the civil rights movement. Choose one event from that time period and one historic figure who played a role in that event. Use the information to write a song to capture your chosen event and how it impacted the civil rights movement. Relate it to a modern-day event.

Your song should have three verses and a chorus. Work with a group to write and practice the song. Perform it for the class.

The Vietnam War

ESSENTIAL QUESTION

Should citizens support the government during wartime?

Think about how this question might relate to the Vietnam War, how it was presented in the press, and how Americans reacted to it.

TALK ABOUT IT

Discuss with a partner what type of information you would need to know to answer this question. For example, one question might be: *What kind of support does a government need from its citizens during wartime?*

DIRECTIONS: Now write down three additional questions that you need to answer to explain whether citizens should have supported the government during the Vietnam War.

MY RESEARCH QUESTIONS

Supporting Question 1:

_____

_____

Supporting Question 2:

_____

_____

Supporting Question 3:

_____

_____

Going to War in Vietnam

DIRECTIONS: Search for evidence in Chapter 16, Lesson 1 to help you answer the following questions.

1A **DESCRIBING** What did nationalism look like in Vietnam?

_____

_____

_____

1B **EXPLAINING CAUSE AND EFFECT** How did Vietnamese nationalism draw the United States into war?

_____

_____

_____

_____

2A **SUMMARIZING** Use your own words to summarize the leadership of Ngo Dinh Diem.

_____

_____

_____

_____

2B **CIVICS** How did the South Vietnamese government change after Diem was overthrown, and how did the United States react?

_____

_____

_____

_____

_____

ESSENTIAL QUESTION

Should citizens support the government during wartime?

As you gather evidence to answer the Essential Question, think about:

- how U.S. citizens reacted to the Vietnam War when it began.
- why Vietnam mattered to U.S. citizens.

My Notes

_____

_____

_____

_____

_____

3 **EVALUATING** What were the arguments for and against entering the Vietnam War?

For Entering the War	Against Entering the War

4 **COMPARING AND CONTRASTING** How did the armies of North Vietnam differ from the soldiers of South Vietnam?

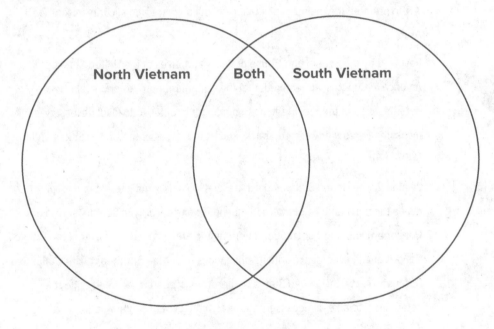

North Vietnam   Both   South Vietnam

Gulf of Tonkin Resolution

Joint resolution to promote the maintenance of international peace and security in southeast Asia, Pub. L. No. 88-408, 78 Stat. 384 (1964).

ESSENTIAL QUESTION

Should citizens support the government during wartime?

DIRECTIONS: Read the following excerpt from a congressional resolution. Then respond to the questions that follow.

EXPLORE THE CONTEXT: President Johnson announced on August 4, 1964, that U.S. naval ships had been attacked by the North Vietnamese in the Gulf of Tonkin. According to the U.S. Constitution, only Congress has the power to authorize war. The president, in the executive branch, is commander in chief of the military, but he cannot decide to go to war without the support of Congress. On August 7, 1964, Congress passed a resolution giving the president broad powers to use the military.

PRIMARY SOURCE: CONGRESSIONAL RESOLUTION

  " To promote the maintenance of international peace and security in southeast Asia. . . .

Resolved by the Senate and House of Representatives of the United States of America in Congress assembled, that the Congress approves and supports the determination of the President, as Commander in Chief, to take all necessary measures to repel any armed attack against the forces of the United States and to prevent further aggression.

Section 2. The United States regards as vital to its national interest and to world peace the maintenance of international peace and security in Southeast Asia. **Consonant** with the Constitution of the United States and the Charter of the United Nations and in accordance with its obligations under the **Southeast Asia Collective Defense Treaty,** the United States is, therefore, prepared, as the President determines, to take all necessary steps, including the use of armed force, to assist any member . . . of the Southeast Asia Collective Defense Treaty requesting assistance in defenses of its freedom.

Section 3. This resolution shall expire when the President shall determine that the peace and security of the area is reasonably assured by international conditions created by action of the United Nations or otherwise, except that it may be terminated earlier by **concurrent** resolution of the Congress. "

—from a joint resolution of the Eighty-eighth Congress of the United States of America

VOCABULARY

consonant: in agreement with

concurrent: happening at the same time

Southeast Asia Collective Defense Treaty: (SEATO) an international organization of nations in Southeast Asia united for collective defense

1 **EVALUATING** What does Congress authorize in this resolution?

_____

_____

_____

2 **ANALYZING INFORMATION** What is the scope of the authorization? How much power does the president have under this resolution?

_____

_____

_____

3 CIVICS What limit does Congress put on the president's power to wage war? What words in the resolution help you understand this limitation?

_____

_____

_____

4 **EVALUATING** What was going on in the world that would make Congress believe that the security of Southeast Asia was vital to U.S. national interests?

_____

_____

_____

_____

5 **PREDICTING** Based on the passage above and what you have read so far, how do you think the Tonkin Resolution ended?

_____

_____

_____

_____

ESSENTIAL QUESTION

Should citizens support the government during wartime?

Reflections on the Vietnam War

DIRECTIONS: Read the following excerpt from a book. Then respond to the questions that follow.

EXPLORE THE CONTEXT: General Cao Van Vien and Lieutenant General Dong Van Khuyen were leaders in the South Vietnamese Army. Both of them served alongside U.S. military leaders during the Vietnam War. Together they wrote a book titled *Reflections on the Vietnam War*.

PRIMARY SOURCE: BOOK EXCERPT

❝As a people burdened by the trauma of a long colonial past, the Vietnamese, North and South, were extremely sensitive about the presence of foreign troops on their soil. This presence was to leave an extensive **sociopolitical** imprint on the hearts and minds of Vietnamese on both sides of the **DMZ**. . . . The South Vietnamese, especially the rural people, did not become conscious of the U.S. military presence until 1962 when U.S. combat support troops were deployed to assist the **RVNAF** in **counterinsurgency** operations and after the Communists stepped up their anti-American propaganda. . . . A small but significant segment fully trusted the American goodwill in helping South Vietnam defeat the Communists while another equally significant segment also believed completely in Communist propagandistic slants. . . .

Not until 1967 and especially 1968 did this majority of the South Vietnamese population come to fully appreciate the value of the U.S. military presence and the fallacy of Communist propaganda. They had seen for themselves how U.S. forces had effectively **interdicted** and driven major Communist units away from populated areas, which restored security to most villages and hamlets. They had witnessed the rehabilitation and construction of roads and bridges which made communication between cities and rural areas much easier and faster. This came as a revealing contrast to Communist sabotage activities. The rural people of South Vietnam also began to benefit directly from various U.S. aid programs which sought to rebuild the damaged countryside and restore agricultural production by putting science and technology at the service of rural life. ❞

—from *Reflections on the Vietnam War*, by General Cao Van Vien and Lieutenant General Dong Van Khuyen

VOCABULARY

sociopolitical: regarding social and political issues

DMZ: demilitarized zone

RVNAF: Republic of Vietnam Armed Forces; the South Vietnamese military forces

counterinsurgency: military action against revolutionaries

interdicted: intercepted or forbade

1 **ANALYZING INFORMATION** According to the authors, what factors contributed to the reluctance of the South Vietnamese people to trust U.S. soldiers?

_____

_____

2 **IDENTIFYING CAUSES** What factors helped build confidence in U.S. soldiers among the South Vietnamese people?

_____

_____

_____

3 ECONOMICS What details from the authors' account indicate a positive economic impact on the South Vietnamese civilian population?

_____

_____

_____

4 **DETERMINING CENTRAL IDEAS** What opinion do the authors hold of Communists? Why?

_____

_____

_____

_____

5 **IDENTIFYING PERSPECTIVES** What perspective do the authors have that adds credibility to their opinion about Vietnamese citizens' reactions to the United States?

_____

_____

_____

_____

Vietnam Divides the Nation

DIRECTIONS: Search for evidence in Chapter 16, Lesson 2 to help you answer the following questions.

1A **INTERPRETING** What images of the Vietnam War did U.S. citizens see on television?

_____

_____

_____

ESSENTIAL QUESTION

Should citizens support the government during wartime?

As you gather evidence to answer the Essential Question, think about:

- how U.S. citizens protested the war.
- the impact of the draft on public opinion about the war.
- how major battles in the war influenced support for the war.

1B **EXPLAINING CAUSE AND EFFECT** How did those images influence public opinion about the war? What other factors drove support for the war down?

_____

_____

_____

_____

_____

2A **EXPLAINING EFFECTS** What was the effect of the Tet Offensive in both Vietnam and the United States?

_____

_____

_____

My Notes

_____

_____

_____

_____

2B **EVALUATING EVIDENCE** How did the Tet Offensive influence U.S. politics in 1968?

_____

_____

_____

_____

3 **EXPLAINING** Complete the chart to explain the differences between the Democratic and Republican National Conventions in 1968.

Democratic National Convention	Republican National Convention

4 **SUMMARIZING** Complete the Cornell Notes organizer to describe the election of 1968 and its aftermath.

Main Ideas	Notes
President Johnson	
Richard Nixon	

Proposed Amendment to The Constitution of the United States, S. J. Res. 7, 92nd Cong. (1971).

ESSENTIAL QUESTION

Should citizens support the government during wartime?

The Twenty-Sixth Amendment to the U.S. Constitution

DIRECTIONS: Read the following excerpt from the U.S. Constitution. Then respond to the questions that follow.

EXPLORE THE CONTEXT: Amending the U.S. Constitution is a difficult process and happens only when the Senate and the House of Representatives overwhelmingly agree that a correction or an improvement is needed. Amendments are then sent to states to be **ratified** by the citizens. The Constitution has been amended 27 times in the course of its history.

We the people

PRIMARY SOURCE: CONSTITUTIONAL AMENDMENT

❝ Resolved by the Senate and House of Representatives of the United States of America in Congress assembled (two-thirds of each House **concurring** therein), That the following article is proposed as an amendment to the Constitution of the United States, which shall be valid to all intents and purposes as part of the Constitution when ratified by the legislatures of three-fourths of the several States within seven years from the date of its submission by the Congress:

'Article—

'SECTION 1. The right of citizens of the United States, who are eighteen years of age or older, to vote shall not be denied or **abridged** by the United States or by any State on account of age.

'SEC. 2. The Congress shall have the power to enforce this article by appropriate legislation.' ❞

—from "The 26th Amendment to the United States Constitution," passed by the Ninety-second Congress, January 21, 1971

VOCABULARY

concurring: agreeing

ratified: formally consented

abridged: restricted

 SUMMARIZING What change does the amendment make to the U.S. Constitution?

_____

_____

2 UNDERSTANDING CONTEXT What does the document say about when the amendment will become law?

_____

_____

_____

3 DESCRIBING What was going on in the world at the time this amendment was passed?

_____

_____

4 COMPARING AND CONTRASTING How were those events the cause of this constitutional amendment? What was the purpose of the amendment?

_____

_____

_____

_____

_____

5 CIVICS What democratic principle guided lawmakers' actions as they wrote this amendment?

_____

_____

_____

_____

6 DRAWING CONCLUSIONS Passing a constitutional amendment is a difficult process for legislators and usually occurs after there is demand for change by voters. Because young people did not have suffrage before this amendment passed, who do you think was the most powerful group in calling for the amendment?

_____

_____

_____

_____

ESSENTIAL QUESTION

Should citizens support the government during wartime?

Johnson Halts Bombing of North Vietnam

DIRECTIONS: Read the following excerpt from a presidential speech. Then respond to the questions that follow.

EXPLORE THE CONTEXT: President Johnson recorded this speech from the White House, and it was broadcast on national television. In his speech, he refers to the two military commanders in Vietnam: General Westmoreland and General Abrams.

PRIMARY SOURCE: SPEECH EXCERPT

❝ I have now ordered that all air, naval, and **artillery** bombardment of North Vietnam cease as of 8 a.m., Washington time, Friday morning; I have reached this decision . . . in the belief that this action can lead to progress toward a peaceful settlement of the Vietnamese war. . . .

[Tonight] I can tell you that a series of hopeful events has occurred in South Vietnam:—The Government of South Vietnam has grown steadily stronger.—South Vietnam's Armed Forces have been substantially increased to the point where a million men are tonight under arms, and the effectiveness of these men has steadily improved.—The superb performance of our own men, under the brilliant leadership of General Westmoreland and General Abrams, has produced truly remarkable results. . . .

Now that progress has come, I know that your prayers are joined with mine and with those of all humanity, that the action I announce tonight will be a major step toward a firm and an honorable peace in Southeast Asia. . . .

Throughout the entire summer and fall I have kept all of the presidential candidates fully **briefed** on developments in Paris as well as in Vietnam. I have made it abundantly clear that no one candidate would have the advantage over others. . . .

I do not know who will be **inaugurated** as the 37th President of the United States next January. But I do know that I shall do all that I can in the next few months to try to lighten his burdens as the contributions of the Presidents who preceded me have greatly lightened mine. I shall do everything in my power to move us toward the peace that the new President—as well as this President and, I believe, every other American—so deeply and urgently desires. ❞

—from a televised speech delivered by President Johnson on October 31, 1968

VOCABULARY

artillery: weapons

inaugurated: sworn in as president

briefed: informed

Johnson, Lyndon B. "The President's Address to the Nation Upon Announcing His Decision to Halt the Bombing of North Vietnam, October 31, 1968." In Public Papers of the Presidents of the United States: Lyndon B. Johnson, 1968-69. Washington, D. C.: Government Printing Office, 1970.

1. **UNDERSTANDING CONTEXT** What announcement is the president making in his speech to the nation? How does he explain his decision?

_____

_____

_____

2. **EVALUATING EVIDENCE** How do you interpret the president's words "a firm and an honorable peace in Southeast Asia"?

_____

_____

_____

3. **EXPLAINING EFFECTS** Look at the date of the speech. Because presidential elections are held in early November, what is the likely impact of the speech on the election?

_____

_____

_____

_____

4. **CIVICS** What democratic principle is on display in this passage? How does the process of elections lead to greater national stability?

_____

_____

_____

_____

5. **INFERRING** What events triggered Johnson's announcement?

_____

_____

The War Winds Down

DIRECTIONS: Search for evidence in Chapter 16, Lesson 3 to help you answer the following questions.

1A **INTERPRETING** What is Vietnamization?

_____

_____

_____

1B **UNDERSTANDING CHANGE** What events made it appear that Nixon was not actually ending the war?

_____

_____

_____

_____

2A **SUMMARIZING** What happened in the My Lai massacre?

_____

_____

_____

2B CIVICS How did protests at home help increase anger over the war?

_____

_____

_____

ESSENTIAL QUESTION

Should citizens support the government during wartime?

As you gather evidence to answer the Essential Question, think about:

- the reasons Nixon moved to end the war.
- the government's decision to fire on American protesters.
- how U.S. citizens remember the Vietnam War today.

My Notes

_____

_____

_____

_____

_____

_____

3 RELATING EVENTS Complete the time line with the correct order of events that led to the end of America's involvement in the Vietnam War.

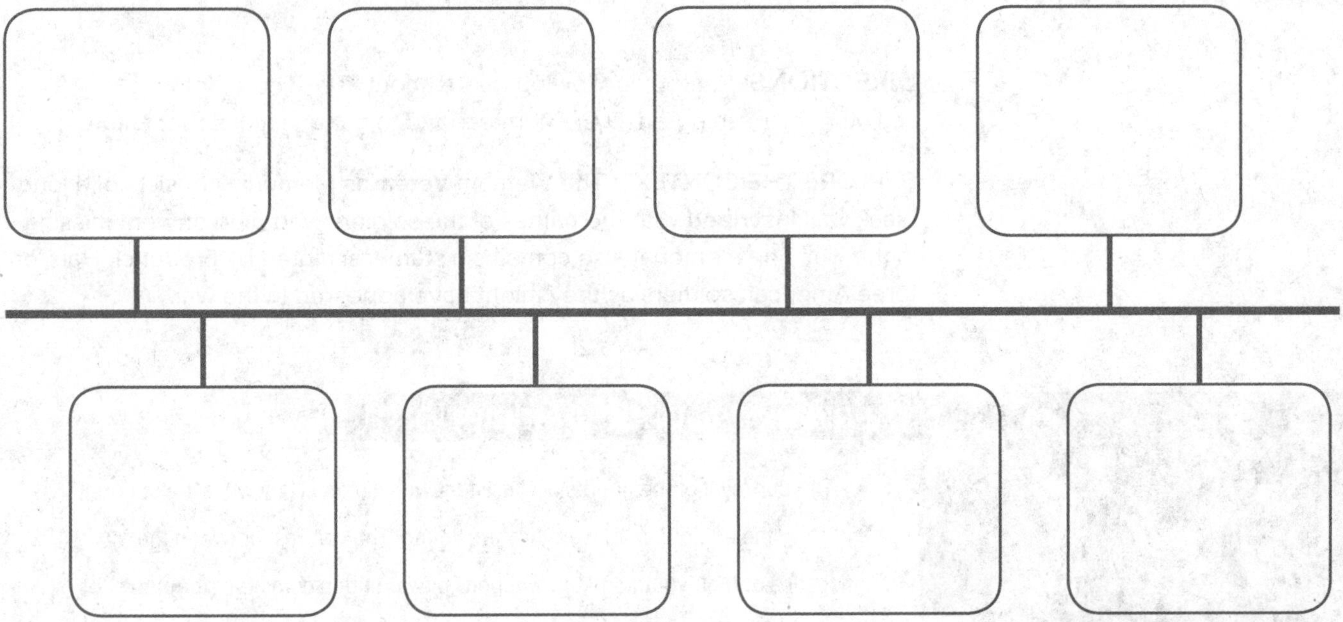

4 EXPLAINING EFFECTS Complete the graphic organizer to identify the long-lasting effects of the Vietnam War.

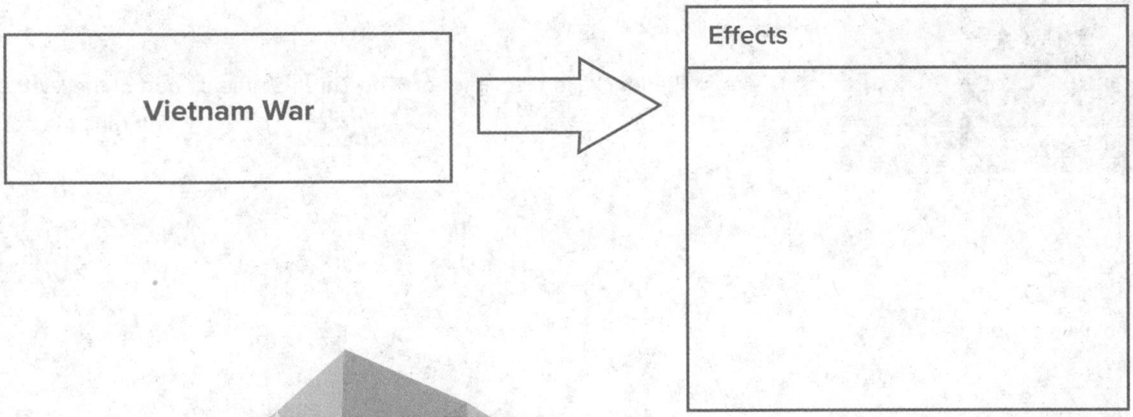

ESSENTIAL QUESTION
Should citizens support the government during wartime?

Inscription on the Vietnam War Memorial

DIRECTIONS: Read the following quote about "The Three Soldiers" sculpture in Washington, D.C. Then respond to the questions that follow.

EXPLORE THE CONTEXT: The Vietnam **Veterans** Memorial consists of a long black wall **inscribed** with the names of the soldiers who died or went missing in the war. The memorial also contains a statue, sculpted by Frederick Hart, of three American soldiers as they might have appeared in the war.

PRIMARY SOURCE: INSCRIPTION

❝ The portrayal of the figures is consistent with history. They wear the uniform and carry the equipment of war; they are young. The contrast between the innocence of their youth and the weapons of war underscores the **poignancy** of their sacrifice. There is about them the physical contact and sense of unity that **bespeaks** the bonds of love and sacrifice that is the nature of men at war. And yet they are each alone. Their strength and their vulnerability are both evident. Their true **heroism** lies in these bonds of loyalty in the face of their aloneness and their vulnerability. ❞

—from Frederick Hart, sculptor of "The Three Soldiers," part of the Vietnam Veterans Memorial

VOCABULARY

inscribed: written or carved

veterans: people who have served their country in the military

poignancy: painful or sad effect

bespeaks: suggests or indicates

heroism: the condition of being a hero

1 CIVICS What is "The Three Soldiers," and what is its purpose?

_____

_____

_____

2 **TESTING HYPOTHESES** How might a war memorial help a country heal from war?

_____

_____

_____

3 **IDENTIFYING PERSPECTIVES** What did the sculptor, Frederick Hart, wish to convey with his statue of the three soldiers?

_____

_____

_____

4 **CITING TEXT EVIDENCE** Which line in the text explains why Hart sculpted three soldiers instead of just one?

_____

_____

_____

5 **INFERRING** The sculptor holds the youth of the soldiers in his statue in contrast to the weapons of war. Why is this an important distinction for him?

_____

_____

_____

6 **EXPLAINING** What did Hart mean when he said, "Their true heroism lies in these bonds of loyalty in the face of their aloneness and their vulnerability"?

_____

_____

_____

_____

ESSENTIAL QUESTION

Should citizens support the government during wartime?

War Powers Resolution

DIRECTIONS: Read the following excerpt from the War Powers Resolution. Then respond to the questions that follow.

EXPLORE THE CONTEXT: The Vietnam War happened in part because Congress, in the mid-1960s, gave the president the power to declare war and utilize the military in any way he saw fit. In 1973, Congress recognized that it needed to assert its authority to stop the war. The War Powers Resolution did just that.

VOCABULARY

imminent: sure to happen

statutory: determined by law

PRIMARY SOURCE: CONGRESSIONAL RESOLUTION

" PURPOSE AND POLICY, SEC. 2. (a) It is the purpose of this joint resolution to fulfill the intent of the framers of the Constitution of the United States and insure that the collective judgment of both the Congress and the President will apply to the introduction of United States Armed Forces into hostilities, or into situations where **imminent** involvement in hostilities is clearly indicated by the circumstances, and to the continued use of such forces in hostilities or in such situations. . . .

(c) The constitutional powers of the President as Commander-in-Chief to introduce United States Armed Forces into hostilities, or into situations where imminent involvement in hostilities is clearly indicated by the circumstances, are exercised only pursuant to (1) a declaration of war, (2) specific **statutory** authorization, or (3) a national emergency created by attack upon the United States, its territories or possessions, or its armed forces.

CONSULTATION, SEC. 3. The President in every possible instance shall consult with Congress before introducing United States Armed Forces into hostilities or into situation where imminent involvement in hostilities is clearly indicated by the circumstances, and after every such introduction shall consult regularly with the Congress until United States Armed Forces are no longer engaged in hostilities or have been removed from such situations. "

—from the War Powers Resolution, a Joint Resolution of Congress, November 7, 1973

War Powers Resolution, Pub. L. No. 93-148, 87 Stat. 555 (1973).

1 **SUMMARIZING** What rule does the resolution impose?

_____

_____

_____

2 **INTERPRETING** According to the resolution, in what three circumstances can the president call for the military to become involved in hostilities with a foreign power?

_____

_____

_____

3 **INTERPRETING** What incident triggered the War Powers Resolution? How does the resolution attempt to address the problem?

_____

_____

_____

4 **UNDERSTANDING CONTEXT** Why do you think a provision to force the president to consult regularly with Congress during wartime was included? What will this provision ensure?

_____

_____

_____

5 CIVICS What bedrock civic principle is expressed in this resolution?

_____

_____

ESSENTIAL QUESTIONS

Should citizens support the government during wartime?

My Notes

_____

_____

_____

_____

_____

_____

_____

_____

_____

_____

_____

_____

_____

_____

_____

① **Think About It**

Review the supporting questions that you developed at the beginning of the chapter. Review the evidence that you gathered in Chapter 16. Were you able to answer each Supporting Question?

If there was not enough evidence to answer your Supporting Questions, what additional evidence do you think you need to consider?

_____

_____

_____

_____

② **Organize Your Evidence**

Complete the graphic organizer below with information you learned about the Vietnam War and how U.S. citizens supported or protested it.

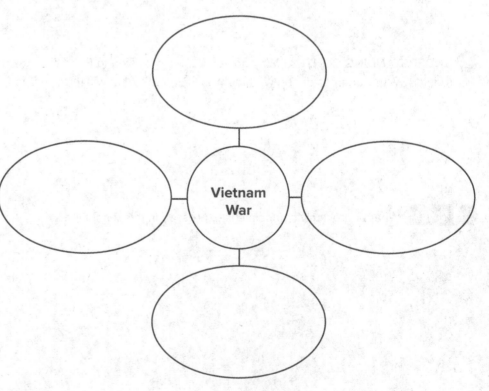

Vietnam War

③ Talk About It

Work in small groups. Talk with your group about the information you included in your graphic organizer. Did you include the same evidence, or were your classmates' responses different from your responses? Which information is most important to understanding the Vietnam War? Why?

_____

_____

_____

_____

④ Connect to the Essential Question

Work in small groups. On a separate piece of paper or on a computer, create a visual essay that answers the Essential Question: Should citizens support the government during wartime? Use the graphic organizer from step 2 and what you discussed with your group to prepare your essay. Find photographs online that represent the causes and effects of the war. Insert these images into your essay. Alternatively, you can locate pictures in hard copy sources. Be sure that the images included in your visual essay are accompanied by captions that help explain what is happening in each image.

_____

_____

_____

_____

_____

_____

_____

_____

_____

_____

CITIZENSHIP
TAKING ACTION

MAKE CONNECTIONS The Vietnam War was a period of intense turmoil in the United States. With many thousands of young men and women participating in the war, most cities and towns in the United States were touched by loss. As a result, many places throughout the country have erected monuments to the men and women who died in the Vietnam War. Some of these monuments are gardens or parks, while others are roads or bridges named after fallen heroes. Still others are statues or sculptures erected in public spaces.

DIRECTIONS: Research the impact of the Vietnam War on the community in which you live. Investigate any war memorials that are part of the civic life in your community. If possible, take a trip to the memorial in or nearest your community, and interview people who were affected by the Vietnam War, whether as soldiers or as citizens. If you do not have access to a memorial, choose one online that you think is powerful.

Write about the monument. Describe how it looks and what it does to honor the people who fought and died in the war. Use images of the monument to illustrate your essay. Finally, share what you've written with your school or town newspaper.

_____

_____

_____

_____

_____

_____

_____

_____

_____

_____

The Politics of Protest

ESSENTIAL QUESTION

How has society changed for students, women, LGBTQ activists, and Latinos?

Think about how this question might relate to the period of time from 1960 until 1980. What led to changes on college campuses? Which groups of people have protested for changes? What kinds of organizations formed to advocate for change?

TALK ABOUT IT

Discuss with a partner the type of information you would need to know to answer these questions. For example, one question might be: *What makes a group form to advocate for change?*

DIRECTIONS: Now write down three additional questions that would help you explain how society has changed for various groups.

MY RESEARCH QUESTIONS

Supporting Question 1:

_____

_____

Supporting Question 2:

_____

_____

Supporting Question 3:

_____

_____

Students and The Counterculture

DIRECTIONS Search for evidence in Chapter 17, Lesson 1 to help you answer the following questions.

1A EXPLAINING CAUSES What inspired the youth movement of the 1960s?

_____

_____

_____

_____

_____

ESSENTIAL QUESTION

How has society changed for students, women, LGBTQ activists, and Latinos?

As you gather evidence to answer the Essential Question, think about:

- the reasons for new social movements of the times.
- how these movements had a lasting impact on American society.

1B RELATING EVENTS How did the size of the baby boom impact the youth movement?

_____

_____

_____

_____

_____

My Notes

_____

_____

_____

_____

_____

_____

2A CIVICS What was the main objective of Students for a Democratic Society?

_____

_____

_____

_____

2B IDENTIFYING CONNECTIONS What ideals did the New Left and the Students for a Democratic Society share with the Free Speech Movement?

_____

_____

_____

_____

3 **COMPARING AND CONTRASTING** Fill in the blank boxes in the graphic organizer below with characteristics of the youth movement and the hippie movement.

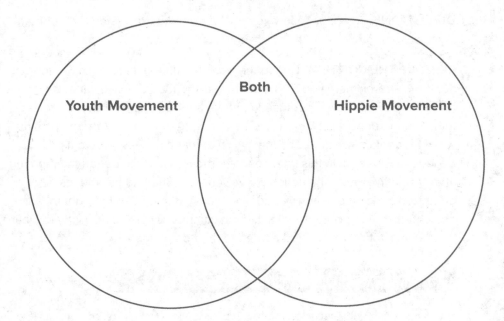

4A **IDENTIFYING** What were some of the main values of hippie culture?

_____

_____

_____

4B **IDENTIFYING CONNECTIONS** What was the long-term impact of hippie culture?

_____

_____

ESSENTIAL QUESTION

How has society changed for students, women, LGBTQ activists, and Latinos?

VOCABULARY

WATS line: flat-rate long-distance service used when it was expensive to call a person outside the local area

mystique: air of mystery and power

besmirch: tarnish; harm one's reputation

leaflets: informational brochures

Interview of Barbara Epstein

DIRECTIONS: Read the following excerpt from the oral history of Barbara Epstein. Then respond to the questions that follow.

EXPLORE THE CONTEXT: During the free speech movement, on September 30, 1964, approximately 10,000 students surrounded a police car at University of California Berkeley and refused to move after a nonstudent was arrested for handing out political literature on campus. At that time, Barbara Epstein was a student at Radcliffe College (which at that time was the Women's College of Harvard). In this interview, she recalls what happened the morning after the sit-in around the police car at Berkeley. She and her friends organized a picket of Harvard's administration, demanding the right to pass out **leaflets** to support political action on campus. By 1:00 p.m., Harvard Dean of Students John Monroe had agreed to their demands.

PRIMARY SOURCE: ORAL HISTORY

❝ . . . the SNCC [Student Nonviolent Coordinating Committee] office in Atlanta had a **WATS line,** and in the middle of the night, when people in SNCC heard about the sit-in at Berkeley, they began calling people around the country who were their contacts. So they called my friends, Max and Simon. Max and Simon got hold of the rest of us. They must have called me first thing in the morning. I was on a steering committee of SDS [Students for a Democratic Society] and by eight o'clock in the morning, the steering committee of SDS was in front of the office of Dean Monroe, who was the dean of students of Harvard, telling him about the FSM [Free Speech Movement] and demanding that we be allowed to conduct political activities on campus. Up until that time, it had been against the rules to, for instance, pass out leaflets on the Harvard campus because the Harvard campus was sacred, so to speak . . . the **mystique** of Harvard was that it was the ivory tower, and how could you possibly do something to **besmirch** that by handing out a leaflet? . . . At any rate, we demanded that we be allowed to conduct political activities on campus, including handing out leaflets, and Dean Monroe agreed very readily. ❞

—from "Free Speech Movement Oral History Project: Barbara Epstein," recorded in 1999

1 GEOGRAPHY What can you infer about the scope of the Students for a Democratic Society from this excerpt?

_____

_____

_____

2 **RELATING EVENTS** How did the events at UC Berkeley influence students who, like Barbara, were attending other colleges?

_____

_____

3 **INFERRING** What can you infer from the fact that Epstein mentions the time?

_____

_____

_____

4 **DETERMINING MEANING** What do you think a steering committee is? Use evidence from the text to explain your answer.

_____

_____

_____

_____

5 **ANALYZING CHANGE** How did the free speech movement change Harvard?

_____

_____

_____

_____

ESSENTIAL QUESTION

How has society changed for students, women, LGBTQ activists, and Latinos?

VOCABULARY

insidious: harmful and convincing

Marxism-Leninism: communism

blatantly: obviously and offensively

abdicated: ignored or passed on to someone else

capitulation: giving in to demands

FBI Statement on Campus Unrest

DIRECTIONS: Read the following excerpt from FBI Director J. Edgar Hoover's statement on campus unrest. Then respond to the questions that follow.

EXPLORE THE CONTEXT: The 1960s saw a great deal of activism on college campuses, including protests that sometimes turned violent. In April 1970, immediately after President Nixon announced the movement of U.S. forces into Cambodia, a series of violent protests occurred on campuses such as Kent State and Jackson State College that resulted in the use of national guardsmen and several student deaths. By the end of May 1970, nearly one-third of the nation's 2,500 college campuses had experienced some sort of protest activity. As a result, President Nixon established the President's Commission on Campus Unrest and tasked the FBI with investigating the causes of the violence and outlining steps that could be taken to resolve grievances through other means.

PRIMARY SOURCE: FBI STATEMENT

" The most widely publicized group active in fanning the flames of student discontent and violence has been the notorious Students for a Democratic Society (SDS). This group came into being in 1962. Since that time, it has spread its **insidious** philosophy to hundreds of campuses across the nation and has moved in rapid succession from a policy of protest to one of active resistance and finally, to the urging of open warfare against our system. Embracing the tenets of **Marxism-Leninism,** its leaders have publicly stated that, if our academic institutions are not restructured, they must be destroyed. In a manner totally alien to the principles of our democracy, it has sought to achieve its goals. SDS groups have been in the forefront of student disruptions and violence. Its leaders have **blatantly** encouraged the use of violent and terrorist tactics . . .

Notwithstanding the fact that the New Left movement is essentially a youth movement made up of irresponsible student activists and an assortment of misguided faculty members and administrators, the American people as a whole must shoulder the responsibility for allowing the situation on our college campuses to degenerate to the tragic conditions now existing in many areas. Far too many Americans have **abdicated** a basic responsibility by adopting a philosophy of indulgence and relaxed discipline and retreating from firm moral standards during the difficult process of preparing their children for a place in society. The arrogance which has manifested itself on our college campuses during the past few years is the product of years of permissiveness and **capitulation** to youth.

This is not to suggest in the least that the great majority of the present generation of youth should be written off. Most of our youth are a credit to their parents and to this country. But a minority, steeped in an attitude of indulgence and materialism, has terrorized whole academic communities, bringing the nation's educational facilities to the brink of chaos. Arrogant, spoiled youth, many not emotionally mature enough to enter an institution of higher learning, are ill prepared to dictate the academic standards or policies of a college or university, and yet many have done just that. "

—from statement by J. Edgar Hoover before the President's Commission on Campus Unrest, July 1970

Statement of J. Edgar Hoover, Director, Federal Bureau of Investigation Before President's Commission on Campus Unrest; 7/1970; Statements Before the Commission [July 1970]; Office Files of the Chairman, 1970 - 1970; Records of Temporary Committees, Commissions, and Boards, Record Group 220.

1 **DETERMINING MEANING** What do you think Hoover means by "fanning the flames"?

_____

_____

2 **IDENTIFYING BIAS** What kinds of words does the FBI director use that might indicate that he is biased against Students for a Democratic Society?

_____

_____

3 CIVICS How does Hoover feel that the Students for a Democratic Society acted in our democracy?

_____

_____

4 **CITING TEXT EVIDENCE** What does the FBI director think of the New Left movement? Cite evidence from the text to support your answer.

_____

_____

_____

_____

_____

_____

5 **CONTRASTING** How does Hoover's perspective compare to Barbara Epstein's?

_____

_____

_____

6 **ANALYZING CHANGE** According to Hoover, how had the youth of America changed? Why?

_____

_____

_____

ESSENTIAL QUESTION

How has society changed for students, women, LGBTQ activists, and Latinos?

As you gather evidence to answer the Essential Question, think about:

- the reasons the feminist movement gained strength in the 1960s.

- the successes and failures of the feminist movement.

My Notes

The Feminist Movement

DIRECTIONS: Search for evidence in Chapter 17, Lesson 2 to help you answer the following questions.

1A **IDENTIFYING** What is feminism?

_____

_____

_____

1B **DETERMINING CONTEXT** What were some of the reasons many women felt the need to push for more rights?

_____

_____

_____

_____

2A **RELATING EVENTS** What did the Equal Rights Amendment specify?

_____

_____

_____

2B CIVICS Why didn't the Equal Rights Amendment pass?

_____

_____

_____

_____

3 **SUMMARIZING** Complete the graphic organizer below describing the landmark policies that were part of the feminist movement.

Landmark Policy	Action	Impact
The Equal Pay Act		
The Civil Rights Act of 1964		
The Equal Rights Amendment		
Title IX		
Griswold v. Connecticut		
Roe v. Wade		
Planned Parenthood v. Casey		

4 **EXPLAINING EFFECTS** How has the women's movement changed society?

_____

_____

_____

5 **EXPLAINING CAUSES** What is one reason there is still a wage gap between men and women?

_____

_____

ESSENTIAL QUESTION

How has society changed for students, women, LGBTQ activists, and Latinos?

Women's Equality Day

DIRECTIONS: Examine the following image of a woman protesting. Then respond to the questions that follow.

EXPLORE THE CONTEXT: In August 1970, 50 years after the Nineteenth Amendment was passed, 50,000 women marched in New York City in an event organized by the National Organization for Women (NOW). This Women's Strike for Equality march was the idea of Betty Friedan, who wanted to demonstrate the scope and power of second-wave feminism. In 1971, Congress passed a resolution designating August 26 each year as Women's Equality Day. The photo below was taken at a march on Women's Equality Day in 1973. In 1968, the Phillip Morris company launched an ad campaign with the slogan "You've come a long way, baby," to advertise a new brand of cigarettes targeting women.

PRIMARY SOURCE: PHOTO

—from Women's Equality Day in Fountain Square in Cincinnati, Ohio on August 26, 1973

1 **RELATING EVENTS** Why do you think the women's movement during the 1960s and 1970s was referred to as "second-wave feminism"?

_____

_____

_____

2 CIVICS How could marching for a cause have an impact?

_____

_____

_____

3 **INTEGRATING INFORMATION** What is ironic about the popular advertising slogan "You've come a long way, baby?"

_____

_____

_____

_____

4 **DETERMINING MEANING** Why do you think the woman's sign reads "You have not come a long way baby"?

_____

_____

_____

5 **IDENTIFYING CONNECTIONS** Why would a woman fighting for rights hold a sign referencing population growth?

_____

_____

_____

ESSENTIAL QUESTION

How has society changed for students, women, LGBTQ activists, and Latinos?

The Passage of Title IX

DIRECTIONS: Read the following excerpt from the article from *Today's education: The journal of the National Education Association.* Then respond to the questions that follow.

EXPLORE THE CONTEXT: One of the most significant accomplishments of the feminist movement was the passage of Title IX on June 23, 1972, which bars sex discrimination in educational programs and activities by any institution receiving federal funds. Title IX ensures that no student is denied educational opportunities based on gender any more than they should be denied opportunities based on race, religion, or country of origin. Title IX applies to financial aid, student services, and athletics and was passed in response to educational inequalities such as limited or prohibited admissions, reduced access to scholarships, and fewer opportunities to participate in sports. The year before Title IX was enacted, there were roughly 310,000 females in the United States playing high school and college sports. By 2012, that number had surpassed 3,373,000.

PRIMARY SOURCE: JOURNAL ARTICLE

❝ Although sex discrimination has been widespread in many areas of public school education, in no area has it been so blatant as in athletics. Until recently, the education **hierarchy** from top to bottom has agreed that exposure to competitive athletics was good for boys but morally and physically bad for girls. Why? On what has this strange **dichotomy** been based? Primarily on myth, it now appears, because, until the last few years, there has been little or no objective, documented research . . .

During the period that high school and collegiate sports for boys and men were developing to their present state, social thinking put women into the home, into **nurturant** [sic] roles, and into places where they could be protected. Along with everything else, they were to be protected from the rough and tumble of **boisterous** play, from the pressures of competition and the striving to win of competitive sports . . .

Misconceptions about anatomy and **physiology** and about the strength and endurance females were capable of developing and displaying also played their part in fostering the idea that girls and young women were to be protected from vigorous activity. ❞

—from *Today's Education,* Nov/Dec 1974

VOCABULARY

hierarchy: leadership system

dichotomy: contradiction

nurturant: nourishing and training

boisterous: loud and energetic

physiology: the bodily processes of a living organism

Blaufarb, Marjorie. "Equal Opportunity for Girls in Athletics." Today's Education, Nov/Dec 1974.   Copyright © McGraw-Hill Education

1 CIVICS In the opinion of the author, which area of discrimination against women needed prompt attention?

_____

_____

_____

2 **ANALYZING SOURCES** Why had many people erroneously believed that competitive athletics were not good for girls?

_____

_____

_____

3 **ANALYZING CENTRAL IDEAS** Why did some people in the past think that girls needed to be protected from competitive sports?

_____

_____

_____

_____

4 **DETERMINING CONTEXT** At the time of this article, what was changing in social thinking?

_____

_____

_____

5 **IDENTIFYING CONNECTIONS** Do you believe that women can play competitive sports without damaging their minds and bodies? Explain your stance.

_____

_____

_____

_____

Latino Americans Organize

DIRECTIONS: Search for evidence in Chapter 17, Lesson 3 to help you answer the following questions.

1A **RELATING EVENTS** Why did emigration from Mexico increase during the first half of the twentieth century?

_____

_____

1B **IDENTIFYING** How were Mexicans discriminated against?

_____

_____

_____

_____

_____

2A **GEOGRAPHY** Besides Mexico, from which other regions did Latinos migrate?

_____

_____

2B **RELATING EVENTS** What caused the increase in Latino migration from these regions?

_____

_____

_____

_____

_____

ESSENTIAL QUESTION

How has society changed for students, women, LGBTQ activists, and Latinos?

As you gather evidence to answer the Essential Question, think about:

- the people who were "left behind" despite a prosperous economy.
- the ways the government attempted to improve economic standards and education.

My Notes

_____

_____

_____

_____

_____

_____

3 **SUMMARIZING** Complete the graphic organizer below with information about the organizations that were formed to defend Latino rights.

Organization	Purpose	Impact
League of United Latin American Citizens		
American GI Forum		
National Farm Workers Association		
Mexican American Youth Organization		
La Raza Unida		

4 **CIVICS** What was the purpose of the Bilingual Education Act of 1968?

_____

_____

5 **ANALYZING** Why do you think that the Bilingual Education Act was controversial?

_____

_____

_____

ESSENTIAL QUESTION

How has society changed for students, women, LGBTQ activists, and Latinos?

VOCABULARY

recuperating: recovering

fast: go without food for an extended length of time

cultivated: prepared land so it could sustain crops

prosperity: financial thriving

Remembering the United Farm Workers Union

DIRECTIONS: Read the following excerpt from an essay about the Farm Workers Union. Then respond to the questions that follow.

EXPLORE THE CONTEXT: César Chávez was the leader of the National Farm Workers Association, which joined with the Agricultural Workers Organizing Committee to form the United Farm Workers Union in 1966. Chávez was a Mexican American migrant farm laborer who fought for the rights of migrant laborers and improved working conditions. He believed in a philosophy of nonviolence and raised awareness through boycotts and strikes. Maria Rifo wrote this essay recalling her experiences with the movement and her time spent around Chávez.

PRIMARY SOURCE: ESSAY

❝I met César Chávez when I worked as a Vista volunteer in New Mexico in 1967. He came to persuade the farmworkers not to break the strike that was starting in California. His attitude and his calm manner inspired me to ask for a job with the union. So when I finished the second year of the contract with Vista, I left for Delano, California. I came to the United Farm Workers mature in years but immature in other ways, without experience of life outside of home and without knowing how to communicate with people in power . . . I didn't want to lose the ideals that led me there in the first place, but I was not skilled at how to use power in order to maintain a positive attitude. In other words, I did not know what to do when doubts came up, and how to ask people in charge about it.

At the beginning of my stay, César was patient and didn't give me very difficult tasks. At first, I was a receptionist in the house where he spent many months **recuperating** from his **fast**. His fasting helped redirect the farmworker movement from the wave of violence that was growing between the farmworkers and the owners. The workers had **cultivated** the vineyards and were the source of the **prosperity** and wealth of the owners. And now the farmworkers were on strike for better working conditions and honest, fair salaries so they could escape from the poverty that they and their families lived in . . .

I think that César taught us by the way he told us to work. In this way he helped us to develop our own insight, our own gift, our own dreams, and our own ideas of what we could do . . .

Delano was divided by the [railroad] tracks. On the eastside was the nuns' school and the Catholic Church, and this place was for the rich people. On the other side of the tracks was the Virgin of Guadalupe, no school for children, just a priest who supported the poor and the union, and this is where the workers lived. Total division.❞

—from "Remembering the United Farm Workers Union," an essay by Maria Rifo

Rifo, Maria. "Remembering the United Farm Workers Union," Essay, Farmworker Movement Documentation Project, University of California San Diego, 2004.

1 DESCRIBING According to Maria, what characteristics did Chávez have that inspired others to follow him?

_____

_____

_____

2 ANALYZING SOURCES What did Maria say she lacked when she began working with the United Farm Workers?

_____

_____

_____

3 RELATING EVENTS How does Maria feel that Chávez's fast affected the farmworker movement?

_____

_____

_____

_____

4 CITING TEXT EVIDENCE How was Maria changed by Chávez? Cite evidence from the text to support your answer.

_____

_____

_____

_____

5 ECONOMICS How was the city of Delano separated?

_____

_____

_____

ESSENTIAL QUESTION
How has society changed for students, women, LGBTQ activists, and Latinos?

Overview of Mexican-American Education

DIRECTIONS: Read the following excerpt from a speech on Mexican American education. Then respond to the questions that follow.

EXPLORE THE CONTEXT: The Bilingual Education Act of 1968, also known as Title VII of the Elementary and Secondary Education Act (ESEA), was the first federal recognition that students with limited English have special educational needs and that bilingual programs that address those needs should be federally funded in the interest of equal educational opportunity. Title VII was the first step toward recognizing that ethnic minorities could seek differentiated services for reasons other than segregation or racial discrimination. The act raised cultural awareness and promoted instruction in languages other than English.

PRIMARY SOURCE: SPEECH

" A little over a year ago President Johnson said, 'The time has come to focus our efforts more intensely on the Mexican-American.' I want to present to you what I see as a result of the President's call for action. . . . I have found during the past year that there is a most encouraging scene for directed improvement of the education of the Mexican-American. There is a rising determination on the part of educators in the Southwest to **implement** programs designed to more effectively meet the educational needs of the bilingual-bicultural student. This determination is in both new and **innovative** programs and in expenditures of money. . . .

But now I want to spend some time talking about what I consider the most important potential for breaking the barrier of cultural and **linguistic** isolation we have in our hands. I'm talking about the Bilingual Education Act, Title VII, ESEA. It provides a national commitment for important change in the educational policy of most school districts. It gives moral and legislative recognition to the assets of a people whose **mother tongue** is not English. It may be the first step toward the desirable and **attainable** goal of a bilingual society. It says to other nations that the United States can and will work toward the education of its people in the richness of differences—not just racial—but linguistic and cultural. "

—from the speech "Mexican-American Education; An Overview," given by Armando Rodriguez at the Workshop to Develop Human Resources among Mexican-American Teachers in the Denver Metropolitan Area, Denver, Colorado, June 1968

VOCABULARY

implement: put in place

innovative: creative and new

linguistic: relating to language

attainable: achievable

mother tongue: language learned as an infant; language of one's homeland

Rodriguez, Armando. "Mexican-American Education; An Overview," speech given by Armando Rodriguez at the Workshop to Develop Human Resources among Mexican-American Teachers in the Denver Metropolitan Area, Denver, Colorado, June 9 - 10. 1968.

1 **INFERRING** What might be the unique needs of a bilingual-bicultural student?

_____

_____

_____

2 CIVICS In what ways does the speaker see educators changing public education to address the needs of these students?

_____

_____

_____

3 **DETERMINING MEANING** What do you think the speaker means by "cultural and linguistic isolation"?

_____

_____

_____

4 **ANALYZING PERSPECTIVES** Is the speaker for or against bilingual education? Why?

_____

_____

_____

5 **IDENTIFYING CONNECTIONS** Do you consider bilingual education essential? Explain your stance.

_____

_____

_____

_____

_____

ESSENTIAL QUESTIONS

How has society changed for students, women, LGBTQ activists, and Latinos?

① Think About It

Review the Supporting Questions that you developed at the beginning of the chapter. Review the evidence that you gathered in Chapter 17. Were you able to answer each Supporting Question?

If there was not enough evidence to answer your Supporting Questions, what additional evidence do you think you need to consider?

_____

_____

_____

_____

_____

② Organize Your Evidence

Use a chart such as the one below to organize the evidence you will use to support your findings about how society changed for students, women, LGBTQ activists, and Latinos.

Group	Change to Society	Effect on the Group	Cite evidence from the text to support your claim
Students			
Women			
LGBTQ Activists			
Latinos			

3 Talk About It

In a small group, talk about all the changes that took place from 1960 through 1980. After the discussion, choose the two you feel had the greatest effect on Americans' lives. Describe both changes, and briefly explain your reasons for choosing them as the most impactful.

_____

_____

_____

_____

_____

4 Connect to the Essential Question

On a separate piece of paper, write a journal entry of at least 350 words from the point of view of someone living during the 1960s or 1970s. Your journal entry should help to answer the Essential Question: _How has society changed for students, women, LGBTQ activists, and Latinos?_ Choose a group that you learned about in this chapter, and write your entry from the perspective of that group. You may choose to write from the perspective of a college student in the 1960s, a woman during the feminist movement, an LGBTQ activist, or a Latino immigrant. Through your journal entry, the audience should be able to understand the historical context of the time and how society was changing. Remember to be respectful when writing about different cultures.

_____

_____

_____

_____

_____

_____

_____

_____

_____

_____

_____

_____

CITIZENSHIP
TAKING ACTION

MAKE CONNECTIONS Throughout the 1960s and 1970s, cultural shifts were often represented in new music. Think of gatherings such as Woodstock, the types of music popular at the time, and the musicians who sang about the counterculture or protesting ideas. You can stream the music of Bob Dylan from this time period, Barry McGuire's "Eve of Destruction," Aretha Franklin's "Respect," or music by other artists such as Merle Haggard and Barry Sadler. In what ways has society changed? Is there something that you feel strongly still needs to change in our society?

Directions Write a song that incorporates facts on societal changes. Choose to write about a particular group or issue about which you feel strongly. Think carefully about the tone that you want to set in your song and how you can include lyrics that will clearly express your ideas. Through your song, the audience should be able to understand the historical context of the era and how people's lives changed. Volunteers may also wish to perform their songs for the class.

Politics and Economics

ESSENTIAL QUESTION

How does society change the shape of itself over time?

Think about how this question might relate to both political and economic events that took place from 1968 to 1980.

TALK ABOUT IT

Discuss with a partner what type of information you would need to know to answer this question. For example, one question might be: *What events were taking place during this time that challenged prevailing ideas or opinions in the country?*

DIRECTIONS: Now write three additional questions that would help you explain why society in the United States might have changed during the period from 1968 to 1980.

MY RESEARCH QUESTIONS

Supporting Question 1:

_____

_____

Supporting Question 2:

_____

_____

Supporting Question 3:

_____

_____

The Nixon Administration

DIRECTIONS: Search for evidence in Chapter 18, Lesson 1 to help you answer the following questions.

1A **DESCRIBING** What was Richard Nixon's appeal to Middle America?

_____

_____

_____

_____

_____

1B **EXPLAINING CAUSE AND EFFECT** In what way did the Southern strategy change the political party system during and after the 1968 election?

_____

_____

_____

_____

_____

_____

2A **RELATING EVENTS** How did Nixon's law and order platform collide with the Warren Court?

_____

_____

_____

_____

2B **SUMMARIZING** How did the Burger Court differ from the Warren Court?

_____

_____

_____

_____

ESSENTIAL QUESTION

How does society change the shape of itself over time?

As you gather evidence to answer the Essential Question, think about:

- what helped Nixon win the 1968 presidential election.
- what challenges Nixon faced in his domestic agenda.
- why Nixon's foreign policy achievements are notable.

My Notes

_____

_____

_____

_____

_____

_____

3 **RELATING EVENTS** Complete the graphic organizer below by describing Nixon's New Federalism plan. In what ways did Nixon's program attempt to overturn the legacy of the Great Society?

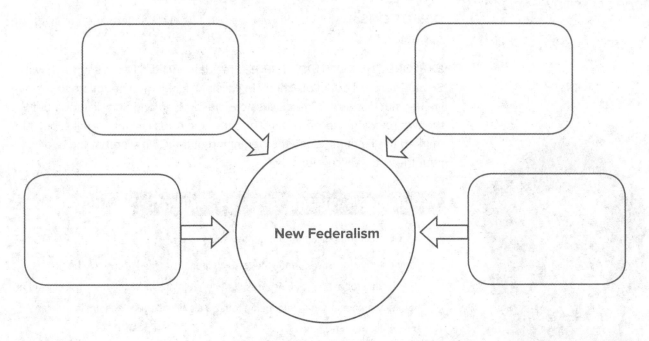

4 CIVICS Complete the chart by explaining how the Warren Court decisions affected U.S. society.

Policy/Doctrine	What Was It?	Outcome
Nixon Doctrine		
Détente		
Proxy wars		
SALT I and II		
Helsinki Accords		

ESSENTIAL QUESTION

How does society change the shape of itself over time?

Strategic Arms Talks

DIRECTIONS: Read the following excerpt from a speech. Then answer the questions that follow.

EXPLORE THE CONTEXT: In 1969, President Richard Nixon sat down with Soviet Premier Leonid Brezhnev in Helsinki, Finland, to negotiate terms over limiting nuclear arms. The discussions became an ongoing dialogue between the two reigning superpowers. The Strategic Arms Limitation Talks, or SALT, marked the first time since the beginning of the Cold War that the two countries held discussions.

PRIMARY SOURCE: SPEECH EXCERPT

❝ Good afternoon, ladies and gentlemen:

As you know, the Soviet-American talks on limiting nuclear arms have been deadlocked for over a year. As a result of negotiations involving the highest level of both governments, I am announcing today a significant development in breaking the deadlock.

The statement that I shall now read is being issued simultaneously in Moscow and Washington: Washington, 12 o'clock; Moscow, 7 p.m.

The Governments of the United States and the Soviet Union, after reviewing the course of their talks on the limitation of **strategic** armaments, have agreed to concentrate this year on working out an agreement for the limitation of the **deployment** of **anti-ballistic missile** systems (ABMs). They have also agreed that, together with concluding an agreement to limit ABMs, they will agree on certain measures with respect to the limitation of offensive strategic weapons.

The two sides are taking this course in the conviction that it will create more favorable conditions for further negotiations to limit all strategic arms. These negotiations will be actively pursued.

This agreement is a major step in breaking the **stalemate** on nuclear arms talks. Intensive negotiations, however, will be required to translate this understanding into a concrete agreement.

This statement that I have just read expresses the commitment of the Soviet and American Governments at the highest levels to achieve that goal. If we succeed, this joint statement that has been issued today may well be remembered as the beginning of a new era in which all nations will devote more of their energies and their resources not to the weapons of war, but to the works of peace. ❞

—from "Remarks Announcing an Agreement on Strategic Arms Limitation Talks," by President Richard Nixon, May 20, 1971

VOCABULARY

anti-ballistic missile: land to air missiles that can contain nuclear warheads

deployment: to place, to use

stalemate: deadlock, standstill

strategic: deliberate, planned

Nixon, Richard M. "Remarks Announcing an Agreement on Strategic Arms Limitation Talks, May 20, 1971." In Public Papers of the Presidents of the United States: Richard M. Nixon, 1971. Washington, D. C.: Government Printing Office, 1971.

1 **DETERMINING CENTRAL IDEAS** Which phrase from the passage states the purpose of the SALT talks?

_____

_____

2 **ANALYZING INFORMATION** According to the document, what was the purpose of these talks?

_____

_____

_____

_____

3 **UNDERSTANDING CONTEXT** Why was Nixon hopeful at the possible outcome of the talks with the Soviet Union?

_____

_____

_____

4 **EVALUATING EVIDENCE** What type of document is this? In what way does this document help you to understand events of this period?

_____

_____

_____

5 CIVICS How does this document illustrate the powers of the executive branch as outlined in the U.S. Constitution?

_____

_____

6 **DRAWING CONCLUSIONS** What is Nixon suggesting in the last sentence of the excerpt?

_____

_____

ESSENTIAL QUESTION

How does society change the shape of itself over time?

New Federalism

DIRECTIONS: Read the following excerpt from a State of the Union address. Then answer the questions that follow.

EXPLORE THE CONTENT: On January 22, 1971, President Nixon delivered his annual State of the Union address to the American people. The primary focus of the address was on Nixon's domestic agenda. The speech outlined policy points that were part of the president's "New Federalism" and how, with its enactment, government would become more efficient.

PRIMARY SOURCE: SPEECH EXCERPT

❝ Based on a long and intensive study with the aid of the best advice obtainable, I have concluded that a sweeping reorganization of the executive branch is needed if the government is to keep up with the times and with the needs of the people.

I propose, therefore, that we reduce the present 12 Cabinet departments to eight.

I propose that the Departments of State, Treasury, Defense, and Justice remain, but that all the other departments be consolidated into four: Human Resources, Community Development, Natural Resources, and Economic Development.

Let us look at what these would be:

—First, a department dealing with the concerns of people—as individuals, as members of a family—a department focused on human needs.

—Second, a department concerned with the community—rural communities and urban communities—and with all that it takes to make a community function as a community.

—Third, a department concerned with our physical environment, with the preservation and balanced use of those great natural resources on which our nation depends.

—And fourth, a department concerned with our prosperity—with our jobs, our businesses, and those many activities that keep our economy running smoothly and well. ❞

—from the State of the Union address by President Richard Nixon, January 22, 1971

Nixon, Richard M. "Annual Message to the Congress on the State of the Union, January 22, 1971." In *Public Papers of the Presidents of the United States: Richard M. Nixon, 1971*. Washington, D. C.: Government Printing Office, 1971.

1 **ANALYZING INFORMATION** Which phrase describes what President Nixon proposes to do? Why is this important?

_____

_____

_____

2 CIVICS Based on the excerpt, what primary issue was Nixon addressing?

_____

_____

_____

3 **EVALUATING EVIDENCE** What is this document? Is this a primary or secondary source?

_____

_____

_____

4 **DETERMINING CENTRAL IDEAS** What is Nixon referring to when he states that "a sweeping reorganization of the executive branch is needed if the government is to keep up with the times and with the needs of the people"?

_____

_____

_____

5 **DRAWING CONCLUSIONS** According to Nixon, how would the proposed new departments enable government to work more efficiently?

_____

_____

_____

6 **DETERMINING CENTRAL IDEAS** What does the formation of the third department suggest?

_____

_____

The Watergate Scandal

DIRECTIONS: Search for evidence in Chapter 18, Lesson 2 to help you answer the following questions.

1A **DETERMINING CONTEXT** What led to the initial uncovering of the Watergate incident?

_____

_____

_____

1B **UNDERSTANDING CONTEXT** What caught reporter Bob Woodward's attention about the Watergate burglary?

_____

_____

_____

_____

2A **DRAWING CONCLUSIONS** What conclusion can you draw about Nixon and the election of 1972 that led to the Watergate break-in?

_____

_____

_____

_____

_____

2B **SUMMARIZING** By what means did Nixon's advisers try to ensure that Nixon would win the 1972 presidential election?

_____

_____

_____

_____

ESSENTIAL QUESTION

How does society change the shape of itself over time?

As you gather evidence to answer the Essential Question, think about:

- the events that led up to the Watergate scandal.
- the impact the Watergate scandal had on the office of the president.

My Notes

_____

_____

_____

_____

_____

_____

3 **RELATING EVENTS** Use the Cornell Notes organizer to describe the individuals associated with the Watergate scandal.

Main Idea	Notes
James McCord	
W. Mark Felt	
Sam J. Ervin	
John Dean	
Alexander Butterfield	

4 **SUMMARIZING** Complete the graphic organizer below to describe some of the key elements of the Watergate scandal.

	Why It's Important	Outcome
Secret CRP fund		
Senate Select Committee on Presidential Campaign Activities		
White House tapes		
Executive privilege		
June 23, 1972		

Feldbaum, Carl B. "Memorandum to the Special Prosecutor." Watergate Special Prosecution Force, Department of Justice, August 9, 1974. https://www.archives.gov/education/lessons/watergate-constitution/memo-transcript.html

ESSENTIAL QUESTION

How does society change the shape of itself over time?

The Presidency and Criminal Proceedings

DIRECTIONS: Read the following excerpt from a memorandum. Then answer the questions that follow.

EXPLORE THE CONTEXT: The Watergate scandal not only cast a pall on the Nixon presidency, it also raised a thornier question about the office of the president in relation to criminal legal proceedings and a president's rights under the Constitution. In this excerpt, the Justice Department outlines the issues at hand to the special prosecutor, Leon Jaworski.

PRIMARY SOURCE: MEMORANDUM

❝The factors which mandate in favor of indictment and prosecution are:

1. The principle of equal justice under law requires that every person, no matter what his past position or office, answer to the criminal justice system for his past offenses. This is a particularly weighty factor if Mr. Nixon's aides and associates, who acted upon his orders and what they conceived to be his interests, are to be prosecuted for the same offenses.

2. The country will be further divided by Mr. Nixon unless there is a final **disposition** of charges of criminality outstanding against him so as to **forestall** the belief that he was driven from his office by erosion of his political base. This final disposition may be necessary to preserve the integrity of the criminal justice system and the legislative process, which together **marshalled** the substantial evidence of Mr. Nixon's guilt.

3. Article I, Section 3, clause 7 of the Constitution provides that a person removed from office by impeachment and conviction 'shall nevertheless be liable and subject to Indictment, Trial, Judgment, and Punishment, according to Law.' The Framers contemplated that a person removed from office because of abuse of his public trust still would have to answer to the criminal justice system for criminal offenses.

4. It cannot be sufficient **retribution** for criminal offenses merely to surrender the public office and trust which has been demonstrably abused. A person should not be permitted to trade in the abused office in return for immunity.

5. The modern nature of the Presidency necessitates massive public exposure of the President's actions through the media. A bar to prosecution on the grounds of such publicity effectively would immunize all future Presidents for their actions, however criminal. Moreover, the courts may be the appropriate forum to resolve questions of pre-trial publicity in the context of an adversary proceeding. ❞

—from "Memorandum to the Special Prosecutor," August 9, 1974

VOCABULARY

disposition: arrangement

forestall: prevent

marshalled [marshaled]: assembled; collected

retribution: justice; reckoning

1 UNDERSTANDING CONTEXT Is this document a primary or secondary source? How does it help you understand the period in which it was written?

_____

_____

_____

2 DETERMINING CENTRAL IDEAS What does the statement "The principle of equal justice under law requires that every person, no matter what his past position or office, answer to the criminal justice system for his past offenses" suggest with regard to the office of the president? Why is this important?

_____

_____

_____

_____

3 INTERPRETING What is the third point stating? Why would that be important for the special prosecutor?

_____

_____

_____

_____

4 CIVICS How might this document have impacted the events of the Watergate scandal?

_____

_____

_____

5 SUMMARIZING What is the importance of the fifth point of the memorandum?

_____

_____

_____

_____

ESSENTIAL QUESTION

How does society change the shape of itself over time?

Pardoning Richard Nixon

DIRECTIONS: Read the following excerpt from a presidential statement. Then answer the questions that follow.

EXPLORE THE CONTENT: For over two years, the nation was gripped by the revelations of the Watergate scandal. The scandal toppled the Nixon administration and forced the president to resign. The scandal also affected many Americans' views of the Oval Office. Recognizing that the Watergate affair was a "national trauma," President Ford quickly sought a resolution that would allow the nation to move on.

PRIMARY SOURCE: SPEECH

66 There are no historic or legal **precedents** to which I can turn in this matter, none that precisely fit the circumstances of a private citizen who has resigned the Presidency of the United States. But it is common knowledge that serious allegations and accusations hang like a sword over our former President's head, threatening his health as he tries to reshape his life, a great part of which was spent in the service of this country and by the mandate of its people.

After years of bitter controversy and divisive national debate, I have been advised, and I am **compelled** to conclude that many months and perhaps more years will have to pass before Richard Nixon could obtain a fair trial by jury in any jurisdiction of the United States under governing decisions of the Supreme Court. . . .

The facts, as I see them, are that a former President of the United States, instead of enjoying equal treatment with any other citizen accused of violating the law, would be cruelly and excessively penalized either in preserving the **presumption** of his innocence or in obtaining a speedy determination of his guilt in order to repay a legal debt to society.

During this long period of delay and potential litigation, ugly passions would again be aroused. And our people would again be **polarized** in their opinions. And the credibility of our free institutions of government would again be challenged at home and abroad.

In the end, the courts might well hold that Richard Nixon had been denied due process, and the verdict of history would even more be inconclusive with respect to those charges arising out of the period of his Presidency . . . 99

—from "Remarks on Pardoning Richard Nixon," by President Gerald Ford, September 8, 1974

VOCABULARY

precedents: examples

compelled: obliged; forced

presumption: belief

polarized: divided

1 **EVALUATING EVIDENCE** What type of document is this?

_____

_____

2 **DETERMINING CONTEXT** How does this resource better help you understand the events surrounding the Watergate scandal?

_____

_____

_____

3 CIVICS What constitutional authority is the president drawing on in this excerpt?

_____

_____

4 **EVALUATING EVIDENCE** Which line(s) in the excerpt suggest that Ford faced a unique dilemma in handling the situation?

_____

_____

_____

5 **DETERMINING CENTRAL IDEAS** What did Ford mean by the following statement? "During this long period of delay and potential litigation, ugly passions would again be aroused. And our people would again be polarized in their opinions. And the credibility of our free institutions of government would again be challenged at home and abroad."

_____

_____

_____

6 **IDENTIFYING PERSPECTIVES** What underlying principle of the Constitution did the president fear Nixon would not receive if he were to be tried?

_____

_____

_____

ESSENTIAL QUESTION

How does society change the shape of itself over time?

As you gather evidence to answer the Essential Question, think about:

- what factors accounted for the economic crisis of the 1970s.

- the ways Presidents Ford and Carter tried to bolster the economy.

- Carter's foreign policy and how it impacted domestic policy.

My Notes

Ford and Carter

DIRECTIONS: Search for evidence in Chapter 18, Lesson 3 to help you answer the following questions.

1A DESCRIBING What was the biggest problem facing the country during the 1970s? Why?

1B ECONOMICS What was the oil embargo? How did this foreign policy translate into domestic policy for Americans?

2A DETERMINING CENTRAL IDEAS What is "stagflation"?

2B EXPLAINING EFFECTS What impact did the New Economic Policy have on American exchange rates?

3 ANALYZING INFORMATION Complete the chart below by aligning the economic policy to the president who supported its use. In some cases, both names may apply.

	Ford	Carter
WIN		
Lowering taxes		
Increasing government spending		
Reducing money supply		
Raising interest rates		
Deregulation		

4 RELATING EVENTS Use the Cornell Notes organizer to describe President Carter's foreign policy during his administration.

Main Idea	Notes
Panama	
Soviet Union	
Middle East	
Iran	

ESSENTIAL QUESTION

How does society change the shape of itself over time?

The Oil Embargo

DIRECTIONS: Study the following photograph. Then answer the questions that follow.

EXPLORE THE CONTEXT: The oil embargo of 1973 put an additional strain on an already struggling U.S. economy. Foreign policy now took into consideration a delicate balancing act comprised of American dependence on foreign oil from the Middle East while maintaining support for Israel. For Americans at the gas pumps, the embargo resulted in rising gas prices and shortages as well as a government plea for drivers to go slower.

PRIMARY SOURCE: PHOTOGRAPH

1 **DETERMINING CENTRAL IDEAS** What is shown in this photograph?

_____

_____

_____

_____

2 **ANALYZING SOURCES** Describe some of the details that you see in the photograph. What clues do they offer about the period in which the photograph was taken?

_____

_____

_____

_____

3 ECONOMICS How does the photograph illustrate the impact of the oil embargo?

_____

_____

_____

4 **IDENTIFYING EFFECTS** Why might the government have asked Americans to drive more slowly?

_____

_____

_____

5 **INFERRING** If this photograph were taken today, what about it might be different?

_____

_____

_____

Carter, Jimmy. "Statement on the Panama Canal Treaty Signing." Speech. September 7, 1977. https://www.jimmycarterlibrary.gov/digital_library/sso/148878/40/SSO_148878_040_01.pdf

ESSENTIAL QUESTION

How does society change the shape of itself over time?

The Panama Canal Treaty

DIRECTIONS: Read the following excerpt from a presidential statement. Then answer the questions that follow.

EXPLORE THE CONTEXT: One of President Carter's foreign policy successes came with the negotiation of the Panama Canal Treaty. For decades, the United States had brushed off claims of being an imperialist power when it came to Panama and the canal. For the United States to stumble in the negotiations meant international disgrace and the potential of violence throughout Latin America. Despite a tough battle in the Senate, however, the treaty was ratified in 1978.

PRIMARY SOURCE: TREATY

"If any agreement between two nations is to last, it must serve the best interests of both nations. The new treaties do that. And by guaranteeing the neutrality of the Panama Canal, the treaties also serve the best interests of every nation that uses the canal.

This agreement thus forms a new partnership to ensure that this vital waterway, so important to all of us, will continue to be well operated, safe, and open to shipping by all nations, now and in the future.

Under these **accords**, Panama will play an increasingly important role in the operation and defense of the canal during the next 23 years. And after that, the United States will still be able to counter any threat to the canal's neutrality and openness for use.

The members of the Organization of American States and all the members of the United Nations will have a chance to subscribe to the permanent neutrality of the canal.

The accords also give Panama an important economic stake in the continued, safe, and efficient operation of the canal and make Panama a strong and interested party in the future success of the waterway.

In the spirit of **reciprocity** suggested by the leaders at the Bogota summit, the United States and Panama have agreed that any future sea-level canal will be built in Panama and with the cooperation of the United States. In this manner, the best interests of both our nations are linked and preserved into the future. "

—from "Statement on the Panama Canal Treaty," by President Jimmy Carter, September 7, 1977

VOCABULARY

accords: agreements

reciprocity: exchange

1. **CITING TEXT EVIDENCE** According to the excerpt, what did President Carter believe to be the biggest obstacle in the treaty negotiations?

_____

_____

_____

2. **GEOGRAPHY** Why might members of the Senate be concerned about ratifying the Panama Canal Treaty?

_____

_____

_____

3. **EVALUATING** According to the excerpt, what will be the status of the canal when it reverts back to Panama? What does the treaty allow the United States to do if there is a problem?

_____

_____

_____

_____

4. **INFERRING** By turning the canal back to Panama, what message was Carter sending to other nations?

_____

_____

_____

5. **INFERRING** Based on this excerpt, why did Carter believe that the treaty would be satisfactory to Panama?

_____

_____

_____

ESSENTIAL QUESTION

How does society change the shape of itself over time?

As you gather evidence to answer the Essential Question, think about:

- how African American civil rights groups adjusted their message.
- the impact of affirmative action programs.
- how Native Americans and Asian Americans made their voices heard during the 1970s.
- what the disability rights movement achieved.

My Notes

_____

_____

_____

_____

_____

_____

_____

New Approaches to Civil Rights

DIRECTIONS: Search for evidence in Chapter 18, Lesson 4 to help you answer the following questions.

1A **DESCRIBING** How did African Americans view their status during the 1970s?

_____

_____

_____

_____

1B GEOGRAPHY In what ways did forced busing change the human landscape in cities?

_____

_____

_____

_____

2A **DETERMINING CENTRAL IDEAS** What is "affirmative action"?

_____

_____

_____

_____

2B **EXPLAINING EFFECTS** What was the *Bakke* case, and how did it address affirmative action?

_____

_____

_____

_____

_____

_____

3 **ANALYZING ISSUES** Complete the chart by describing the event concerning Native Americans that took place in each year.

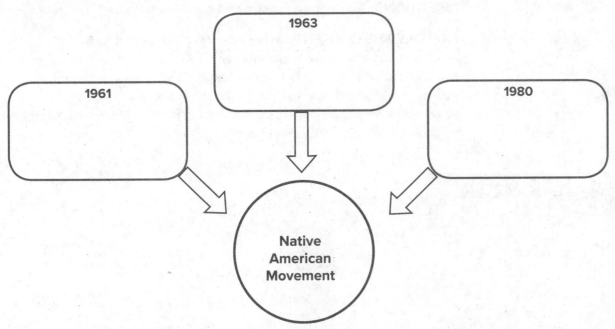

4 **EXPLAINING CAUSE AND EFFECT** What set Asian American groups apart from other groups seeking equal rights? How did this affect their struggle for equal rights?

_____

_____

_____

5 **RELATING EVENTS** Complete the Cornell Notes organizer to describe the results of the Disability Rights Movement.

Main Idea	Notes
Rehabilitation Act of 1973	
American Coalition of Citizens with Disabilities	
Bureau for the Education of the Handicapped	
Education for All Handicapped Children Act	
Americans with Disabilities Act	

ESSENTIAL QUESTION

How does society change the shape of itself over time?

The Alcatraz Occupation

DIRECTIONS: Study the photograph. Then answer the questions that follow.

EXPLORE THE CONTENT: On November 9, 1969, a group of Native Americans, led by a Mohawk member named Richard Oake, took a charter boat to Alcatraz Island. Their arrival marked the beginning of an almost two-year standoff between the group and the U.S. government. The group demanded that the government deed the island to them. The government refused and, in June 1971, removed the occupiers.

PRIMARY SOURCE: PHOTOGRAPH

1 **INFERRING** How might this photograph reflect what had happened to Native Americans over the years?

_____

_____

_____

_____

2 **ANALYZING SOURCES** What is meant by the phrase "United Indian Property"?

_____

_____

_____

_____

3 **CIVICS** What aspects of society are demonstrated in the photograph?

_____

_____

_____

4 **DETERMINING CENTRAL IDEAS** Why do you think this photograph was taken?

_____

_____

_____

6 **EXPLAINING ISSUES** What other clues in the photograph illustrate the conflict between Native Americans and the federal government?

_____

_____

_____

_____

_____

ESSENTIAL QUESTION

How does society change the shape of itself over time?

Ford on Busing

DIRECTIONS: Read the following excerpt from a presidential statement. Then answer the questions that follow.

EXPLORE THE CONTEXT: Although President Ford was a strong supporter of equal education opportunities, he remained a vocal opponent of forced busing. Heavily criticized for this stance, Ford decided to find a legal standing for his position. He continued to defend the right of parents to educate their children wherever they wanted. Finally, in June 1976, President Ford sent proposed legislation to Congress designed to limit forced busing.

PRIMARY SOURCE: STATEMENT EXCERPT

❝In recent years, we have seen many communities in the country lose control of their public schools to the Federal courts because they failed to voluntarily correct the effects of willful and official denial of the rights of some children in their schools.

It is my belief that in their earnest desire to carry out the decisions of the Supreme Court, some judges of lower Federal courts have gone too far. They have:

• resorted too quickly to the remedy of massive busing of public school children;

• extended busing too broadly; and

• maintained control of schools for too long.

It is this overextension of court control that has transformed a simple judicial tool, busing, into a cause of widespread controversy and slowed our progress toward the total elimination of segregation. . . .

I therefore ask the Congress, as the elected representatives of the American people, to join with me in establishing guidelines for the lower Federal Courts in the desegregation of public schools throughout the land—acting within the framework of the Constitution and particularly the Fourteenth Amendment to the Constitution. . . .

Both the advocates of more busing and the advocates of less busing feel they hold a strong moral position on this issue. . . .

Whether busing helps school children get a better education is not a settled question. The record is mixed. Certainly, busing has assisted in bringing about the desegregation of our schools. But it is a tragic reality that, in some areas, busing under court order has brought fear to both black students and white students—and to their parents.

No child can learn in an atmosphere of fear. Better remedies to right Constitutional wrongs must be found. ❞

—from a statement about busing by President Gerald Ford, June 24, 1976

Ford, Gerald R. "Presidential Statement: Ford on Busing." Speech, June 24, 1976.

1 **CITING TEXT EVIDENCE** According to Ford, why are cities and towns unable to regulate their schools?

_____

_____

_____

_____

2 CIVICS Why does Ford refer to the Fourteenth Amendment in his remarks?

_____

_____

_____

3 **EVALUATING** According to Ford, what mistake did the federal courts make in trying to remedy the problem?

_____

_____

_____

4 **IDENTIFYING CONNECTIONS** In his remarks, is Ford siding with the states or with the federal government?

_____

_____

_____

5 **SUMMARIZING** Based on this excerpt, how does Ford acknowledge that busing affects student morale?

_____

_____

_____

Environmentalism

DIRECTIONS: Search for evidence in Chapter 18, Lesson 5 to help you answer the following questions.

1A **DESCRIBING** What legal action marked the beginning of the environmental movement?

_____

_____

_____

1B **DRAWING CONCLUSIONS** How did the Yannacones' court battle help the environmental movement?

_____

_____

_____

_____

_____

2A **EXPLAINING** What was *Silent Spring*?

_____

_____

_____

_____

2B **GEOGRAPHY** According to Rachel Carson, what was the impact of human activity on the environment?

_____

_____

_____

_____

_____

ESSENTIAL QUESTION

How does society change the shape of itself over time?

As you gather evidence to answer the Essential Question, think about:

- what contributed to the growing awareness of the environment.
- the environmental movement and what it hoped to accomplish.
- the government's response to the environmental movement.

My Notes

_____

_____

_____

_____

_____

_____

_____

3 ANALYZING ISSUES Complete the chart below to show how the government responded to environment issues.

Action	What Did It Do?
National Environmental Policy Act	
Clean Air Act	
Clean Water Act of 1972	
Endangered Species Act	

4 RELATING EVENTS Complete the Cornell Notes organizer to explain the pros and cons of the nuclear energy debate.

Main Idea	Notes
Nuclear Energy: Pros	
Nuclear Energy: Cons	

5 INFERRING In what way did Three Mile Island intensify the debate over nuclear energy?

_____

_____

_____

ESSENTIAL QUESTION

How does society change the shape of itself over time?

Strip Mining

DIRECTIONS: Study the following photograph. Then answer the questions that follow.

EXPLORE THE CONTEXT: In 1975, despite overwhelming support, President Ford vetoed a proposed law that would impose stricter regulations on the coal mining industry, especially strip mining. Ford argued that passing the law would cause loss of jobs, increased utility bills, and an even larger dependence on foreign oil. The bill's failure to pass was a blow for environmental groups. However, in 1977, President Jimmy Carter passed a similar bill.

PRIMARY SOURCE: PHOTOGRAPH

Wally McNamee/Corbis Historical/Getty Images

1 **DETERMINING CENTRAL IDEAS** Who are the people in the photograph and what do they hope to accomplish?

_____

_____

_____

2 **EVALUATING EVIDENCE** Why do you think the people in the photograph are gathered at this point in time?

_____

_____

_____

3 **DETERMINING EFFECTS** What do the protestors say will result if stricter regulations are imposed on the industry?

_____

_____

_____

4 GEOGRAPHY What reasons might those who support stricter regulations of the strip mining industry give for their position?

_____

_____

_____

_____

5 **IDENTIFYING CONNECTIONS** How do you think the United States can strike a balance between our need for electricity and our concern for the environmental impact of producing it?

_____

_____

_____

_____

ESSENTIAL QUESTION

How does society change the shape of itself over time?

Valley of Drums Cleanup

DIRECTIONS: Study the following press release. Then answer the questions that follow.

EXPLORE THE CONTEXT: What started out as a business enterprise on a 17-acre field in Kentucky eventually became a symbol for environmental damage caused by the unrestricted dumping of hazardous materials. Known as "The Valley of the Drums," the site was used by environmental proponents to call attention to the haphazard disposal of toxic chemicals and their impact on people, drinking water, soil, and animal and plant life.

PRIMARY SOURCE: PRESS RELEASE

66 An expenditure of $400,000 will be made from the new Superfund for emergency cleanup work at Kentucky's top priority hazardous waste site—the Valley of the Drums, near Louisville.

Anne M. Gorsuch, Administrator of the U.S. Environmental Protection Agency, said today EPA will spend the money to pay for removal of about 1,500 drums containing chemical waste to reduce the possibility of fire.

The Valley of the Drums drew national attention in 1979 as one of the country's worst abandoned hazardous waste sites. Thousands of drums—accumulated over a 10-year period—were strewn in pits and trenches over a 23-acre site in Bullitt County.

The drums of the site scheduled for cleanup are deteriorating quickly. When it rains, they overflow and leak into Wilson Creek, a tributary of the Ohio River. They contain such chemicals as benzene, toluene and methylmethacrylate. 99

—from "EPA Schedules Emergency Cleanup at Valley of the Drums," a press release by the Environmental Protection Agency, September 18, 1981

1 **CITING TEXT EVIDENCE** Which sentence shows the importance of cleaning up "The Valley of the Drums"?

_____

_____

_____

_____

2 GEOGRAPHY In what ways might "The Valley of the Drums" impact the local environment? How might it affect a larger region?

_____

_____

_____

_____

_____

_____

3 **PREDICTNG** What other threat might be posed by the site?

_____

_____

_____

4 **INFERRING** What does this press release tell the reader about the state of environmental protection in 1979?

_____

_____

_____

_____

ESSENTIAL QUESTIONS

How does society change the shape of itself over time?

① Think About It

Review the supporting questions that you developed at the beginning of the chapter. Review the evidence that you gathered in Chapter 18. Were you able to answer each of your Supporting Questions?

If there was not enough evidence to answer your Supporting Questions, what additional evidence do you think you need to consider?

_____

_____

_____

_____

② Organize Your Evidence

Complete the chart to organize the evidence you will use to support your Position Statement. Pick an example of a program that is appropriate to that focus and which you are most interested in. Then fill in the chart.

Focus	Challenging Issue	Outcome
Watergate crisis		
Human rights		
Affirmative action		

Minority protests		
Environment		

❸ Write About It

Choose one of the topics from the chart you completed. Write two paragraphs about that topic. In the first paragraph, briefly describe what the issue is and the government's response to that issue. In the second paragraph, consider what steps would have to occur to lead to a different result, and explain why.

_____

_____

_____

_____

_____

❹ Connect to the Essential Question

Work in small groups. Create a compare and contrast poster on a topic studied in the chapter. Your poster should illustrate the issue at hand and how change can be effective (or not) with regard to that issue. Your compare and contrast poster should focus on the Essential Question: _How does society change the shape of itself over time?_ As a group, share the poster with your class, and be prepared to answer questions about it.

_____

_____

_____

_____

_____

TAKE ACTION

MAKE CONNECTIONS   One of the rights American citizens are guaranteed is freedom of speech. Protest movements, attending town hall meetings, writing to government representatives—these are all different ways that citizens draw the government's attention to needed change. Can you think of groups calling for change today? Who are they, and why do they want change to happen? Are their demands new, older, or a mixture of both?

DIRECTIONS: Work in a small group. Discuss one current issue that demonstrates the following idea: as society changes, so do attitudes. Together, write a statement paper describing the issue and how society reflects changing attitudes in regard to it. Does a majority or a minority in society support the issue? Why might people feel the way they do? How might their feelings change over time? Explain both sides. After you have finished, share your statement paper with the class.

The Resurgence of Conservatism

ESSENTIAL QUESTION

How do you think the resurgence of conservative ideas has changed society?

Think about the liberal nature of the 1960s and 1970s. Why would the 1980s see a resurgence of conservatism? How do political and social ideas impact the everyday lives of average citizens?

TALK ABOUT IT

With a partner, discuss the sort of information you would need in order to discover what conservative ideas looked like in the 1980s as well as the impact conservative ideas had on society. For example, you might ask, "How did conservative ideas differ from the leading ideas of previous decades?"

DIRECTIONS: Now write three additional questions that will help you to explain the resurgence of conservatism.

MY RESEARCH QUESTIONS

Supporting Question 1:

_____

_____

Supporting Question 2:

_____

_____

Supporting Question 3:

_____

_____

The New Conservatism

DIRECTIONS: Search for evidence in Chapter 19, Lesson 1 to help you answer the following questions.

1A **SUMMARIZING** Use the chart to list the major differences between conservatism and liberalism.

Conservatism	Liberalism

1B **IDENTIFYING CONNECTIONS** What effect did the Cold War have on Americans' values and priorities?

_____

_____

_____

_____

2A **INTERPRETING** What ideals or principles were the foundation of the conservatism of the 1980s?

_____

_____

_____

_____

ESSENTIAL QUESTION

How do you think the resurgence of conservative ideas has changed society?

As you gather evidence to answer the Essential Question, think about:

- the differences between liberalism and conservatism.
- how the Cold War impacted citizens' priorities and values.
- the role of religion in the rise of conservatism.

My Notes

_____

_____

_____

_____

_____

_____

2B **UNDERSTANDING CHANGE** What was happening in American society that led to the rise in conservatism?

_____

_____

_____

3 **EXPLAINING CAUSES** Complete the graphic organizer with the causes that drew many religious Americans to embrace conservatism.

Causes

→

Conservatism

4 ECONOMICS How did the economic impact of World War II contribute to the shift in American values and priorities in the Sunbelt?

_____

_____

_____

_____

5 **SUMMARIZING** What was the importance of think tanks?

_____

_____

_____

_____

International Treaty: SALT II

ESSENTIAL QUESTION

How do you think the resurgence of conservative ideas has changed society?

DIRECTIONS: Read the excerpt of this treaty between the United States and the Soviet Union, also known as the Union of Soviet Socialist Republics (the USSR). Then respond to the questions that follow.

EXPLORE THE CONTEXT: The Cold War between the United States and the Soviet Union began just after World War II. Both sides were deeply suspicious of the intentions of the other. The threat of nuclear war hung over both countries.

VOCABULARY

parties: countries

anti-ballistic missile systems: systems that use missiles to destroy incoming nuclear missiles before they reach their destination

strategic offensive arms: nuclear weapons

non-proliferation: slowing down of the production of weapons

disarmament: reducing stores of weapons

PRIMARY SOURCE: INTERNATIONAL TREATY

❝ The United States of America and the Union of Soviet Socialist Republics, hereinafter referred to as the **Parties**,

Conscious that nuclear war would have devastating consequences for all mankind,

Proceeding from the Basic Principles of Relations Between the United States of America and the Union of Soviet Socialist Republics of May 29, 1972,

Attaching particular significance to the limitation of strategic arms and determined to continue their efforts begun with the Treaty on the Limitation of **Anti-Ballistic Missile Systems** and the Interim Agreement on Certain Measures with Respect to the Limitation of **Strategic Offensive Arms**, of May 26, 1972,

Convinced that the additional measures limiting strategic offensive arms provided for in this Treaty will contribute to the improvement of relations between the Parties, help to reduce the risk of outbreak of nuclear war and strengthen international peace and security,

Mindful of their obligations under Article VI of the Treaty on the Non-Proliferation of Nuclear Weapons,

Guided by the principle of equality and equal security,

Recognizing that the strengthening of strategic stability meets the interests of the Parties and the interests of international security,

Reaffirming their desire to take measures for the further limitation and for the further reduction of strategic arms, having in mind the goal of achieving general and complete **disarmament**,

Declaring their intention to undertake in the near future negotiations further to limit and further to reduce strategic offensive arms,

Have agreed as follows:

Article I

Each Party undertakes, in accordance with the provisions of this Treaty, to limit strategic offensive arms quantitatively and qualitatively, to exercise restraint in the development of new types of strategic offensive arms, and to adopt other measures provided for in this Treaty. ❞

—from a treaty between the United States and the Union of Soviet Socialist Republics, signed in Vienna in 1979

Carter, Jimmy, and L. Brezhnev. 1979. "Treaty Between the United States of America and the Union of Soviet Socialist Republics on the Limitation of Strategic Offensive Arms, Together with Agreed Statements and Common Understandings Regarding the Treaty," U.S. Department of State.

1 **ANALYZING TEXT STRUCTURE** What is the purpose of the introductory text?

_____

_____

2 **SUMMARIZING** What do both sides agree to do in Article I?

_____

_____

_____

3 **IDENTIFYING CAUSES** Given what you about this time period, why was this treaty created?

_____

_____

_____

4 **CONSTRUCTING HYPOTHESES** How do you think conservatives may have felt about this treaty?

_____

_____

_____

_____

5 CIVICS What are some of the ways in which conservative citizens could have responded to this treaty if they disagreed with its contents?

_____

_____

_____

_____

6 ECONOMICS How might this treaty affect the economy of the United States?

_____

_____

_____

_____

ESSENTIAL QUESTION

How do you think the resurgence of conservative ideas has changed society?

Presidential Speech on Gun Control

DIRECTIONS: Read the excerpt from President Johnson's remarks about the Gun Control Act of 1968. Then respond to the questions that follow.

EXPLORE THE CONTEXT: President Johnson pressed Congress in the late 1960s to pass a comprehensive gun control law. He was the last president before President Obama to take on the issue of gun control. Johnson was motivated by many high-profile shootings during his lifetime, including the assassinations of President John F. Kennedy, Dr. Martin Luther King, Jr., and Robert Kennedy. Johnson had urged his staff and Congress to act quickly, before the gun lobby had time to organize, but the gun lobby still managed to influence the bill.

PRIMARY SOURCE: PRESIDENTIAL SPEECH

66 Some of you may be interested in knowing-really-what this bill does:

—It stops murder by mail order. It bars the **interstate** sale of all guns and the bullets that load them.

—It stops the sale of lethal weapons to those too young to bear their terrible responsibility.

—It puts up a big 'off-limits' sign, to stop **gunrunners** from dumping cheap foreign '**$10 specials**' on the shores of our country.

Congress adopted most of our recommendations. But this bill—as big as this bill is—still falls short, because we just could not get the Congress to carry out the requests we made of them. I asked for the national registration of all guns and the licensing of those who carry those guns. For the fact of life is that there are over 160 million guns in this country—more firearms than families. If guns are to be kept out of the hands of the criminal, out of the hands of the insane, and out of the hands of the irresponsible, then we just must have licensing. If the criminal with a gun is to be tracked down quickly, then we must have registration in this country.

The voices that blocked these **safeguards** were not the voices of an aroused nation. They were the voices of a powerful lobby, a gun lobby, that has **prevailed** for the moment in an election year. 99

—from "Remarks Upon Signing the Gun Control Act of 1968," by President Lyndon B. Johnson

VOCABULARY

interstate: passing between two or more states

gunrunners: people who transport and sell illegal guns and ammunition

$10 specials: inexpensive weapons, usually sold illegally

safeguards: protections

prevailed: was victorious

Johnson, Lyndon Baines. 1968. "Remarks Upon Signing the Gun Control Act of 1968, October 22, 1968," in *Public Papers of the Presidents of the United States: Lyndon B. Johnson, 1968-1969*. Washington: U.S. Government Printing Office.

1 DETERMINING CENTRAL IDEAS What is President Johnson's view on gun control?

_____

_____

_____

_____

2 ANALYZING TEXT STRUCTURE What evidence and persuasive techniques does Johnson use to express his view?

_____

_____

_____

3 CITING TEXT EVIDENCE Does President Johnson's speech show liberalism or conservatism? Cite evidence from the text to support your response.

_____

_____

_____

_____

4 INTERPRETING What would be the opinion of a leader who holds the opposite viewpoint from Johnson's?

_____

_____

_____

5 CIVICS Today, conservatism is often associated with Second Amendment rights. Why do you think that is so?

_____

_____

_____

_____

_____

The Reagan Years

DIRECTIONS: Search for evidence in Chapter 19, Lesson 2 to help you answer the following questions.

1 **IDENTIFYING CAUSES** Complete the graphic organizer to show the various factors that caused Reagan to become a conservative president.

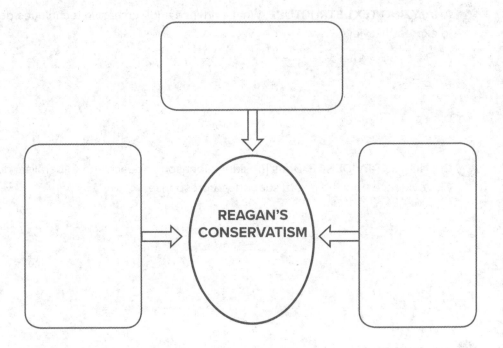

REAGAN'S CONSERVATISM

2A **ECONOMICS** What is the economic theory behind Reaganomics?

_____

_____

_____

_____

ESSENTIAL QUESTION

How do you think the resurgence of conservative ideas has changed society?

As you gather evidence to answer the Essential Question, think about:

- the impact of conservatism on the economy.

- how conservatism influenced military policy.

- how the government changed under President Reagan.

My Notes

_____

_____

_____

_____

_____

_____

2B RELATING EVENTS Use the graphic organizer to show the connection between Reaganomics and conservative ideas.

```
┌─────────────────────┐
│  Conservative Idea  │
│                     │                    ┌───────────────┐
│                     │         ──────▶    │               │
│                     │                    │  Reaganomics  │
│                     │                    │               │
└─────────────────────┘                    └───────────────┘
```

3A INTERPRETING How did Reagan's attitude toward the Soviet Union align with conservatism?

_____

_____

_____

3B IDENTIFYING CONNECTIONS How did Reagan's attitude toward the Soviet Union impact his policies?

_____

_____

_____

4 EXPLAINING EFFECTS How might Reagan's military policy have influenced conservatism?

_____

_____

_____

_____

5 CIVICS What options were available to liberals who disagreed with how the government was run?

_____

_____

_____

Economic Recovery Tax Act of 1981

Reagan, Ronald. 1981. "Remarks on Signing the Economic Recovery Tax Act of 1981," in Public Papers of the President of the United States: Ronald Reagan, 1981. Washington: U.S. Government Printing Office.

ESSENTIAL QUESTION

How do you think the resurgence of conservative ideas has changed society?

DIRECTIONS: Read the excerpt from President Reagan's remarks on the Economic Recovery Tax Act. Then respond to the questions that follow.

EXPLORE THE CONTEXT: During his campaign, Reagan promised the American people that he would improve the economy. Reagan did not make much progress on that promise for the first year and a half of his term, but in August 1981, Congress passed the Economic Recovery Tax Act. The law was a departure from both the liberal economic policies of the previous decade and previous Republican policies. Statistics show Reagan's popularity decreased just after he signed the bill, possibly because many people were not entirely reassured by Reaganomics.

PRIMARY SOURCE: PRESIDENTIAL REMARKS

❝ These bills that I'm about to sign—not every page—this is the budget bill, and this is the tax program—but I think they represent a turnaround of almost a half a century of a course this country's been on and mark an end to the excessive growth in government bureaucracy, government spending, government taxing.

And we're **indebted** for all of this—I can't speak too highly of the leadership, Republican leadership in the Congress and of those Democrats who so courageously joined in and made both of these truly **bipartisan** programs. But I think in reality, the real credit goes to the people of the United States who finally made it plain that they wanted a change and made it clear in Congress and spoke with a more authoritative voice than some of the **special interest groups** that they wanted these changes in government.

This represents $130 billion in savings over the next 3 years. This represents $750 billion in tax cuts over the next 5 years. And this is only the beginning, because from here on now we are going to have to implement all of these, and it's going to be a job to make this whole turnaround work. It's going to be the number one priority—or continue to be the number one priority—of our administration.

And again, I express my gratitude to the Congress, the 97th Congress, and to the administration, the people who worked so hard to make these come about. ❞

—from "Remarks on Signing the Economic Recovery Tax Act of 1981," by President Ronald Reagan, August 1981

VOCABULARY

indebted: owed gratitude

bipartisan: involving both political parties

special interest group: people who share the same concerns and work together to affect public policy

1 **ECONOMICS** According to Reagan's speech, how is the Economic Recovery Tax Act of 1981 a departure from earlier policy?

_____

_____

_____

2 **SUMMARIZING** To whom does Reagan give credit for the success in passing the bill?

_____

_____

3 **ANALYZING TEXT** What can you tell about Reagan's attitude toward Congress?

_____

_____

_____

_____

4 **DETERMINING MEANING** Why do you think Reagan and Congress chose to call the law the Economic Recovery Tax Act? What are the connotations of the use of the word "recovery"?

_____

_____

_____

_____

5 **IDENTIFYING CONNECTIONS** What evidence of conservative values can you glean from this excerpt?

_____

_____

_____

_____

_____

ESSENTIAL QUESTION

How do you think the resurgence of conservative ideas has changed society?

Soviet Invasion of Afghanistan

DIRECTIONS: Read the transcript of the radio address given by President Reagan. Then respond to the questions that follow.

EXPLORE THE CONTEXT: The Soviet Union invaded Afghanistan in 1979 in an attempt to end the ongoing civil war there. The Soviets hoped to have another Communist government near their border. The United States was committed to containing communism, so the Soviet Union's invasion of Afghanistan was perceived as a threat to U.S. foreign policy. President Reagan gave a radio address on the subject.

PRIMARY SOURCE: RADIO ADDRESS

❝Today Soviet troops inside Afghanistan number nearly 120,000. And in the face of this brutal **onslaught**, the Afghan people still refuse to surrender—is surely a miracle. And in this holiday season of renewed faith in miracles, it is surely fitting for us to honor and pray for those brave men and women. These courageous people have shown the world that the Soviets can never achieve the outright **subjugation** of the Afghan mind and spirit that they seek. The Afghan people are too proud, too fiercely determined to fight on. The Soviets understand this. They know that, in a sense, the battle for Afghanistan has shifted from the mountains of Afghanistan itself to the wider field of world opinion. So it is that the Soviets are prolonging the war and **blacking out** news about the daily **atrocities** which they're committing. They're waiting for world attention to slip, for our outrage to **wane**. Then, they believe the support which the free world has been providing to the freedom fighters will dwindle. The Soviets at that point will have effectively cut off the freedom fighters' lifelines, and although the **mujahidin** may never surrender, the Soviets will have achieved indisputable control of the country. An entire nation will have been strangled.

My friends, in the name of human freedom, we cannot, we must not, allow that to happen. From the first, the United States has insisted on a settlement of the Afghan conflict that ensures the complete withdrawal of all Soviet troops. We're doing all that we can to see that a settlement comes about. Indeed, in my discussions with Mr. Gorbachev in Geneva, I made it clear that the presence of Soviet forces in Afghanistan represent an obstacle to the improvement of American-Soviet relations. As long as the Soviets insist upon a policy of aggression, they must face the fact that free men will oppose them. The Soviet Union has always presented itself as a champion of anticolonialism and national liberation; history presents a different picture. ❞

—from radio address made by President Ronald Reagan, 1985

VOCABULARY

onslaught: strong, intense attack

subjugation: the act of gaining control of through force

blacking out: censoring; preventing

atrocities: horrible acts

wane: fade away

mujahidin: Middle Eastern guerrilla fighters

Reagan, Ronald. "Radio Address to the Nation on the Soviet Occupation of Afghanistan, December 28, 1985," in *Public Papers of the Presidents of the United States: Ronald Reagan, 1985.* Washington: U.S. Government Printing Office.

1 **DETERMINING CENTRAL IDEAS** What can you determine from the text about the conflict between Afghanistan and the Soviet Union?

_____

_____

_____

_____

_____

2 **IDENTIFYING BIAS** What is Reagan's opinion about the role of the United States in the conflict?

_____

_____

_____

_____

_____

3 **DESCRIBING** Who is the intended audience of this address, and how can you tell? Be as specific as possible, and use examples from the text to support your answer.

_____

_____

_____

_____

4 **IDENTIFYING CONNECTIONS** How does this radio address connect to Reagan's "peace through strength" foreign policy?

_____

_____

_____

_____

5 CIVICS What role did radio addresses play in politics on the national stage?

_____

_____

_____

_____

Life in the 1980s

DIRECTIONS: Search for evidence in Chapter 19, Lesson 3 to help you answer the following questions.

1A **SUMMARIZING** What changes in media occurred in the 1980s?

_____

_____

_____

_____

_____

_____

1B **UNDERSTANDING CONTEXT** What changes in retail businesses and the economy happened in the 1980s?

_____

_____

_____

_____

_____

2 **DRAWING CONCLUSIONS** What conclusions might conservatives have drawn based on the changes in the economy, media, and retail in the United States? Use the graphic organizer below to show the connections.

Based on the Changes in . . .	The Conclusion Conservatives Drew
Economy:	
Retail:	
Media:	

ESSENTIAL QUESTION

How do you think the resurgence of conservative ideas has changed society?

As you gather evidence to answer the Essential Question, think about:

- how the baby boomers influenced the U.S. economy and media.
- why new activist groups formed.
- the role of conservatism in changes with technology and the media.

My Notes

_____

_____

_____

_____

_____

_____

3A CIVICS What new groups of people became activists in the 1980s?

_____

_____

3B RELATING EVENTS What factors contributed to those groups of people becoming activists?

Activist Group	Factors That Contributed to Their Activism

4 INTERPRETING How did the government's response to activism reflect the conservatism of the time?

_____

_____

_____

_____

ESSENTIAL QUESTION

How do you think the resurgence of conservative ideas has changed society?

VOCABULARY

telecommunications: communication of words, images, and/or sounds across a distance

liberalization: state of becoming more liberal or relaxing the rules

affiliates: members

entrepreneurs: people who start a business or take on the risks of owning a business

virtual: in effect

Testimony Before Subcommittee on Telecommunications

DIRECTIONS: Read the excerpts from Pluria Marshall's testimony. Then respond to the questions that follow.

EXPLORE THE CONTEXT: Pluria W. Marshall, Sr., is a civil rights activist and media professional who created the National Black Media Coalition to increase the reach of African American media professionals. In the testimony below before the subcommittee on **telecommunications**, Marshall speaks in favor of the "7-station rule." This rule, established in the 1950s, prohibited any one person or company from owning more than seven television stations, seven A.M. radio stations, or seven F.M. radio stations. This rule prevented groups from joining together to create regional station coalitions.

PRIMARY SOURCE: CONGRESSIONAL TESTIMONY

66 STATEMENT OF PLURIA W. MARSHALL Before the Subcommittee on Telecommunications:

As Chairman of the National Black Media Coalition, I am honored to have this opportunity to place our views on television station ownership before the Subcommittee on Telecommunications, Consumer Protection and Finance. Of the nation's approximately 1,100 television stations, only ten are currently owned by Black Americans. This is a national tragedy. In television, ownership determines the diversity of content, and Black America has much to say which has remained unstated to the general audience reachable by television.

Because Blacks are unlikely to own or control access to the various new technologies such as . . . cable television (in all but a few markets), we must depend on commercial television for whatever opportunity we will have to reach our own people, and the general audience, with our message.

It is for this reason that the National Black Media Coalition, on behalf of its 87 **affiliates** and thousands of members across the country, urged the Federal Communications Commission to proceed with an abundance of caution in implementing any **liberalization** of the so-called '7 station' rule. It appeared self-evident to everyone but this Commission that a change in the rule would have the effect of allowing the many large companies currently at or near their ownership limits to bid for medium and small market stations—the very stations which are within the grasp of Black **entrepreneurs**. The few Blacks prepared to bid for these stations now find themselves competing only against other small broadcasters for these opportunities. If the '7' rule is lifted, Blacks and small broadcasters will compete with big broadcasters—with their more favorable banking relationships and financing terms—for the few stations being sold at prices Blacks can afford. The result: a **virtual** halt to new TV station ownership by Blacks and other minorities. 99

—from testimony of Pluria W. Marshall, Sr., before the Subcommittee on Telecommunications, Consumer Protection, and Finance of the Committee on Energy and Commerce, September 1984

Marshall, Pluria W. 1984. Statement of Pluria W. Marshall Before the Subcommittee on Telecommunications, Consumer Protection, and Finance of the Committee on Energy and Commerce, House of Representatives, September 19, 1984. Ninety-eighth Congress, second session, on H.R. 6122 ... H.R. 6134. Washington: U.S. Government Printing Office.   Copyright © McGraw-Hill Education

1 **DETERMINING MEANING** What does Marshall mean when he refers to the lack of diversity in television as a "national tragedy"?

_____

_____

_____

2 **IDENTIFYING EFFECTS** Why was Marshall pleading on behalf of African American broadcasters for the committee to retain the 7-station rule?

_____

_____

_____

3 **CITING TEXT EVIDENCE** What does Marshall fear will happen if the committee revokes the 7-station rule? Cite text evidence in your response.

_____

_____

_____

_____

4 **INTERPRETING** What implications does Marshall's testimony suggest for the African American community in the 1980s?

_____

_____

_____

_____

5 CIVICS How might television and other entertainment mediums encourage people to join a cause?

_____

_____

_____

_____

ESSENTIAL QUESTION

How do you think the resurgence of conservative ideas has changed society?

Congressional Hearing on Antigay Violence

DIRECTIONS: Read the excerpts from the letter that was included in the Congressional hearing. Then respond to the questions that follow.

EXPLORE THE CONTEXT: The LGBTQ (lesbian, gay, bisexual, transgender, queer) community had been defending their civil rights since the 1960s. The Stonewall Riot sparked an activist movement to increase acceptance of the LGBTQ community. Many gay rights groups sprouted up around the country. However, the rise of conservatism in the 1980s brought with it an increase in violent acts and discrimination against the LGBTQ community.

PRIMARY SOURCE: LETTER INCLUDED IN CONGRESSIONAL HEARING

❝As the statewide Gay rights group in Michigan, we hear of many stories of anti-Gay violence, ranging from phone harassment to robberies to murder. In addition we believe that the total number of incidents is on the increase as a result of some amount of hysteria over the AIDS **epidemic**.

If we had known about your hearings earlier, we would have liked to send one of our people to the hearing in D.C. We have files with newspaper clippings of anti-Gay violence, and we have people who have personally had to deal with violence against them.

In my own case, my partner and I suffered through a month of harassment during the summer of 1981 in a working class neighborhood of Columbus, Ohio. Several teenage youths made crank calls, made verbal threats, burglarized our home twice, and finally set our trash cans on fire. Repeated calls to the police resulted only in a week long **incarceration** for one of the youths and advice to us that we move, which we did.

Enclosed are a half dozen clippings from the Kalamazoo area dealing with the murder trial of three young men who brutally murdered an area Gay man last year. Despite the brutality of the crime and much evidence, the resulting **acquittal** of one man and hand-slapping of the other two proved that justice for Gay people is **tenuous** at best.

We would like to receive a copy of the proceedings and we hope that the hearings will bring about not only understanding of the enormous problem of anti-Gay violence but action to improve the situation. ❞

—from a 1986 letter included in the transcript of a Congressional hearing before the Subcommittee on Criminal Justice

VOCABULARY

epidemic: wide spread of an infectious disease

incarceration: state of being held in prison

acquittal: freedom from legal charges

tenuous: weak; insubstantial

U.S. House. Committee on the Judiciary. Subcommittee on Criminal Justice. 1987. Anti-Gay Violence: Hearing. 99th Cong., 2nd sess., October 9, 1986. Washington: U.S. G.P.O.

1 DETERMINING CENTRAL IDEAS What can you infer about the speaker of the testimony?

_____

_____

2 INTERPRETING What was the environment like for the LGBTQ community in the 1980s?

_____

_____

3 DETERMINING POINT OF VIEW What were the speaker's hopes for the hearing?

_____

_____

_____

4 IDENTIFYING CONNECTIONS How does the speaker's hope align with the resurgence of conservatism in the 1980s?

_____

_____

_____

_____

5 RELATING EVENTS What about conservative ideas posed a challenge to the LGBTQ community?

_____

_____

_____

_____

6 CIVICS What do you think could be done today to combat antigay violence?

_____

_____

_____

The End of the Cold War

DIRECTIONS: Search for evidence in Chapter 19, Lesson 4 to help you answer the following questions.

1A SUMMARIZING What promises did President George H. W. Bush make to the American people?

_____

_____

_____

_____

1B IDENTIFYING CONNECTIONS What was the impact of those promises?

_____

_____

_____

_____

_____

_____

2 COMPARING AND CONTRASTING How were President Bush's actions in the Persian Gulf War similar to and different from Reagan's military philosophy?

_____

_____

_____

_____

_____

_____

ESSENTIAL QUESTION

How do you think the resurgence of conservative ideas has changed society?

As you gather evidence to answer the Essential Question, think about:

- the effect the Soviet Union's collapse had on conservatism.
- the changes that the end of the Cold War brought to the world.
- the challenges President George H. W. Bush faced.

My Notes

_____

_____

_____

_____

_____

_____

3A `ECONOMICS` Use the graphic organizer to explain how the end of the Cold War impacted the U.S. economy.

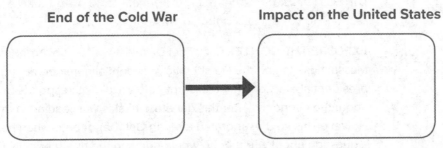

End of the Cold War   **Impact on the United States**

3B **EXPLAINING CAUSES** How did Bush's plan for the capital gains tax connect to conservatism?

_____

_____

_____

_____

_____

4 **INTERPRETING** What did President Clinton's victory in the 1992 election suggest about the country's view of conservatism?

_____

_____

_____

_____

Presidential Candidates Debates: "Presidential Debate in Winston-Salem, North Carolina," September 25, 1988. Online by Gerhard Peters and John T. Woolley, The American Presidency Project. http://www.presidency.ucsb.edu/ws/?pid=29411.

ESSENTIAL QUESTION

How do you think the resurgence of conservative ideas has changed society?

VOCABULARY

moderator: person who presides over a meeting, discussion, or debate

deficit: lack of money coming in to cover expenses

revenue: the government's income from taxes and other sources

monies: plural of money

Transcript of Presidential Debate

DIRECTIONS: Read the excerpts from this 1988 presidential debate. Then respond to the questions that follow.

EXPLORE THE CONTEXT: Michael Dukakis was the governor of Massachusetts and the Democratic presidential nominee during the 1988 presidential election. In the excerpt below, Dukakis responds to a question about the economy. After this debate, Dukakis was leading in the polls. However, his lead evaporated after an October debate when he responded to a question about whether he would demand the death penalty if his wife was murdered. President George H. W. Bush won the election.

PRIMARY SOURCE: PRESIDENTIAL DEBATE

❝ JOHN MASHEK [**moderator**]: 'Governor Dukakis, another troublesome issue for voters this year is the bulging federal **deficit**. In a Dukakis administration, you say taxes will be raised only as a last resort. Would you identify for us then please three specific programs that you are willing to cut to bring that deficit down?'

DUKAKIS: 'Yes, I've been very specific about those, John. And let me lay out for you my own strategy for bringing that deficit down, because as a chief executive that's balanced ten budgets in a row, I've had to make those tough decisions and those tough choices.

First, I've suggested that there are certain weapons systems which we don't need and we can't afford. Mr. Bush has been critical of me for that, but I think those are the kinds of tough choices you have to make. I've also suggested that there are weapons systems that we should proceed on, and I've outlined those in detail.

Secondly, we've got to invest in economic growth in this country, in every part of this country. Building that kind of growth expands **revenues** and helps to bring down that deficit.

Thirdly, we have to bring interest rates down, and we will as we come up with a good, solid plan with the Congress for bringing that deficit down.

And, finally, we've got to go out there and collect billions and billions of dollars in taxes owed that aren't being paid to this country. It's very unfair to the average taxpayer who pays his taxes and pays them on time to permit these **monies** to go uncollected. I've also suggested that on the domestic side there are areas where we can make some cuts. We ought to be able to come up with an agricultural policy in this country that gives our farm families a fair price and a decent future without spending $20 to $25 billion a year, which is what we've been doing under this administration. We can help people to live better lives, and at the same time save money by helping hundreds of thousands of families on welfare to get off of welfare, and to become productive citizens again. ❞

—from the presidential debate of September 25, 1988

1 **SUMMARIZING** What is Dukakis's economic plan?

_____

_____

_____

_____

_____

2 ECONOMICS How does Dukakis's economic plan compare with Reaganomics?

_____

_____

_____

_____

_____

_____

3 **EVALUATING EVIDENCE** How well does Dukakis answer Mashek's question?

_____

_____

_____

4 **IDENTIFYING CONNECTIONS** What conservative value does Dukakis mention in his speech?

_____

_____

_____

5 **EXPLAINING CAUSE AND EFFECT** How did conservative values impact the 1988 presidential debate?

_____

_____

_____

Bush, George H.W. 1989. "Inaugural Address," January 20. Public Papers of the Presidents: George H.W. Bush. George Bush Presidential Library and Museum. https://bush41library.tamu.edu/archives/public-papers/1

ESSENTIAL QUESTION

How do you think the resurgence of conservative ideas has changed society?

Bush's Inaugural Address

DIRECTIONS: Read the excerpt from President George H. W. Bush's Inaugural Address. Then respond to the questions that follow.

EXPLORE THE CONTEXT: George H. W. Bush had served as President Reagan's vice president. He won the 1988 presidential election by a landslide. A solid economy and President Reagan's endorsement helped him to win. Bush promised to continue the legacy of President Reagan. One of the ways he promised to do this was by refusing to raise taxes. The excerpt below is from his Inaugural Address.

PRIMARY SOURCE: INAUGURAL ADDRESS

66 No President, no government can teach us to remember what is best in what we are. But if the man you have chosen to lead this government can help make a difference; if he can celebrate the quieter, deeper successes that are made not of gold and silk but of better hearts and finer souls; if he can do these things, then he must.

America is never wholly herself unless she is engaged in high moral principle. We as a people have such a purpose today. It is to make kinder the face of the Nation and gentler the face of the world. My friends, we have work to do. There are the homeless, lost and roaming. There are the children who have nothing, no love and no normalcy. There are those who cannot free themselves of enslavement to whatever addiction—drugs, welfare, the **demoralization** that rules the slums. There is crime to be conquered, the rough crime of the streets. There are young women to be helped who are about to become mothers of children they can't care for and might not love. They need our care, our guidance, and our education, though we bless them for choosing life.

The old solution, the old way, was to think that public money alone could end these problems. But we have learned that that is not so. And in any case, our funds are low. We have a deficit to bring down. We have more **will** than wallet, but will is what we need. We will make the hard choices, looking at what we have and perhaps allocating it differently, making our decisions based on honest need and **prudent** safety. And then we will do the wisest thing of all. We will turn to the only resource we have that in times of need always grows: the goodness and the courage of the American people. 99

—from President George H. W. Bush's 1989 Inaugural Address

VOCABULARY

demoralization: state of feeling discouraged

will: desire

prudent: wise

1 **DETERMINING CENTRAL IDEAS** What is the main idea of this section of Bush's inaugural address?

_____

_____

2 **SUMMARIZING** What point does Bush make about the social problems of the 1980s?

_____

_____

_____

_____

3 **IDENTIFYING CONNECTIONS** What conservative ideas appear in the inauguration speech?

_____

_____

_____

_____

4 **ECONOMICS** How do the conservative ideas in Bush's speech compare to Dukakis's statements in the presidential debate?

_____

_____

_____

_____

_____

_____

5 **DETERMINING MEANING** What does Bush mean when he says, "America is never wholly herself unless she is engaged in high moral principle"?

_____

_____

_____

6 **INTERPRETING** What aspects of the speech might a liberal disagree with, and why?

_____

_____

_____

ESSENTIAL QUESTIONS

How do you think the resurgence of conservative ideas has changed society?

❶ Think About It

Review the supporting questions you developed at the beginning of the chapter. Review the evidence you gathered in Chapter 19. Were you able to answer each Supporting Question? If there was not enough evidence to answer your Supporting Questions, what additional evidence do you think you need to consider?

_____

_____

_____

_____

_____

_____

❷ Organize Your Evidence

Complete the chart below with information you learned about conservative ideas, changes to the economy, and social problems in the 1980s.

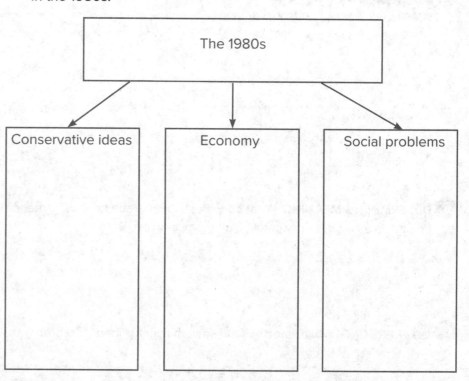

The 1980s

Conservative ideas

Economy

Social problems

❸ Write About It

Work in small groups. Research an issue that was considered a social problem in the 1980s and is still an issue today. Consider these questions: *How has the issue changed over time? What progress still needs to be made? How would liberal and conservative officials believe the issue could be solved?* Write at least two paragraphs explaining both sides of the issue. Compare your paragraphs with your group.

_____

_____

_____

_____

_____

_____

_____

_____

_____

_____

_____

_____

_____

❹ CONNECT TO THE ESSENTIAL QUESTION

Following your work in step 3, choose the same issue or a different issue to focus on. Then create a social media thread that helps answer the Essential Question: *How do you think the resurgence of conservative ideas has changed society?*

Write a social media thread with more than 10 entries in which you explain one aspect of an issue from either a liberal or conservative point of view. Include at least two hotlinks. Remember all entries must be 140 characters or less, but images and hotlinks do not count toward that limit. Connect your entries to the impact conservatism had on the 1980s.

CITIZENSHIP
TAKE ACTION

MAKE CONNECTIONS The resurgence of conservatism occurred in part because many Americans were discontent with society and worried about social issues. Often, citizens will vote for the presidential candidate they feel will best improve their individual lives. Those citizens spoke with their voices and their votes, resulting in a huge impact on the social and economic state of the country.

DIRECTIONS Find a specific issue, cause, or problem in your community or the country with which you are discontented. Write a letter to someone (member of Congress, president, school board official, and so on) who has the authority to enact solutions to the problem. In your letter, describe the problem and its connection to your life.

Use the Internet and available library resources to research your issue and suggest at least one solution based on your research. Use academic (college and university) and government Web sites in addition to books. Work hard to determine whether a source is biased for or against your stance on the issue. If you find a source that is heavily biased, consider using a different source. Include a bibliography on a separate page after your letter. In this way, the official can refer to the original source and read more about it.

A Time of Change

ESSENTIAL QUESTION

How have immigration, technology, and global trade changed the world?

Think about how this question might relate to the societal changes that took place between 1980 and 2000.

TALK ABOUT IT

Discuss with a partner the type of information you would need to know to answer these questions. For example, one question might be: *Which social problems drew the most attention?*

DIRECTIONS: Now write down three additional questions that you need to answer to explain the impact of the changes that occurred during this time.

MY RESEARCH QUESTIONS

Supporting Question 1:

_____

_____

Supporting Question 2:

_____

_____

Supporting Question 3:

_____

_____

The Clinton Years

DIRECTIONS: Search for evidence in Chapter 20, Lesson 1 to help you answer the following questions.

1A SUMMARIZING What were some of Bill Clinton's priorities as president?

_____

_____

_____

1B EVALUATING EVIDENCE Which parts of his agenda were successful, and which were not?

_____

_____

_____

_____

_____

_____

_____

2A ANALYZING CHANGE Which methods do advocacy groups use to bring about change?

_____

_____

_____

_____

_____

_____

ESSENTIAL QUESTION

How have immigration, technology, and global trade changed the world?

As you gather evidence to answer the Essential Question, think about:

- the main priorities of the Clinton administration.
- how government policies affect or are affected by other changes in society.

My Notes

_____

_____

_____

_____

_____

2B **SUMMARIZING** Use the graphic organizer to identify and describe some advocacy groups and where they fall on the political spectrum.

Liberal	Neutral	Conservative

3 **ANALYZING INFORMATION** Explain what the Republican Contract with America offered.

_____

_____

4 CIVICS On what grounds was Clinton impeached, and how did the impeachment efforts fail?

_____

_____

_____

_____

5 **EXPLAINING** Complete the chart by explaining President Clinton's foreign policy in regard to each area.

President Clinton's Foreign Policy	
Haiti	
Bosnia	
Kosovo	
The Middle East	

ESSENTIAL QUESTION

How have immigration, technology, and global trade changed the world?

Hillary Clinton on Child Care

DIRECTIONS: Read the following excerpt from a speech by Hillary Clinton. Then respond to the questions that follow.

EXPLORE THE CONTEXT: Hillary Clinton played a more prominent role in the White House than most former first ladies. She held an office in the West Wing and was appointed by her husband to lead a task force on health care reform. Other issues important to her included women's rights and support for working families. She also wrote books during her time as first lady. The following remarks were made at a conference focusing attention on the needs of children and families for affordable childcare.

PRIMARY SOURCE: SPEECH EXCERPT

❝I'd like to take a minute for all of us to think about what's happening in America this morning, and about what happens every morning. Parents are making the preparations to get to work, and those preparations include for most working families putting their children in the care of others. And most, even before they're out the door, are worrying about the **logistics** of the care that their children will receive. Some are even worrying about the safety or quality of that care. There are many who are wondering whether they would get better quality care if they could pay more. Others are struggling to determine how they'll be able to afford next month's payment. And there are many who are in the work force who worry every day about how they'll care for their child and hold down the job that they need. Many parents will go to work, but have trouble focusing on work because they are worried about the sniffle that their daughter had or wondering how their son is **faring**.

And before we finish today, many more working parents will keep looking **anxiously** at the clock and will murmur into telephones the instructions that their children need after school, because their concerns don't end at the end of the day for their children's school time, because parents won't get home, so that they have to worry about what happens to keep their child safe and well **occupied** during those hours, as well.❞

—from a speech by First Lady Hillary Clinton, given at the White House Conference on Child Care on October 23, 1997

VOCABULARY

logistics: operations

faring: doing

anxiously: nervously

occupied: busy or entertained

Clinton, Hillary. 1997. "Remarks by the President and First Lady at White House Conference on Child Care." October 23. Washington: White House. Office of the Press Secretary. https://clinton4.nara.gov/WH/EOP/First_Lady/html/generalspeeches/1997/19971023-16352.html

1 **IDENTIFYING PERSPECTIVES** What is Clinton's purpose in asking her listeners to imagine what goes through the minds of working parents?

_____

_____

_____

_____

2 **INFERRING** Based on the excerpt, what do you think Clinton would suggest as a solution to the problems she's describing?

_____

_____

_____

_____

3 **ECONOMICS** What connection does Clinton see between money and childcare?

_____

_____

_____

_____

_____

4 **RELATING EVENTS** How do the issues Clinton is describing relate to the feminist movement of the 1960s and 1970s that you read about in an earlier chapter?

_____

_____

_____

_____

5 **IDENTIFYING CONNECTIONS** From your reading of the chapter and Clinton's speech, describe populations that may be especially affected by the struggle to find quality childcare.

_____

_____

_____

Clinton, William J. 1995. "Remarks by the President at the Brady Law One-Year Anniversary Commemoration." February 28. Washington: White House. Office of the Press Secretary. https://clinton6.nara.gov/1995/02/1995-02-28-president-at-brady-law-one-year-anniversary-event.html

ESSENTIAL QUESTION

How have immigration, technology, and global trade changed the world?

VOCABULARY

crucial: critical

naysayers: people who doubt

The Brady Law One-Year Anniversary Commemoration

DIRECTIONS: Read the following excerpt from a magazine article. Then respond to the questions that follow.

EXPLORE THE CONTEXT: In 1981, James Brady was serving as press secretary when he was shot during an assassination attempt on President Ronald Reagan. He later became a strong advocate for gun-control legislation. In 1987, he succeeded in getting a gun-control bill introduced to Congress. Many opposed the bill for fear that it would impinge on citizens' Second Amendment rights. The bill required a handgun buyer to wait five business days while authorities checked his or her background. It was signed into law in 1993.

PRIMARY SOURCE: SPEECH EXCERPT

❝ You know, I'd like to begin by saying a special word about Jim Brady. He dedicated his life to public service. In no small measure because of that dedication, 14 years ago his life was in danger and his life changed forever. In spite of all the hardship and the pain that followed, he never looked back, but instead decided he should fight on, determined to do his part to prevent the tragedy that struck him from striking other people. More than any other person in the United States, we celebrate today the courage and determination of Jim Brady, and we are in his debt.

Thank you, sir . . .

I am committed to this law and committed to what it represents. You know, our big problems here in Washington often stem from the fact that we don't think about what promotes responsibility and what creates opportunity, and what enables people to make the most of their own lives. The Brady Bill does all that.

A **crucial** part of our job here in Washington is to help arm the American people through our police officers to fight crime and violence. The Brady Law, in that sense, is one of the things that I'm proudest of that has happened since I have been President. We put an end to seven years of politics as usual, of people saying one thing and doing another when the Brady Law passed. It's not a complex piece of legislation, but it took seven years—seven years—to pass the Congress.

And all the **naysayers** talked about how terrible it would be. Well, now we know that, as the Secretary said, over 40,000 convicted felons, fugitives, drug dealers, gang members, stalkers, were prevented from purchasing handguns in the Brady Law's first eleven months. I should point out that the real national number is bigger than that because, as you know, there are some states that have companion laws that go along with that, and the estimates are that, nationwide in the states with Brady-like laws and the Brady Law, the total is more like 70,000. ❞

—from a speech given by President Clinton at the Brady Law One-Year Anniversary Commemoration, Office of the Press Secretary, February 1995

1 **DETERMINING CONTEXT** Why did Bill Brady spend so much of his time working to pass a gun-control bill?

_____

_____

_____

2 **CITING TEXT EVIDENCE** How did Bill Brady dedicate himself to public service? Cite examples from the text to support your answer.

_____

_____

_____

_____

_____

3 CIVICS Why do you think the Brady Bill took seven years to pass through Congress?

_____

_____

4 **ANALYZING SOURCES** Of the many issues President Clinton dealt with during his presidency, why do you think he considered this bill one of his proudest accomplishments?

_____

_____

_____

5 **EXPLAINING CAUSE AND EFFECT** At the time of this speech, what effect does President Clinton believe the Brady Bill had on crime?

_____

_____

_____

A New Wave of Immigration

DIRECTIONS: Search for evidence in Chapter 20, Lesson 2 to help you answer the following questions.

1A **EXPLAINING** What was the national origins quota system of immigration? How did it change in the 1960s?

_____

_____

_____

1B **EXPLAINING EFFECTS** What was the result of this change in immigration law?

_____

_____

2A Before 1980, who was considered a refugee?

_____

_____

2B **DIFFERENTIATING** How did the Refugee Act of 1980 broaden the definition of a refugee?

_____

_____

_____

_____

ESSENTIAL QUESTION

How have immigration, technology, and global trade changed the world?

As you gather evidence to answer the Essential Question, think about:

- changes in immigration law and immigrant populations.

- how these changes have influenced society.

My Notes

_____

_____

_____

_____

_____

_____

3 CIVICS Complete the graphic organizer below by describing the results of other immigration reforms.

Law	Action
The Immigration Act of 1965	
McCarran-Walter Act of 1952	
The Immigration Reform and Control Act of 1986	
The Illegal Immigration Reform and Immigrant Responsibility Act of 1996	
The USA PATRIOT Act of 2001	

4 GEOGRAPHY Why do you think states such as California, Texas, New York, New Jersey, and Florida have experienced a larger influx of immigrants than other states?

_____

_____

_____

5 DETERMINING CONTEXT What are some of the issues that have divided public opinion about how to address the challenges of increased unauthorized immigration?

_____

_____

_____

_____

ESSENTIAL QUESTION

How have immigration, technology, and global trade changed the world?

VOCABULARY

imposed: forced

awe: amazement

Hai Phan's American Dream

DIRECTIONS: Read the following excerpt from Hai Phan's life story. Then respond to the questions that follow.

EXPLORE THE CONTEXT: The second half of the twentieth century saw a shift in where immigrants to the United States came from. Instead of coming mostly from Europe as they did before, they were now coming mostly from Latin America and Asia. One reason was the Vietnam War. As a result of the war, approximately 600,000 immigrants came to the United States from Vietnam, Laos, and Cambodia in the decade after 1974. Hai Phan's story was collected by Made Into America, an organization centered in California. One of its goals is to compile, present, and share stories about immigration that generate an understanding of the ways immigrants contribute to society.

PRIMARY SOURCE: LIFE STORY

❝ The sounds of gunfire, cannons, and people in your town screaming are signs that your life is going to change. My mother is from Vietnam and had her life change because of war. She is now living happily here in America . . .

My mom was born in South Vietnam in 1974. 'The life back then was great,' my mom said. Hai was born the oldest of eight kids. As a child she played hide-and-seek, hop scotch, store, and regular games that kids play in America. 'Life was very good, but I don't remember much because I was five,' Hai said. After North Vietnam took over the South, life became terrible. My mother had to work at the age of eight in a convenience store to help her family. She went to school for half a day, then worked the rest of the day. The food was limited selling no meat, only rice and vegetables . . .

The U.S. came to Vietnam with the idea to help people get away from the terrible life being **imposed** upon them. They gave my mom's family the choice to leave Vietnam, so they took it. My mom boarded an airplane that was bound for Houston in 1991. When Hai first looked outside the windows of the plane, she said that she was in **awe** of how many cars were there. When they landed, Hai saw that everything was enormous compared to Vietnam. They were greeted with a welcoming sponsor family who helped them in the first months.
The first thing Hai wanted to do was learn English as a second language. After six months of learning the language, she had her first opportunity to test her English. She worked for a sewing company then at a burger joint. She worked so well that they gave her a promotion to customer service. That's where she said she learned how to communicate properly with people. ❞

—from "Hai Phan's American Dream," written by Hai Phan's daughter

1 **ANALYZING STRUCTURE** Why did the author choose to begin her mother's life story the way she did?

_____

_____

_____

2 **EXPLAINING CAUSES** What was the main cause of the changes in Hai Phan's life?

_____

_____

_____

3 **SUMMARIZING** What difficulties did Hai Phan's family face that convinced them they should leave their home?

_____

_____

_____

_____

4 **ECONOMICS** How did Hai make a living as an immigrant in the United States?

_____

_____

_____

5 **COMPARING AND CONTRASTING** What differences did Hai Phan first notice between Vietnam and the United States?

_____

_____

6 **IDENTIFYING CONNECTIONS** How have immigrants such as Hai Phan changed the United States?

_____

_____

_____

ESSENTIAL QUESTION

How have immigration, technology, and global trade changed the world?

VOCABULARY

vital: very important

sacrosanct: sacred enough to never change

perceived: believed by an observer

harassment: verbal or physical attacks

The USA PATRIOT Act of 2001

DIRECTIONS: Read the following excerpt from the USA PATRIOT Act of 2001. Then respond to the questions that follow.

EXPLORE THE CONTEXT: The USA PATRIOT Act stands for "Uniting and Strengthening America by Providing Appropriate Tools Required to Intercept and Obstruct Terrorism." It was drawn up and signed into law as a response to the terrorist attacks of September 11, 2001. President George W. Bush hoped that the legislation would empower law enforcement and intelligence agencies to better protect the nation against future terrorist attacks. Despite the bill's passage, some in Congress remained concerned that it did not do enough to combat terrorism, while others believed that it went too far in giving the government broad powers to investigate U.S. citizens.

PRIMARY SOURCE: LEGISLATION

66 SEC. 102. SENSE OF CONGRESS CONDEMNING DISCRIMINATION AGAINST ARAB AND MUSLIM AMERICANS.

(a) FINDINGS.—Congress makes the following findings:

1. Arab Americans, Muslim Americans, and Americans from South Asia play a **vital** role in our Nation and are entitled to nothing less than the full rights of every American.

2. The acts of violence that have been taken against Arab and Muslim Americans since the September 11, 2001, attacks against the United States should be and are condemned by all Americans who value freedom.

3. The concept of individual responsibility for wrongdoing is **sacrosanct** in American society, and applies equally to all religious, racial, and ethnic groups.

4. When American citizens commit acts of violence against those who are, or are **perceived** to be, of Arab or Muslim descent, they should be punished to the full extent of the law.

5. Muslim Americans have become so fearful of **harassment** that many Muslim women are changing the way they dress to avoid becoming targets.

6. Many Arab Americans and Muslim Americans have acted heroically during the attacks on the United States, including Mohammed Salman Hamdani, a 23-year-old New Yorker of Pakistani descent, who is believed to have gone to the World Trade Center to offer rescue assistance and is now missing.

(b) SENSE OF CONGRESS.—It is the sense of Congress that—

1. the civil rights and civil liberties of all Americans, including Arab Americans, Muslim Americans, and Americans from South Asia, must be protected, and that every effort must be taken to preserve their safety;

2. any acts of violence or discrimination against any Americans be condemned; and

3. the Nation is called upon to recognize the patriotism of fellow citizens from all ethnic, racial, and religious backgrounds. 99

—The United States PATRIOT Act, United States Government Printing Office, 2001

USA PATRIOT Act of 2001. 2001. Public Law 107-56, 107th Cong., 1st sess., October 26.

1. **INFERRING** Why do you think the writers of the PATRIOT Act believed it necessary to include this section?

_____

_____

_____

_____

2. **CITING TEXT EVIDENCE** How did the September 11 attacks personally impact the lives of Muslim Americans? Cite evidence from the USA PATRIOT Act to support your answer.

_____

_____

_____

3. **DETERMINING CONTEXT** Why do you think the writers of the legislation included the story about Mohammed Salman Hamdani?

_____

_____

4. **SUMMARIZING** What three actions does this section of the PATRIOT Act call for?

_____

_____

_____

_____

5. CIVICS What does the act request of all U.S. citizens?

_____

_____

_____

_____

6. **IDENTIFYING CONNECTIONS** How do you think the experiences of Middle Eastern, Muslim, or South Asian immigrants have compared with the experiences of other immigrants?

_____

_____

_____

ESSENTIAL QUESTION

How have immigration, technology, and global trade changed the world?

As you gather evidence to answer the essential question, think about:

- which new technologies came about between 1980 and 2000.

- how these technologies changed the way we communicate and do business.

My Notes

Technology and Globalization

DIRECTIONS: Search for evidence in Chapter 20, Lesson 3 to help you answer the following questions.

1A **ANALYZING CHANGE** How have computers changed since they were first invented?

1B **EXPLAINING EFFECTS** How have computers changed society?

2A **RELATING EVENTS** How did the Internet begin?

2B **ANALYZING CHANGE** How has the Internet changed society?

3 **EXPLAINING** What is globalization, and how has technology influenced it?

4 ECONOMICS Complete the graphic organizer below with names of some of the various trade agreements and organizations that have formed to manage a global economy and promote trade.

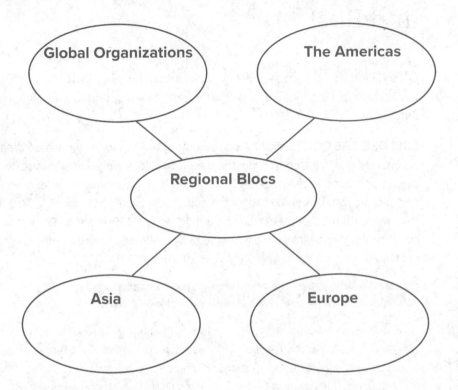

5 **ANALYZING ISSUES** What are some of the environmental issues that have had a global impact?

_____

_____

_____

ESSENTIAL QUESTION

How have immigration, technology, and global trade changed the world?

The Push-Pull Effects of the Information Technology Boom and Bust

DIRECTIONS: Read the following excerpt from an article about the effects of the information technology boom and bust. Then respond to the questions that follow.

EXPLORE THE CONTEXT: The development of the World Wide Web created an entirely new "dot-com" industry. Based in Silicon Valley, new start-ups began operating in the mid-1990s and fueled an economic bubble, or period of rapid growth. Driven by the information technology industry, the **GDP** also rose more than 20 percent during the mid- to late 1990s. While some "dot-com" companies were successful, the failure of many online companies to be profitable led to a market crash in April of 2000.

PRIMARY SOURCE: ARTICLE EXCERPT

66 The information technology (IT) sector played a remarkable role in the growth of the U.S. economy during the late 1990s. Between 1996 and 2000 the IT-producing sector was responsible for an estimated 1.4 percentage points of the nation's average annual real GDP growth of 4.6 percent, largely driven by business investment in IT products. Since 2000, however, the IT sector has been struggling. In particular, the level of IT Manufacturing **output** declined rapidly as business investment spending on IT declined sharply during the 2001 recession. In 2002 it is estimated that IT-producing industries contributed only 0.1 percentage points to the economy's 2 percent annual growth (Economics and Statistics Administration 2003).

The IT boom of the 1990s led to a dramatic rise in employment in IT-producing industries, and the **subsequent** IT **retrenchment** resulted in a large decline in employment in the early 2000s. Between 1993 and 2000, the average number of workers in IT-producing industries in the U.S. grew by approximately 50 percent, which is almost two and a half times as fast as employment in private sector non-IT industries.

From 2000 to 2003, average employment in IT-producing industries declined by 21 percent, compared to a two percent decline in non-IT industries. Such extraordinary movement in the labor market presents unique **incentives** and opportunities for workers, and could serve as motivation for workers to migrate to take advantage of promising labor market opportunities and/or to escape labor market declines. The pull on workers to communities experiencing positive economic opportunities and the push of workers out during economic declines has been referred to as

'push-pull' migration, and has been analyzed in a variety of different contexts. 99

—from an article by Julie L. Hotchkiss, M. Melinda Pitts, and John C. Robertson, published by the Federal Reserve Bank of Atlanta, February 2006

VOCABULARY

GDP: Gross Domestic Product, or total value created by a country

output: production

subsequent: immediately following

retrenchment: pulling back

incentives: reasons to do something

Hotchkiss, Julie L., M. Melinda Pitts, and John C. Robertson. "The Push-Pull Effects of the Information Technology Boom and Bust: Insight from Matched Employer-Employee Data." Working Paper 2006-1, Federal Reserve Bank of Atlanta, 2006.

1 `ECONOMICS` How big a role did the IT sector play in the economic boom of the 1990s?

_____

_____

2 **ANALYZING SOURCES** Why did the economy begin to struggle in 2000?

_____

_____

_____

3 **COMPARING AND CONTRASTING** How much did the IT sector contribute to the economy after this decline?

_____

_____

_____

4 **CITING TEXT EVIDENCE** What effect did the burst of the technology bubble have on employment? Cite evidence from the text to support your answer.

_____

_____

_____

_____

_____

5 **DESCRIBING** What is "push-pull" migration?

_____

_____

_____

6 **ANALYZING CHANGE** Based on this source, what is one way technology changed the world?

_____

_____

_____

ESSENTIAL QUESTION

How have immigration, technology, and global trade changed the world?

Implications of the Kyoto Protocol on Climate Change

DIRECTIONS: Read the following excerpt from a senate hearing on the Kyoto Protocol. Then respond to the questions that follow.

EXPLORE THE CONTEXT: In the 1990s, many scientific experts agreed that increased carbon dioxide emissions from factories and power plants were changing Earth's climate, but others disagreed. The issue was controversial because of the cost of controlling emissions. In 1997, the EU and many countries signed the Kyoto Protocol, which called for mandatory targets on greenhouse gas emissions. President Clinton did not submit the protocol for ratification because most senators opposed it. President George W. Bush withdrew the United States from the agreement entirely.

PRIMARY SOURCE: SENATE HEARING EXCERPT

66 I would like, Mr. Chairman and members of the committee, to deal very briefly with some **misperceptions**. The first is that the Kyoto Protocol will **imperil** the ability of our military to meet its worldwide responsibilities. This is absolutely untrue. We took special pains, working with the Defense Department and with our uniformed military, both before and in Kyoto, to fully protect the unique position of the United States as the world's only superpower with global military responsibilities. We achieved everything they outlined as necessary to protect military operations and our national security . . .

A second misperception is that somehow the protocol will create a 'super U.N. secretariat,' threatening U.S. **sovereignty** and national decision making through alleged intrusive verification procedures and prior approval of individual emissions trades. This also is not so . . . the review process is not by some secretariat, it is **intergovernmental** . . .

A third concern is that somehow on the one hand we are told it will threaten U.S. sovereignty by **dictating** national decisions on implementation, and yet, on the other, it lacks mechanisms or teeth to verify compliance. In fact, the protocol strikes an appropriate balance between these two extremes . . . the protocol leaves to the parties themselves to decide how best to meet their targets based on national circumstances. If somebody else wants to do it by heavy carbon taxes or heavy central regulation, that is their business. We are going to do it by market driven mechanisms alone. 99

—from a speech by Senator Chuck Hagel before the Committee on Foreign Relations, February 11, 1998

VOCABULARY

misperceptions: false beliefs

imperil: endanger

sovereignty: self-rule

intergovernmental: between governments

dictating: commanding

1 **CITING TEXT EVIDENCE** Is Senator Hagel for or against the Kyoto Protocol? Cite evidence from the text to support your answer.

_____

_____

_____

_____

_____

2 **SUMMARIZING** According to the excerpt, what were the main misperceptions that people had about the Kyoto Protocol?

_____

_____

_____

3 **INFERRING** What can you infer from this source about the prevailing view of regulation in the United States?

_____

_____

_____

_____

4 **ECONOMICS** What do you think Senator Hagel means by "market driven mechanisms"?

_____

_____

_____

5 **RELATING EVENTS** How has increased global trade impacted the environment?

_____

_____

_____

ESSENTIAL QUESTIONS

How have immigration, technology, and global trade changed the world?

1 Think About It

Review the supporting questions that you developed at the beginning of the chapter. Review the evidence that you gathered in Chapter 20. Were you able to answer each Supporting Question?

If there was not enough evidence to answer your Supporting Questions, what additional evidence do you think you need to consider?

2 Organize Your Evidence

Complete the chart below with information you learned about how immigration, technology, and global trade have changed the world.

	Major events or changes	How did it change the world?	Evidence to support your claim
Immigration			
Technology			
Global trade			

3 Write About It

Of all the events that took place between 1980 and 2000, which two do you feel led to the most far-reaching changes in society? Describe these events, and explain your reasons for believing they have had the most impact.

_____

_____

_____

_____

_____

_____

_____

4 Connect to the Essential Question

Using one of the changes you detailed above, create a graph in which you compare and contrast the United States in 1980 to the United States in 2000 and today. Your graph should clearly demonstrate how society has changed and show at least five points of comparison. For example, in the 1980s, home computers could be used to play videogames, program, and word process. Today, they can be used to do all those things as well as research, shop, pay bills, and do so much more. Use original visuals as well as interesting and accurate copy to inform your audience of the changes brought about by your topic. Your graph should be creative and show strong insight into the topic you chose.

_____

_____

_____

_____

_____

_____

_____

CITIZENSHIP
TAKE ACTION

MAKE CONNECTIONS As you have learned from this chapter, dramatic changes in technology and global trade have not only affected world economies, but they have also affected the environment. Increased manufacturing and industrialization have led to major environmental changes around the globe. Opinions vary as to the causes of changing climates and the extent of the damage, but most scientists believe that the changes are happening as a direct result of human activity. Research ways that human activity can harm the environment. Then write a short public service announcement to raise awareness about the issue and inspire others to change their behaviors.

DIRECTIONS Choose one human activity you believe has strongly affected the environment, and outline the cause(s) and possible solution(s). Then write a short public service announcement (PSA) to raise awareness about the issue. Write your PSA in such a way that you will inspire others to act on the information and change their own behaviors. Share your PSA with your class. You may also wish to share your PSA with the local community.

America's Challenges for a New Century

How have disputes over ideas, values, and politics resulted in change?

Think about the challenges that face Americans today. How does technology present both problems and solutions? How do our climate and natural disasters present challenges to governments and to citizens?

TALK ABOUT IT

With a partner, discuss the sort of information you would need to discover how Americans have moved toward change due to disputes over ideas, values, and politics. For example, you might ask, "How did global challenges lead to change in America?"

DIRECTIONS: Now write three additional questions that will help you to explain how ideas, values, and politics have resulted in change.

MY RESEARCH QUESTIONS

Supporting Question 1:

_____

_____

Supporting Question 2:

_____

_____

Supporting Question 3:

_____

_____

Bush's Global Challenges

DIRECTIONS: Search for evidence in Chapter 21, Lesson 1 to help you answer the following questions.

1A **COMPARING AND CONTRASTING** What is the difference between the electoral vote and the popular vote?

_____

_____

_____

_____

_____

1B **IDENTIFYING CONNECTIONS** How did the Bush win the presidency without winning the popular vote? How did that fact lead to the court case *Bush* v. *Gore*?

_____

_____

_____

_____

_____

2A **SUMMARIZING** Summarize the events of September 11, 2001. How did Americans react?

_____

_____

_____

2B **UNDERSTANDING CHANGE** What are the goals of terrorism? How do terrorists achieve their goals?

_____

_____

_____

ESSENTIAL QUESTION

How have disputes over ideas, values, and politics resulted in change?

As you gather evidence to answer the Essential Question, think about:

- how political differences can lead to disputes.
- how countries react to major military attacks.
- the way that terrorism can change how people behave.

My Notes

_____

_____

_____

_____

_____

_____

_____

3 **EXPLAINING CAUSES** Complete the graphic organizer with details about the U.S. government's response to the September 11, 2001, attacks.

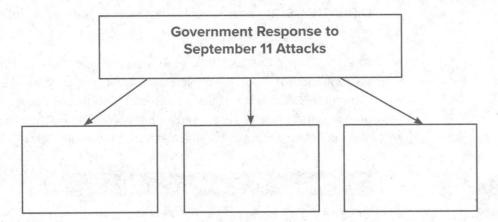

```
                    ┌─────────────────────────────┐
                    │   Government Response to     │
                    │   September 11 Attacks       │
                    └─────────────────────────────┘
                       │          │          │
                       ▼          ▼          ▼
            ┌──────────┐  ┌──────────┐  ┌──────────┐
            │          │  │          │  │          │
            │          │  │          │  │          │
            │          │  │          │  │          │
            └──────────┘  └──────────┘  └──────────┘
```

4 ECONOMICS What factors led to a weak American economy at the end of the Bush years? .

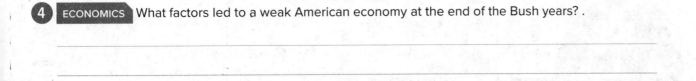

_____

_____

_____

ESSENTIAL QUESTION

How have disputes over ideas, values, and politics resulted in change?

September 11 Press Release

DIRECTIONS: Read the press release from September 11, 2001. Then respond to the questions that follow.

EXPLORE THE CONTEXT: When terrorists attacked the World Trade Center on September 11, 2001, President Bush was visiting children at Emma Booker Elementary School. The attack occurred at 8:46 A.M. His press secretary prepared this press release just over half an hour later. They were not aware that the Pentagon would be attacked about 12 minutes later.

PRIMARY SOURCE: PRESS RELEASE

" For Immediate Release

Office of the Press Secretary

September 11, 2001

Remarks by the President after Two Planes Crash into World Trade Center

Emma Booker Elementary School

Sarasota, Florida

9:30 A.M. EDT

THE PRESIDENT: Ladies and gentlemen, this is a difficult moment for America. I, unfortunately, will be going back to Washington after my remarks. Secretary Rod Paige and the **Lt. Governor** will take the **podium** and discuss education. I do want to thank the folks here at Booker Elementary School for their hospitality.

Today we've had a national tragedy. Two airplanes have crashed into the World Trade Center in an apparent **terrorist** attack on our country. I have spoken to the Vice President, to the Governor of New York, to the Director of the FBI, and have ordered that the full resources of the federal government go to help the victims and their families, and to conduct a full-scale investigation to hunt down and to find those folks who committed this act.

Terrorism against our nation will not stand.

And now if you would join me in a moment of silence. May God bless the victims, their families, and America. Thank you very much.

END 9:31 A.M. EDT "

—from *Remarks by the President after Two Planes Crash into World Trade Center,* September 11, 2001

VOCABULARY

Lt. Governor: state elected official who is second in command to the governor

podium: small platform on which a speaker stands

terrorist: person who uses violence for political aims

1 **SUMMARIZING** What does President Bush announce in his press release?

_____

_____

2 **IDENTIFYING CAUSES** Who wrote the document? What is that person's job? What details are included in this document that help to convey the details of the president's remarks?

_____

_____

_____

_____

3 **INTERPRETING** What details does the document share about the president's understanding of the terrorist attacks? How did he learn more about the event?

_____

_____

_____

4 **ANALYZING** What does the president mean when he says that he has "ordered that the full resources of the federal government go to help the victims and their families"?

_____

_____

5 CIVICS What is the president's responsibility in the face of an attack on the homeland? Does the document meet that responsibility? Why or why not?

_____

_____

_____

_____

6 **IDENTIFYING CONNECTIONS** What change does this document mark in the history of America?

_____

_____

_____

USA PATRIOT Act of 2001. 2001. Public Law 107-56, 107th Cong., 1st sess., October 26.

Copyright © McGraw-Hill Education

ESSENTIAL QUESTION

How have disputes over ideas, values, and politics resulted in change?

USA PATRIOT Act: Counterterrorism

DIRECTIONS: Read the excerpt from the USA PATRIOT Act. Then respond to the questions that follow.

EXPLORE THE CONTEXT: President Bush asked Congress to pass legislation to help him fight terrorism at home and abroad. Bush created the Department of Homeland Security, and legislators created funding to help the president pay for his terrorism efforts with a bill called the USA PATRIOT Act. The letters of the bill stand for Uniting and Strengthening America by Providing Appropriate Tools Required to Intercept and Obstruct Terrorism.

PRIMARY SOURCE: LEGISLATION

" TITLE I—ENHANCING DOMESTIC SECURITY AGAINST TERRORISM

SEC. 101. COUNTERTERRORISM FUND.

(a) ESTABLISHMENT; AVAILABILITY.—There is hereby established in the Treasury of the United States a separate fund to be known as the "**Counterterrorism** Fund", amounts in which shall remain available without **fiscal year** limitation—

(1) to reimburse any Department of Justice component for any costs incurred in connection with—

(A) reestablishing the operational capability of an office or facility that has been damaged or destroyed as the result of any **domestic** or international terrorism incident;

(B) providing support to counter, investigate, or prosecute domestic or international terrorism, including, without limitation, paying rewards in connection with these activities; and

(C) conducting terrorism threat assessments of Federal agencies and their facilities; and

(2) to reimburse any department or agency of the Federal Government for any costs incurred in connection with **detaining** in foreign countries individuals accused of acts of terrorism that violate the laws of the United States.

(b) NO EFFECT ON PRIOR **APPROPRIATIONS**.—Subsection (a) shall not be **construed** to affect the amount or availability of any appropriation to the Counterterrorism Fund made before the date of the enactment of this Act. "

—from the USA PATRIOT Act

VOCABULARY

domestic: happening inside a country

counterterrorism: against or designed to prevent terrorism

fiscal year: year used for accounting or tax purposes

appropriations: money used for a specific purpose

construed: understood

detaining: holding someone in custody for questioning

1 DETERMINING CENTRAL IDEAS What does the passage of this legislation allow for?

_____

_____

2 INTERPRETING What costs do the legislators expect that the funds will pay for? Name at least three of them.

_____

_____

_____

3 EVALUATING Explain the final sentence of the passage. What important clarification does it make?

_____

_____

_____

_____

4 CIVICS How does the legislation demonstrate the effective separation of powers in the three branches of government?

_____

_____

_____

_____

5 ECONOMICS What are the economic effects of the legislation?

_____

_____

_____

_____

_____

6 EXPLAINING CAUSES What was the motivation for creating the document?

_____

_____

_____

_____

Focusing on Afghanistan and Iraq

DIRECTIONS: Search for evidence in Chapter 21, Lesson 2 to help you answer the following questions.

1A **ANALYZING ISSUES** What were the initial goals when the United States first launched its war in Afghanistan?

_____

_____

_____

_____

1B **ANALYZING CHANGE** How did the objectives of the war change after the Taliban government was toppled?

_____

_____

_____

_____

2A **INTERPRETING** What are weapons of mass destruction? How did the search for them lead to war with Iraq?

_____

_____

_____

_____

2B **RELATING EVENTS** After toppling Iraq's government and finding no weapons of mass destruction, what new problems did the United States face in Iraq?

_____

_____

_____

_____

ESSENTIAL QUESTION

How have disputes over ideas, values, and politics resulted in change?

As you gather evidence to answer the Essential Question, think about:

- how the values of the Taliban contrasted with American values.
- how Americans escalated the war with Iraq.
- the dispute over how and why to wage war in Iraq.

My Notes

_____

_____

_____

_____

_____

3A **EXPLAINING EFFECTS** Use the graphic organizer to show how the Iraq War affected the Iraqi government and society.

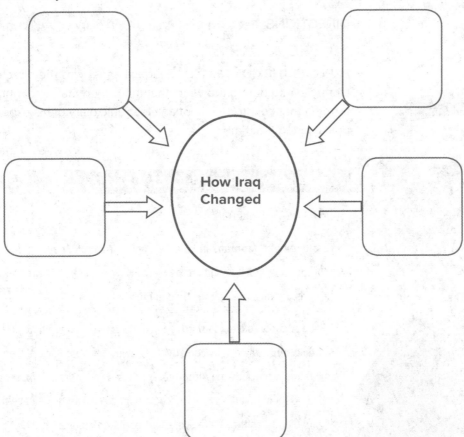

3B **CIVICS** Using information that you gathered in the graphic organizer, summarize how Iraqi society was improved and weakened as a result of the war.

_____

_____

_____

ESSENTIAL QUESTION

How have disputes over ideas, values, and politics resulted in change?

Iraq War Diary

DIRECTIONS: Read the excerpt from the diary entry. Then respond to the questions that follow.

EXPLORE THE CONTEXT: Dr. Saad Eskander was the director of the National Library in Iraq during the years that the United States fought a war against terror in that country. He kept an electronic diary of his experiences as blog posts during that time.

PRIMARY SOURCE: DIARY ENTRY

" 11 November 2006

I left Rome to **Amman**, and the next day, I arrived to the Baghdad International Airport. It is well known that the highway, which links the airport to the Baghdad City, is the most dangerous road in the world.

For a security reason, I asked the taxi driver to drop me at the first military **checkpoint**, which is by car 3 minutes away from the Airport. One must not trust anybody, especially the Airport taxi drivers. At the checkpoint, my driver was waiting for me with his car. The security police asked us to leave the area immediately, as they were suspicious of abandoned car at the checkpoint. The highway was in a chaotic state, as everyone tried to leave the Airport area . . .

I asked the driver to take me to my office straightaway. Minutes after we left the highway, two terrorists bombed a police checkpoint in the **Al-Yarmook** district, killing 60 people and injuring 90 others. My driver and I decided to take another route via the **Al-Karradah** district. Once again, just as we entered the Al-Karradah district, two car-bombs exploded killing and injuring a lot of civilians. I decided not to go to my office, as the other main routes were extremely dangerous. Indeed, on the same day and in the very busy **Al-Sa'adun** area, two more car-bombs exploded, killing and injuring many people. It was a very nice welcome and back to reality. **"**

VOCABULARY

Amman: capital city of Jordan; city through which most business travelers went during the war in Iraq

checkpoint: entrance where travelers go through security

Al-Yarmook, Al-Karradah, Al-Sa'adun: districts in Baghdad, the capital city of Iraq

1 **SUMMARIZING** How would you describe Dr. Eskander's journey home through Baghdad?

_____

_____

_____

2 **IDENTIFYING PERSPECTIVES** Why do you think Dr. Eskander recorded his experiences in a diary? What do you think was his motivation for writing?

_____

_____

_____

_____

3 CIVICS How were military checkpoints used during wartime? What areas of the city were likely the most restrictive?

_____

_____

_____

_____

4 **UNDERSTANDING CONTEXT** What does the author mean by the last line in his diary entry?

_____

_____

5 **INTERPRETING** Based on the details in the diary entry, describe the nature of the war in Baghdad.

_____

_____

_____

6 **INFERRING** How is the war that Dr. Eskander describes different from World War I or the Vietnam War?

_____

_____

_____

ESSENTIAL QUESTION

How have disputes over ideas, values, and politics resulted in change?

Conclusion of Diplomacy

DIRECTIONS: Read the transcript of the letter to Congress written by President Bush. Then respond to the questions that follow.

EXPLORE THE CONTEXT: Congress authorized the president to use military force in Iraq. However, the international community urged the United States to pressure Iraq to find a diplomatic solution to the conflict instead.

PRIMARY SOURCE: LETTER TO CONGRESS

"Dear Mr. Speaker:

Consistent with section 3(b) of the Authorization for Use of Military Force Against Iraq Resolution of 2002 **(Public Law 107-243)**, and based on information available to me, including that in the enclosed document, I determine that:

(1) reliance by the United States on further diplomatic and other peaceful means alone will neither (A) adequately protect the national security of the United States against the continuing threat posed by Iraq nor (B) likely lead to enforcement of all relevant **United Nations Security Council resolutions** regarding Iraq; and

(2) acting **pursuant** to the Constitution and Public Law 107-243 is consistent with the United States and other countries continuing to take the necessary actions against international terrorists and terrorist organizations, including those nations, organizations, or persons who planned, authorized, committed, or aided the terrorist attacks that occurred on September 11, 2001.

Sincerely,

GEORGE W. BUSH "

—from a letter to Congress from President George W. Bush, March 18, 2003

VOCABULARY

pursuant: based on

United Nations Security Council: international unit charged with keeping peace among nations

resolutions: formal statements voted into action by an official group

Public Law 107-243: legislation that authorized the president to use U.S. military against Iraq

Bush, George W. 2006. "Letter to Congressional Leaders on the Conclusion of Diplomatic Efforts With Regard to Iraq," March 18, 2003. Public Papers of the Presidents of the United States: George W. Bush. Bk. 1. Washington: U.S. G.P.O.

1 **DETERMINING CENTRAL IDEAS** This letter is a continuation of a conversation between the U.S. Congress and President George W. Bush. What is the extra request that President Bush asks for in this letter?

_____

_____

_____

2 **CITING TEXT EVIDENCE** What is the purpose of the actions that President Bush proposes? Use text evidence in your response.

_____

_____

_____

3 **CIVICS** What principle of the democratic process is demonstrated by this letter?

_____

_____

_____

4 **INTERPRETING** Why did the president reference the terrorist attacks that occurred on September 11, 2001?

_____

_____

_____

5 **UNDERSTANDING CHANGE** Once the president's request was granted by Congress, how did it change the actions of the military and the nation as a whole?

_____

_____

_____

_____

_____

Domestic Challenges

DIRECTIONS: Search for evidence in Chapter 21, Lesson 3 to help you answer the following questions.

1A **INTERPRETING** How did the Iraq War influence the 2004 election?

_____

_____

_____

1B **SUMMARIZING** After winning his second term, what errors did President Bush make regarding Guantanamo Bay and wiretapping?

_____

_____

_____

2A **SUMMARIZING** President Bush faced several important events in his second term. Use the graphic organizer below to take notes about President Bush's actions. For each event, explain what happened and why his decisions were controversial.

Event	Notes
Hurricane Katrina	
Kelo v. City of New London	
Supreme Court Appointments	

ESSENTIAL QUESTION

How have disputes over ideas, values, and politics resulted in change?

As you gather evidence to answer the Essential Question, think about:

- how national security was enhanced by housing prisoners at Guantanamo Bay.
- why the U.S. government implemented domestic surveillance.
- how a natural disaster such as Hurricane Katrina led to domestic disputes.

My Notes

_____

_____

_____

_____

_____

_____

_____

2B **DRAWING CONCLUSIONS** In addition to these challenges, what additional factors led to huge losses for the Republicans in the 2006 midterm elections?

_____

_____

3 ECONOMICS Complete the cause-and-effect graphic organizer to identify the factors that caused the economic recession during the end of President Bush's second term.

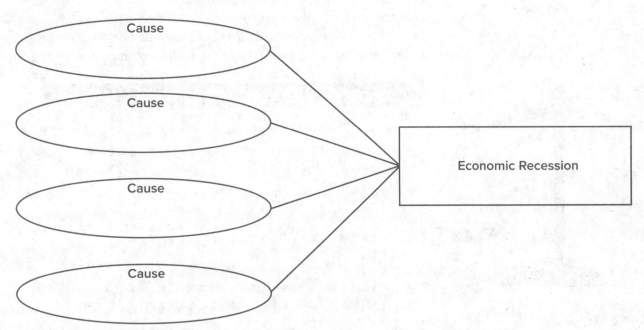

Cause

Cause

Cause

Cause

Economic Recession

4 **CONSTRUCTING HYPOTHESES** Which of these factors was the most damaging to the country's economy? Explain your stance.

_____

_____

ESSENTIAL QUESTION

How have disputes over ideas, values, and politics resulted in change?

Congressional Hearing on Guantanamo Bay

DIRECTIONS: Read the excerpts from Representative Duncan Hunter's testimony to the Committee on Armed Services. Then respond to the questions that follow.

EXPLORE THE CONTEXT: During the wars in Afghanistan and Iraq, President Bush decided to hold captured members of al-Qaeda at the prison in Guantanamo Bay, Cuba. Many Americans objected to this decision because they believed that all prisoners had rights and should be treated with dignity. Some elected officials visited the prison and reported their impressions to Congress.

PRIMARY SOURCE: CONGRESSIONAL HEARING

66 This past weekend, I had the opportunity to lead . . . a bipartisan delegation . . . to Guantanamo to examine firsthand the treatment of **detainees** there. What I saw was not, quote, the **gulag** of our times. Instead, we saw a world-class **detention** facility where detainees representing a threat to our national security are well fed, given access to top-notch medical facilities and given an opportunity to obtain legal representation . . .

While there, we ate from the same menu as the detainees. And I have to say that, having eaten the detainee food . . . and looking at the weight gain charts, it is evident that the detainees have gained an average of five pounds apiece over the last year. Not only are they well fed but receiving first-rate medical services comparable to **Health Maintenance Organizations** (HMOs) in the United States. . . .

Detainees also receive rights that American servicemen and women captured in battle would not receive. One hundred percent of the detainees have been given written notice of their right to contest their detention in a United States court of law as well as instructions on how to obtain a lawyer **pro bono**. And as I understand it . . . over 100 detainees now, in fact, have lawyers. 99

—from the opening statement of Honorable Duncan Hunter, Representative from California, Chairman of the Committee of Armed Services
June 29, 2005

VOCABULARY

detainees: people held in a location, usually for political reasons

gulag: labor camp in which prisoners do hard work

Health Maintenance Organizations: organization that delivers medical services

detention: custody

pro bono: done for free; usually work by a lawyer for a low-income person

1 **ANALYZING INFORMATION** How does Representative Hunter present his experience at the prison at Guantanamo Bay?

U.S. House. Committee on Armed Services. 2007. Detainee Operations at Guantanamo Bay: Hearing. 109th Cong., 1st sess., June 29, 2005. Washington: U.S. G.P.O.

2 DETERMINING MEANING What does Hunter mean by his testimony: "What I saw was not, quote, the gulag of our times"?

_____

_____

_____

3 INFERRING What point is Hunter making by describing the food and the medical care at the prison?

_____

_____

_____

_____

_____

4 CIVICS What aspects of civil rights are evident in Hunter's detail about the detainees who are receiving the service of pro bono lawyers?

_____

_____

_____

5 IDENTIFYING EFFECTS What effect does Hunter want his testimony to have on Congress and the American public?

_____

_____

_____

6 COMPARING AND CONTRASTING Compare the description of Guantanamo Bay to the reports from Abu Ghraib as mentioned in the student edition. How do they differ? How does this testimony highlight the contrast?

_____

_____

_____

Bush, George W. "Address to the Nation on Hurricane Katrina, September 15, 2005." In Selected Speeches of President George W. Bush, 2001 – 2008. Washington, D.C. https://georgewbush-whitehouse.archives.gov/infocus/bushrecord/documents/Selected_Speeches_George_W_Bush.pdf

President Bush Discusses Hurricane Relief

ESSENTIAL QUESTION

How have disputes over ideas, values, and politics resulted in change?

VOCABULARY

congregations: churchgoers

rumble: roll noisily

dirge: sad music

symbolizing: representing

DIRECTIONS: Read the excerpts from President George W. Bush's address to the nation. Then respond to the questions that follow.

EXPLORE THE CONTEXT: Hurricane Katrina struck the Gulf Coast in August 2005. Many officials underestimated the strength of the storm and did not issue evacuations soon enough to get everyone out of harm's way. Government agencies faced harsh criticism for their initial response to the emergency.

PRIMARY SOURCE: PRESIDENTIAL ADDRESS

66 Good evening. I'm speaking to you from the city of New Orleans -- nearly empty, still partly under water, and waiting for life and hope to return. Eastward from Lake Pontchartrain, across the Mississippi coast, to Alabama into Florida, millions of lives were changed in a day by a cruel and wasteful storm.

...Tonight so many victims of the hurricane and the flood are far from home and friends and familiar things. You need to know that our whole nation cares about you, and in the journey ahead you're not alone. To all who carry a burden of loss, I extend the deepest sympathy of our country. To every person who has served and sacrificed in this emergency, I offer the gratitude of our country. And tonight I also offer this pledge of the American people: Throughout the area hit by the hurricane, we will do what it takes, we will stay as long as it takes, to help citizens rebuild their communities and their lives. And all who question the future of the Crescent City need to know there is no way to imagine America without New Orleans, and this great city will rise again.

The streets of Biloxi and Gulfport will again be filled with lovely homes and the sound of children playing. The churches of Alabama will have their broken steeples mended and their **congregations** whole. And here in New Orleans, the street cars will once again **rumble** down St. Charles, and the passionate soul of a great city will return.

In this place, there's a custom for the funerals of jazz musicians. The funeral procession parades slowly through the streets, followed by a band playing a mournful **dirge** as it moves to the cemetery. Once the casket has been laid in place, the band breaks into a joyful "second line" – **symbolizing** the triumph of the spirit over death. Tonight the Gulf Coast is still coming through the dirge -- yet we will live to see the second line. 99

—from George W. Bush's Address to the Nation, September 15, 2005

1 DETERMINING CENTRAL IDEAS What is the purpose of the president's address to the nation?

_____

_____

_____

2 ANALYZING TEXT STRUCTURE The president addresses various groups in his address. In what order does he address this audience? Do you think the order of his remarks was deliberate?

_____

_____

_____

_____

_____

3 GEOGRAPHY Why do you think the custom of the funeral dirge is an appropriate connection for the president to make in this instance?

_____

_____

_____

4 CITING TEXT EVIDENCE What other references made by President Bush are intended to paint a picture of hope for those affected by the hurricane?

_____

_____

_____

5 IDENTIFYING CONNECTIONS Why do you think it is typical for Americans to respond to a national disaster by volunteering for rebuilding efforts and contributing monetarily for the needs of its victims?

_____

_____

_____

_____

ESSENTIAL QUESTIONS

How have disputes over ideas, values, and politics resulted in change?

① Think About It

Review the supporting questions you developed at the beginning of the chapter. Review the evidence you gathered in Chapter 21. Were you able to answer each Supporting Question? If there was not enough evidence to answer your Supporting Questions, what additional evidence do you think you need to consider?

② Organize Your Evidence

Complete the web below with information you learned about the disputes of the early 2000s.

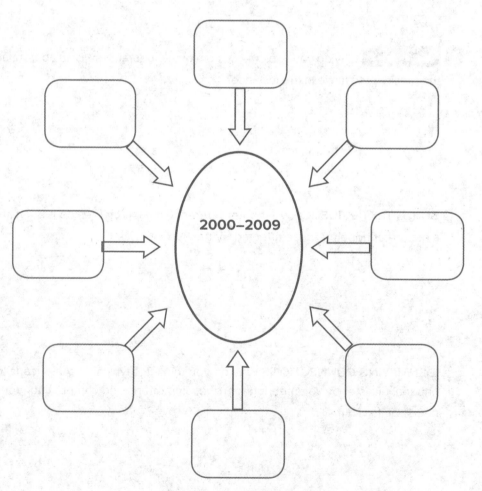

③ Write About It

Research an issue from the first 10 years of the twenty-first century (2000–2009). Consider these questions: *What disputes pushed Americans to change their values? Were there other disputes that changed the shape of politics? How did war and natural disaster lead to political change?* Write at least two paragraphs answering these questions.

_____

_____

_____

_____

_____

④ Talk About It

Work in small groups. Compare the paragraphs you wrote above with your group. What did you learn from the paragraphs of others in your group?

_____

_____

_____

_____

⑤ Connect to the Essential Question

Following your work in step 3, select one of the main events from this time period that caused disputes. Then write a feature newspaper article of at least 350 words that helps to answer the Essential Question: *How have disputes over ideas, values, and politics resulted in change?*

A feature newspaper article is usually filled with details about a single subject. Include facts from the text as well as several other research sources to flesh out your article. Be sure to choose reliable research sources and evaluate each source for bias. Finally, revise your article to use a single compelling voice, include a strong opening statement, and a powerful conclusion.

CITIZENSHIP
TAKE ACTION

MAKE CONNECTIONS The attacks of September 11, 2001, stunned the world. On the day of the attacks, commerce halted, air transportation was grounded, trains stopped running, and people all over the world waited breathlessly to learn about the reason for the attacks. Most adults today have a vivid memory of where they were and what they were doing on September 11. Perhaps they were commuting to work or dropping their children off at school. As the news of the attacks spread, nearly every person was shocked and horrified.

DIRECTIONS Conduct an interview of an adult friend, parent, or community member who remembers the attacks of September 11. Create questions that will draw out details about where they were, what they were doing, how their life was interrupted, and how they felt about the attack on the country. Record their answers digitally, or take close notes about their answers.

Write the interview answers into a Question and Answer article. Give your interview a title, and write an introductory paragraph about your interviewee. After you write the article, have your interviewee read it to ensure that you have captured the information correctly.

_____

_____

_____

_____

_____

_____

_____

_____

_____

Obama and Beyond

ESSENTIAL QUESTION

How have disputes over ideas, values, and politics resulted in change?

Think about how this question might relate to the events that took place from the presidential election of 2008 to the presidential election of 2016 and beyond.

TALK ABOUT IT

Discuss with a partner what type of information you would need to know to answer this question. For example, one question might be: *What events taking place during this time challenged traditional values in U.S. society?*

DIRECTIONS: Now write down three additional questions that would help you explain how differences in ideas, values, and politics influenced society between 2008 and 2016.

MY RESEARCH QUESTIONS

Supporting Question 1:

_____

_____

Supporting Question 2:

_____

_____

Supporting Question 3:

_____

_____

ESSENTIAL QUESTION

How have disputes over ideas, values, and politics resulted in change?

As you gather evidence to answer the Essential Question, think about:

- why the election of Barack Obama was historic.
- what domestic issues confronted the Obama administration early on.
- what challenges President Obama faced in governing.

My Notes

Obama's First Term

DIRECTIONS: Search for evidence in Chapter 22, Lesson 1 to help you answer the following questions.

1A **DESCRIBING** What was considered to be one of the most important election issues in 2008? Why?

1B **DESCRIBING** What was President Obama's response to the economic crisis?

2A **DETERMINING CENTRAL IDEAS** What was the primary domestic issue President Obama hoped to reform? Why?

2B **SUMMARIZING** Why did some Americans object to Obama's health care plan?

3 EXPLAINING CAUSE AND EFFECT Complete the graphic organizer below by explaining how these events affected the growth of the national debt.

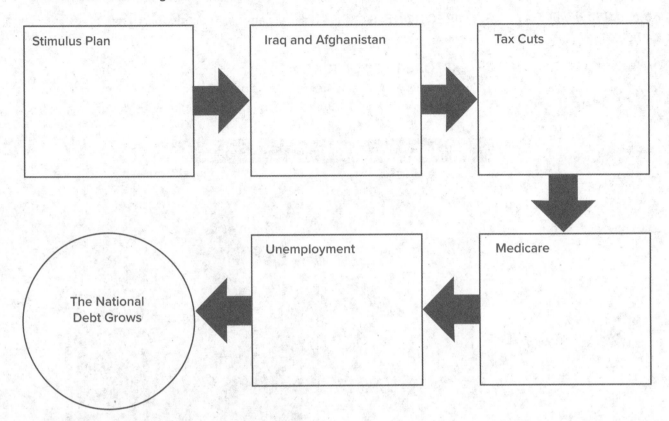

Stimulus Plan	Iraq and Afghanistan	Tax Cuts

The National Debt Grows	Unemployment	Medicare

4 CIVICS Complete the chart below by explaining how each Supreme Court decision affected U.S. citizens.

The Roberts Court		
Decision	Court Ruling	What Group Benefits?
Citizens United v. *Federal Elections Commission*		
National Federation of Independent Business v. *Sebelius* (case deciding the constitutionality of the individual mandate in the health care law)		

ESSENTIAL QUESTION
How have disputes over ideas, values, and politics resulted in change?

Obama Is Sworn In

DIRECTIONS: Study the political cartoon. Then respond to the questions that follow.

EXPLORE THE CONTEXT: In 2008, the United States made history by electing its first African American president, Barack Obama. The election was also notable for historic turnout at the polls throughout the country.

PRIMARY SOURCE: POLITICAL CARTOON

— "Barack Obama Being Sworn in as President of the United States," by Matt Wuerker, 2009

1 **DETERMINING MEANING** What type of source is this? Is it a primary or secondary source? How can you tell?

_____

_____

_____

_____

2 **ANALYZING SOURCES** How does Wuerker portray the event shown in the cartoon?

_____

_____

_____

3 **CIVICS** What aspect of a civil society is demonstrated in this cartoon?

_____

_____

_____

4 **DETERMINING CENTRAL IDEAS** What is the significance of the human pyramid shown in the cartoon? Identify at least three of the figures.

_____

_____

_____

_____

_____

5 **UNDERSTANDING CONTEXT** What is the purpose of showing the figures hidden under the podium?

_____

_____

_____

_____

ESSENTIAL QUESTION

How have disputes over ideas, values, and politics resulted in change?

Citizens United

DIRECTIONS: Read the following excerpt from a speech. Then respond to the questions that follow.

EXPLORE THE CONTEXT: In March 2010, Democratic Senator Patrick Leahy spoke out about the Supreme Court decision known as *Citizens United* v. *Federal Elections Commission*. In the following excerpt, Leahy discusses his reaction to and thoughts about the decision.

PRIMARY SOURCE: HEARING EXCERPT

"And I believe the *Citizens United* decision turns the idea of Government of, by, and for the people on its head. It creates new rights for Wall Street at the expense of the people on Main Street. It threatens to allow unprecedented influence from foreign corporations into our elections. . . . And I think Americans concerned about fair elections have rightfully recoiled.

Our Constitution begins with the words, 'We, the People of the United States.' In designing the Constitution, States ratifying it, adopting the Bill of Rights, and creating our democracy, we spoke of and thought of and guaranteed fundamental rights to the American people, not to corporations.

There are reasons for that. Corporations are not the same as individual human Americans. Corporations do not have the same rights, the same morals, or the same interests. And corporations cannot vote in our democracy.

Teddy Roosevelt proposed the first campaign finance reforms, limiting the role of corporations in the political process. . . . Eight years ago, it was these same values that informed bipartisan efforts in Congress, on behalf of the American people, to enact the landmark McCain-Feingold Act . . .

Six years ago, in *McConnell* v. *Federal Election Commission*, the Supreme Court upheld the key provisions of the McCain-Feingold Act against a First Amendment challenge. Now, a thin majority of the Supreme Court, made possible by President Bush's appointment of Justice Samuel Alito, reversed course on the same question. . . . As Justice Stevens noted in dissent, 'The only relevant thing that has changed since . . . *McConnell* is the composition of the Court.' The Constitution has not changed. In fact, nowhere in Constitution do we even mention corporations. "

—from "'We the People'? Corporate Spending in American Elections after Citizens United," a hearing before the Committee on the Judiciary, opening remarks by Senator Patrick Leahy, March 10, 2010

1 **ANALYZING SOURCES** Which phrase describes what Leahy believes the recent court decision has done? Why is this important?

_____

_____

_____

_____

2 CIVICS Based on the excerpt, on what grounds does Leahy believe the Court has overstepped?

_____

_____

_____

3 **EVALUATING EVIDENCE** What is this document? Is this a primary or secondary source? What does the information in the document suggest about the issue of campaign financing?

_____

_____

_____

_____

4 **DETERMINING MEANING** What does the quote "As Justice Stevens noted in dissent, 'The only relevant thing that has changed since . . . _McConnell_ is the composition of the Court" suggest?

_____

_____

_____

5 **UNDERSTANDING CONTEXT** Why does Senator Leahy believe there's cause for concern over the Supreme Court decision in _Citizens United_?

_____

_____

_____

_____

ESSENTIAL QUESTION

How have disputes over ideas, values, and politics resulted in change?

As you gather evidence to answer the Essential Question, think about:

- the international issues that President Obama faced.
- the challenges that Europe faced, and how these challenges affected the United States.

My Notes

A Troubled World

DIRECTIONS: Search for evidence in Chapter 22, Lesson 2 to help you answer the following questions.

1A **UNDERSTANDING CONTEXT** What was the basis for President Obama's foreign policy?

_____

_____

_____

_____

1B **IDENTIFYING EFFECTS** What was the purpose of increasingly using drones to go after enemies? Was this change in policy effective?

_____

_____

_____

_____

2A **DETERMINING MEANING** What was the Arab Spring? How did the United States respond?

_____

_____

_____

_____

_____

2B **SUMMARIZING** What is the Islamic State? Why is it important?

_____

_____

_____

_____

3 RELATING EVENTS Complete the Cornell Notes organizer to describe the political unrest in Eastern Europe.

Main Idea	Notes
Ukraine	
Crimea	

4 SUMMARIZING Complete the graphic organizer below to summarize the crises faced by the European Union.

Event	What Happened	Outcome
Debt crisis		
Euro crisis		
Refugees		
Terrorism		

G8. 2011. "Declaration of the G8 on the Arab Spring." G8 Summit, May 26-27, Deauville, France.

ESSENTIAL QUESTION

How have disputes over ideas, values, and politics resulted in change?

The Arab Spring

DIRECTIONS: Read the following declaration. Then respond to the questions that follow.

EXPLORE THE CONTEXT: Beginning in late 2010, the world watched as a series of prodemocracy demonstrations erupted throughout the Middle East. The groups were protesting corrupt regimes. The protesters called for nothing less than a complete reform of their countries' governments. These events were called the Arab Spring. The following spring, members of the Group of Eight, or G8—a group of the most industrialized countries in the world—commented on the movement.

PRIMARY SOURCE: DECLARATION EXCERPT

❝ 1) The changes under way in the Middle East and North Africa (MENA) are historic and have the potential to open the door to the kind of transformation that occurred in Central and Eastern Europe after the fall of the Berlin Wall. The aspiration of people for freedom, human rights, democracy, job opportunities, empowerment and dignity, has led them to take control of their own destinies in a growing number of countries in the region. It resonates with and reinforces our common values.

2) We, members of the G8, strongly support the aspirations of the 'Arab spring' as well as those of the Iranian people. We hear the voice of the citizens, support their determination for equality and stand by their legitimate call for democratic, open societies and inclusive economic modernisation. We particularly commend the role played by young people and women in these transformational movements.

3) Today we launched the 'Deauville Partnership' with the people of the region, based on our common goals for the future, in the presence of the Prime Ministers of Egypt and Tunisia, the two countries that originated the movement, and of the Secretary General of the Arab League. We stand ready to extend this long term global Partnership to all countries of the region engaging in a transition toward free, democratic and tolerant societies ('Partnership Countries'), beginning with Egypt and Tunisia, in association with countries wishing to support transition in the region. This Partnership enshrines common values of freedom and democracy and is founded on the respect for the sovereignty of States and peoples, whose protection is the common responsibility of governments. It builds on initiatives already undertaken by G8 members. ❞

—from "Declaration of the G8 on the Arab Spring," May 2011

1 **EVALUATING EVIDENCE** What type of document is this? Why might it be important?

_____

_____

_____

_____

2 **DETERMINING CONTEXT** How does this resource better help you understand the events of the Arab Spring and the Western response to it?

_____

_____

_____

_____

_____

3 **ECONOMICS** What would be gained by the G8's pledge to help to the protesters?

_____

_____

_____

_____

4 **EVALUATING EVIDENCE** What does the document tell you about the state of the Middle East and who was involved in the Arab Spring movement?

_____

_____

_____

_____

_____

5 **INFERRING** What does the term _Arab Spring_ suggest?

_____

_____

_____

Obama, Barack. 2016. "Remarks by President Obama at Leaders Summit on Refugees." United Nations. September 20. Washington: White House, Office of the Press Secretary.

Copyright © McGraw-Hill Education

ESSENTIAL QUESTION

How have disputes over ideas, values, and politics resulted in change?

Summit on Refugees

DIRECTIONS: Read the following excerpt from a presidential speech. Then respond to the questions that follow.

EXPLORE THE CONTEXT: In one of his final addresses on foreign policy, President Barack Obama traveled to New York City to speak to the United Nations about the refugee crisis. In the following excerpt, Obama outlines why the crisis needs to be addressed, not just by the United States but by the world as a whole.

PRIMARY SOURCE: SPEECH EXCERPT

66 Mr. Secretary General; heads of state and heads of government; distinguished guests; ladies and gentlemen: As you saw in the video, we are facing a crisis of epic proportions. More than 65 million people have been driven from their homes—which is more than any time since the Second World War. Among them are more than 21 million refugees who have fled their countries . . .

And I'm here today—I called this summit—because this crisis is one of the most urgent tests of our time—our capacity for collective action. To test, first and foremost, our ability to end conflicts, because so many of the world's refugees come from just three countries ravaged by war—Syria, Afghanistan and Somalia. . . .

It's a test of our international system where all nations ought to share in our collective responsibilities, because the vast majority of refugees are hosted by just 10 countries who are bearing a very heavy burden—among them Turkey, Pakistan, Lebanon, Iran, Ethiopia. Countries that often have fewer resources than many of those who are doing little or nothing. . . .

And if we were to turn refugees away simply because of their background or religion, or, for example, because they are Muslim, then we would be reinforcing terrorist propaganda that nations like my own are somehow opposed to Islam, which is an ugly lie that must be rejected in all of our countries by upholding the values of pluralism and diversity.

And finally, this crisis is a test of our common humanity—whether we give in to suspicion and fear and build walls, or whether we see ourselves in another. 99

—from "Remarks by President Obama at Leaders Summit on Refugees,"
United Nations, New York City, September 20, 2016

1 **UNDERSTANDING CONTEXT** Is this document a primary or secondary source? How does it help you understand the period?

_____

_____

_____

2 **INFERRING** What might President Obama have meant when he said, "It's a test of our international system where all nations ought to share in our collective responsibilities"?

_____

_____

_____

3 **INTERPRETING** How does this excerpt reveal the president's views on U.S. foreign policy in regard to the refugee crisis?

_____

_____

_____

4 **INFERRING** Which sentence suggests that the international response to the refugee crisis is much larger than the problem itself?

_____

_____

_____

5 CIVICS What American civic values is President Obama advocating in his remarks about religion and Islam?

_____

_____

_____

ESSENTIAL QUESTION

How have disputes over ideas, values, and politics resulted in change?

As you gather evidence to answer the Essential Question, think about:

- what factors led to the polarization of American politics.
- the Tea Party movement and what it hoped to accomplish.
- the protest movements that arose as a response to growing inequality in the United States.

My Notes

Obama's Domestic Policy Challenges

DIRECTIONS: Search for evidence in Chapter 22, Lesson 3 to help you answer the following questions.

1A **DESCRIBING** What was one major aftereffect of the recession in the United States?

1B **DRAWING CONCLUSIONS** Why did the middle class continue to struggle as the economy improved?

2A **ECONOMICS** What was one consequence of the economic recovery for the wealthy and the middle class?

2B **SUMMARIZING** How did the Occupy Wall Street movement try to draw attention to the growing income gap in the United States? What was significant about the name of the group?

3 RELATING EVENTS Complete the Cornell Notes organizer to explain the issues surrounding civil rights in the United States.

The Rise of the New Civil Rights Movement	
Main Idea	**Notes**
Hate crimes	
Same-sex marriage	
Windsor v. *United States*	
Obergefell v. *Hodges*	

4 SUMMARIZING Complete the graphic organizer below by identifying two Supreme Court decisions concerning the Second Amendment and explaining what each one did.

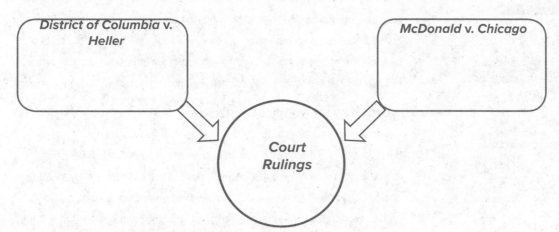

District of Columbia v. Heller

McDonald v. Chicago

Court Rulings

5 CONSTRUCTING HYPOTHESES How might the Black Lives Matter movement be seen as an extension of the civil rights movements of the 1960s and 1970s?

_____

_____

_____

_____

_____

ESSENTIAL QUESTION

How have disputes over ideas, values, and politics resulted in change?

VOCABULARY

analogues: things that are similar to or equivalent of

capriciously: erratically

enumerated: spelled out; catalogued

certiorari: a writ seeking judicial review

District of Columbia v. Heller

DIRECTIONS: Read the following excerpt from a court decision. Then respond to the questions that follow.

EXPLORE THE CONTEXT: In an important victory for supporters of the Second Amendment, the decision handed down in *District of Columbia* v. *Heller* answered a decades-long debate: Was an individual gun owner subject to the same protection as members of a militia or well-regulated army? Washington, D.C., had instituted a citywide ban on owning guns. Gun groups and owners sued, insisting they had a right to possess guns for protection in their own homes. The U.S. Supreme Court agreed by a slim margin. The vote was 5 to 4.

PRIMARY SOURCE: COURT DECISION EXCERPT

❝ "2. Like most rights, the Second Amendment right is not unlimited. It is not a right to keep and carry any weapon whatsoever in any manner whatsoever and for whatever purpose: For example, concealed weapons prohibitions have been upheld under the Amendment or state **analogues**. The Court's opinion should not be taken to cast doubt on longstanding prohibitions on the possession of firearms by felons and the mentally ill, or laws forbidding the carrying of firearms in sensitive places such as schools and government buildings, or laws imposing conditions and qualifications on the commercial sale of arms. *Miller*'s holding that the sorts of weapons protected are those 'in common use at the time' finds support in the historical tradition of prohibiting the carrying of dangerous and unusual weapons.

3. The handgun ban and the trigger-lock requirement (as applied to self-defense) violate the Second Amendment. The District's total ban on handgun possession in the home amounts to a prohibition on an entire class of "arms" that Americans overwhelmingly choose for the lawful purpose of self-defense. Under any of the standards of scrutiny the Court has applied to **enumerated** constitutional rights, this prohibition—in the place where the importance of the lawful defense of self, family, and property is most acute—would fail constitutional muster. Similarly, the requirement that any lawful firearm in the home be disassembled or bound by a trigger lock makes it impossible for citizens to use arms for the core lawful purpose of self-defense and is hence unconstitutional. Because Heller conceded at oral argument that the D. C. licensing law is permissible if it is not enforced arbitrarily and **capriciously**, the Court assumes that a license will satisfy his prayer for relief and does not address the licensing requirement. Assuming he is not disqualified from exercising Second Amendment rights, the District must permit Heller to register his handgun and must issue him a license to carry it in the home. ❞

—from *District of Columbia* v. *Heller*, **Certiorari** to the United States Court of Appeals for the District of Columbia Circuit

1 **DETERMINING MEANING** Which sentence shows that the Court recognizes that, even under the Second Amendment, there can still be limitations on gun ownership? Why is this important?

_____

_____

_____

_____

2 **ANALYZING SOURCES** What is the Court's attitude toward bans on firearms? Why is this important?

_____

_____

_____

_____

_____

_____

3 CIVICS What principle of the Constitution is being supported here?

_____

_____

4 **DETERMINING CENTRAL IDEAS** Why was this an important victory for advocates of gun rights?

_____

_____

_____

_____

5 **ANALYZING INFORMATION** Which sentence concerning disassembled weapons was key to the Court's decision in determining that the ban was unconstitutional?

_____

_____

_____

_____

Providing that the House of Representatives Disagrees with the Majority Opinion in Obergefell et al. v. Hodges, and for Other Purposes, 114th Cong., 1st sess., H.R. 359.

ESSENTIAL QUESTION

How have disputes over ideas, values, and politics resulted in change?

Same-Sex Marriage

DIRECTIONS: Read the following excerpt from a House resolution. Then respond to the questions that follow.

EXPLORE THE CONTEXT: In 2015, the Supreme Court overturned an earlier court decision on same-sex marriage by proclaiming that same-sex couples have the right to marry. The Court based its decision on the Constitution's Fourteenth Amendment. While many supported and cheered the decision, others did not. For example, the House of Representatives issued a resolution criticizing the Court's decision.

PRIMARY SOURCE: RESOLUTION EXCERPT

" Whereas the traditional definition of marriage is a union between one man and one woman;

Whereas the opinion of the majority of the Supreme Court in United States v. Windsor, written by Justice Kennedy, affirmed that 'The definition of marriage is the foundation of the State's broader authority to regulate the subject of domestic relations with respect to the '[p]rotection of offspring, [and] property interests' . . .

Whereas the opinion of the majority of the Supreme Court in Obergefell et al. v. Hodges et al. (in this resolution referred to as 'Obergefell') distorts the meaning of the word 'marriage' to create an unconstitutional right to same-sex marriage. . . .

Whereas the dissenting opinion by Chief Justice Roberts in Obergefell states that '[T]his Court is not a legislature. Whether same-sex marriage is a good idea should be of no concern to us. Under the Constitution, judges have power to say what the law is, not what it should be.' . . .

Whereas the opinion of the majority in Obergefell is a clear case of judicial activism; and Whereas the majority of the Supreme Court in Obergefell acted legislatively, which is an unconstitutional violation of the principle of separation of powers. "

—from House Resolution 359 Providing that the House of Representatives disagrees with the majority opinion in *Obergefell et al.* v. *Hodges*, and for other purposes, by Representative Steve King

1 **CITING TEXT EVIDENCE** According to the resolution, what is at issue with regard to the Supreme Court decision?

_____

_____

_____

2 CIVICS Why did the Court have the constitutional authority to hand down its decision?

_____

_____

_____

3 **EVALUATING** According to the resolution, in addition to redefining what constitutes a marriage, what else does the Court's decision allow? Why is this important?

_____

_____

_____

4 **INFERRING** According the resolution, what is the problem with "judicial activism"?

_____

_____

_____

5 **INTERPRETING** What did Chief Justice Roberts mean when he stated, "[T]his Court is not a legislature. Whether same-sex marriage is a good idea should be of no concern to us. Under the Constitution, judges have power to say what the law is, not what it should be"? How might opponents disagree?

_____

_____

_____

_____

The 2016 Presidential Election

DIRECTIONS: Search for evidence in Chapter 22, Lesson 4 to help you answer the following questions.

1A **DESCRIBING** What was notable about the field of candidates running for their party's nomination for president in 2016?

_____

_____

_____

_____

1B **DRAWING CONCLUSIONS** Why did the 2016 Democratic race take on tones of the 2008 race for Hillary Clinton?

_____

_____

_____

_____

2A **IDENTIFYING CAUSES** Why was Donald Trump's candidacy such a surprise for the Republicans?

_____

_____

_____

_____

2B **SUMMARIZING** What did Trump's candidacy say about the state of the Republican Party during the 2016 election?

_____

_____

_____

_____

ESSENTIAL QUESTION

How have disputes over ideas, values, and politics resulted in change?

As you gather evidence to answer the Essential Question, think about:

- the candidates running for president in 2016.
- the outcome of the 2016 presidential elections.
- what the election outcome suggested about the increasing polarization of American politics.

My Notes

_____

_____

_____

_____

_____

_____

3 **RELATING EVENTS** Complete the chart below by describing the differences between Hillary Clinton and Bernie Sanders.

The Democratic Candidates				
	Background	Platform	Appealed to	Challenges
Hillary Clinton				
Bernie Sanders				

4 **EXPLAINING** What was surprising about the election night returns?

_____

_____

5 **SUMMARIZING** Complete the chart below by summarizing some of the differences between the candidacies of Hillary Clinton and Donald Trump.

A Look at the Candidates				
	Party	Platform	Appealed to	Challenges
Hillary Clinton				
Donald Trump				

Obama, Barack. 2016. "Remarks by the President at the Democratic National Convention," July 28. Washington: White House: Office of the Press Secretary.

ESSENTIAL QUESTION

How have disputes over ideas, values, and politics resulted in change?

Healing the Divide

DIRECTIONS: Read the following excerpt from a speech given at the Democratic National Convention. Then respond to the questions that follow.

EXPLORE THE CONTEXT: On July 28, 2016, President Barack Obama took the podium to introduce the Democratic candidate for the 2016 presidential election, Hillary Clinton. President Obama's message was one of inclusion and invitation—in part to heal any divisions still lingering among Clinton and Sanders supporters.

PRIMARY SOURCE: SPEECH EXCERPT

❝ THE PRESIDENT: And most of all, I see Americans of every party, every background, every faith who believe that we are stronger together—black, white, Latino, Asian, Native American; young, old; gay, straight; men, women, folks with disabilities, all pledging allegiance, under the same proud flag, to this big, bold country that we love. (Applause.) That's what I see. That's the America I know! (Applause.)

And there is only one candidate in this race who believes in that future, has devoted her life to that future; a mother and a grandmother who would do anything to help our children thrive; a leader with real plans to break down barriers, and blast through glass ceilings, and widen the circle of opportunity to every single American—the next President of the United States, Hillary Clinton. (Applause.)

AUDIENCE: Hillary! Hillary! Hillary!

THE PRESIDENT: That's right! . . .

You know, nothing truly prepares you for the demands of the Oval Office. You can read about it. You can study it. But until you've sat at that desk, you don't know what it's like to manage a global crisis, or send young people to war. But Hillary has been in the room; she's been part of those decisions. She knows what's at stake in the decisions our government makes—what's at stake for the working family, for the senior citizen, or the small business owner, for the soldier, for the veteran. And even in the midst of crisis, she listens to people, and she keeps her cool, and she treats everybody with respect. And no matter how daunting the odds, no matter how much people try to knock her down, she never, ever quits. (Applause.)

That is the Hillary I know. That's the Hillary I've come to admire. And that's why I can say with confidence there has never been a man or a woman—not me, not Bill, nobody—more qualified than Hillary Clinton to serve as President of the United States of America. ❞

—from remarks by President Barack Obama at the Democratic National Convention, July 28, 2016

1 **CITING TEXT EVIDENCE** What is the importance of the president's opening statement? Why?

_____

_____

_____

_____

2 CIVICS What civic virtues are displayed in the president's speech?

_____

_____

3 **EVALUATING** Which sentences indicate what Clinton would do if elected president?

_____

_____

_____

_____

_____

_____

4 **IDENTIFYING CONNECTIONS** Why does the president believe that Clinton is uniquely suited to be president?

_____

_____

_____

_____

5 **PREDICTING** How might this speech be seen by someone unsure of whether to vote for Clinton?

_____

_____

_____

_____

Highsmith (Carol M.) Archive, Library of Congress, LC-DIG-highsm-41412

ESSENTIAL QUESTION

How have disputes over ideas, values, and politics resulted in change?

The Second Amendment and Gun Ownership

DIRECTIONS: Study the following sign. Then respond to the questions that follow.

EXPLORE THE CONTEXT: Donald Trump's surprising win in the 2016 presidential race led many political scientists, pollsters, and journalists to try and understand the forces behind his victory. Many of those who cast their votes for Trump believed they had been left behind by the government. Trump captured a majority of white male voters; he also fared better with older voters, who tend to be more conservative.

PRIMARY SOURCE: PHOTOGRAPH

1 DETERMINING MEANING What type of historic document is this? Is it a primary or secondary source?

_____

_____

_____

2 ANALYZING SOURCES What does this photograph tell the viewer about the election and the Trump candidacy?

_____

_____

_____

3 CIVICS What constitutional principles are illustrated here?

_____

_____

_____

4 DETERMINING CENTRAL IDEAS What point do you think the photographer is trying to make with this photograph?

_____

_____

_____

5 UNDERSTANDING CONTEXT How does the sign stand in contrast to the political slogan?

_____

_____

_____

ESSENTIAL QUESTION

How have disputes over ideas, values, and politics resulted in change?

As you gather evidence to answer the Essential Question, think about:

- how President Trump's choices for cabinet reflect who he is.
- the concerns surrounding Russia and the 2016 presidential election.
- the challenges Trump faced in his first months in office.

My Notes

_____

_____

_____

_____

_____

_____

_____

The Trump Administration

DIRECTIONS: Search for evidence in Chapter 22, Lesson 5 to help you answer the following questions.

1A **DESCRIBING** What was one of the first issues that Trump faced upon taking office?

_____

_____

_____

1B **DRAWING CONCLUSIONS** How did Trump's leadership style differ from those of other presidents?

_____

_____

_____

2A **IDENTIFYING CONNECTIONS** How did Trump's background influence his choice of cabinet members?

_____

_____

_____

2B **PREDICTING** How might the first days of the Trump administration predict his remaining time in office?

_____

_____

_____

_____

_____

3 **RELATING EVENTS** Complete the Cornell Notes organizer to explain why there were concerns about Russia's involvement in the election.

The Problem with Russia	
Main Ideas	**Notes**
2016 election	
Trump's cabinet appointments	
Economic sanctions	

4 CIVICS How did Neil Gorsuch's nomination to the Supreme Court change the rules surrounding confirmation hearings for Supreme Court justices?

_____

_____

_____

_____

5 **SUMMARIZING** Complete the graphic organizer to explain some of the challenges faced by the Trump administration with regard to foreign policy.

Trump's Foreign Policy Challenges	
Nation	**Challenge**
China	
Mexico	
Russia	
Syria	

ESSENTIAL QUESTION

How have disputes over ideas, values, and politics resulted in change?

Russian Interference in U.S. Election

DIRECTIONS: Read the following excerpt from a bill. Then respond to the questions that follow.

EXPLORE THE CONTEXT: Charges that the Russians had interfered in the 2016 presidential elections angered many Americans. Calls for Congressional investigations as well as for the FBI to step in increased. The Trump administration tried to downplay the issue to little avail. In Congress, some representatives called for a bill to specifically address the problem.

PRIMARY SOURCE: BILL EXCERPT

66 SEC. 3. PURPOSES.

(a) ACTIVITIES OF RUSSIAN GOVERNMENT.—The purpose of the Commission is to examine any attempts or activities by the Russian government, persons or entities associated with the Russian government, or persons or entities within Russia to use electronic means to influence, interfere with, or sow distrust in elections for public office held in the United States in 2016, including the following:

   (1) Electronic hacks by the Russian government, persons or entities associated with the Russian government, or other persons or entities within Russia into—

(A) the electronic systems of the Democratic National Committee;

    (B) the electronic systems of the Democratic Congressional Campaign Committee;

    (C) the electronic systems of Mr. John Podesta, campaign chairman for Democratic Presidential nominee Hillary Clinton;

    (D) the electronic systems of former Secretary of State Colin Powell; and

    (E) the electronic systems of Arizona, Illinois, and Florida, particularly voter database information.

(2) Efforts by the Russian government, persons or entities associated with the Russian government, or persons or entities within Russia to put forward, disseminate, or promote false news about the campaigns for elections for public office held in the United States in 2016.

(3) Efforts by the Russian government to work with other governments, entities, and individuals to carry out activities described in paragraphs (1) and (2).

(b) ACTIVITIES OF OTHERS.—In addition to the purpose described in subsection (a), the purpose of the Commission is to examine attempts or activities by governments other than the Russian government, persons associated with governments other than the Russian government, and other entities and individuals to use electronic means to influence, interfere with, or sow distrust in elections for public office held in the United States in 2016. 99

—from "A Bill to establish the National Commission on Foreign Interference in the 2016 Election," by Representative Eric Swalwell

U.S. House. 2016. To establish the National Commission on Foreign Interference in the 2016 Election. 114th Cong., 2nd sess., H. 6447.

1 **DETERMINING MEANING** Which sentence reveals the purpose behind the bill?

_____

_____

_____

_____

_____

2 **ANALYZING SOURCES** What type of document is this?

_____

_____

_____

_____

3 CIVICS What democratic principle guided the actions of the group that introduced the bill?

_____

_____

4 **DETERMINING CENTRAL IDEAS** What role did technology appear to play in this event?

_____

_____

_____

_____

5 **INFERRING** What is the importance of section 3b when it says that "governments other than the Russian government" may be investigated?

_____

_____

_____

_____

ESSENTIAL QUESTION

How have disputes over ideas, values, and politics resulted in change?

A Travel Ban

DIRECTIONS: Read the following excerpt from a bill. Then respond to the questions that follow.

EXPLORE THE CONTEXT: On January 27, 2017, President Trump issued an executive order banning entry of citizens from certain Muslim countries into the United States for 90 days. President Trump cited the need for increased security. Thousands of protesters flocked to airports all over the country to protest and help visitors who had been detained. The following excerpt is from a bill presented in Congress responding to Trump's order.

PRIMARY SOURCE: BILL EXCERPT

❝ SECTION 1. SHORT TITLE. This Act may be cited as the "No Funds for UnConstitutional Executive Orders Act".

SEC. 2. FINDINGS.

Congress finds the following:

(1) The first 10 words of the Bill of Rights state: 'Congress shall make no law respecting an establishment of religion'.

(2) In Larson v. Valente, the Supreme Court stated: 'The clearest command of the Establishment Clause is that one religious denomination cannot be officially preferred over another.'.

(3) On January 27, 2017, President Donald J. Trump signed into force an Executive order imposing a selective ban on immigration from majority-Muslim nations.

(4) On January 27, 2017, President Trump signed into force an Executive order that permits the Secretaries of State and Homeland Security to admit individuals to the United States as refugees if they are a religious minority in their home nation, because that is in the 'national interest'.

(5) On January 27, 2017, the Christian Broadcasting Network published an interview between David Brody and President Trump entitled Brody File Exclusive: President Trump Says Persecuted Christians Will Be Given Priority As Refugees in which President Trump says persecuted Christians will be given priority for admission to the United States over other religions.

(6) The Executive order entitled 'Protecting the Nation from Foreign Terrorist Entry into the United States' authored and signed by President Trump violates the Establishment Clause of the United States Constitution. ❞

—from a bill titled "To Prohibit the Use of Federal Funds to Implement, Administer, or Enforce the Executive Order Entitled 'Protecting the Nation from Foreign Terrorist Entry into the United States' Signed by President Donald J. Trump," by Representative Grace Meng

1 **CITING TEXT EVIDENCE** According to the excerpt, what is the purpose of the document?

_____

_____

_____

2 **CIVICS** Which document does the excerpt cite as a basis for the proposed bill? What does this mean?

_____

_____

_____

_____

3 **EVALUATING** According to the commission, how does the bill encourage religious discrimination?

_____

_____

_____

4 **IDENTIFYING CONNECTIONS** What does the proposed bill give as evidence that Trump intended to stop only Muslims from certain countries from entering the United States?

_____

_____

_____

5 **INTERPRETING** Based on this excerpt, what are the writers of the bill suggesting about President Trump's order?

_____

_____

_____

ESSENTIAL QUESTIONS

How have disputes over ideas, values, and politics resulted in change?

1 Think About It

Review the supporting questions that you developed at the beginning of the chapter. Review the evidence that you gathered in Chapter 22. Were you able to answer each Supporting Question?

If there was not enough evidence to answer your Supporting Questions, what additional evidence do you think you need to consider?

_____

_____

_____

_____

2 Organize Your Evidence

Complete the chart below with information you have learned about how cultural, economic, and social changes affected the United States between the years 2008 and 2016.

Issue	Dispute	Outcome
Gay and lesbian rights		
African American rights		
Universal health insurance		
Income gap		

❸ Talk About It

Work in small groups. Talk with your group about the information you included in your chart. Did you include the same evidence, or were your classmates' responses different from your responses? Which information is most important to understanding the societal changes that took place between 2008 and 2016? Why?

_____

_____

_____

_____

❹ Connect to the Essential Question

On a separate piece of paper or on a computer, create a compare-and-contrast chart that helps answer the Essential Question: _How have disputes over ideas, values, and politics resulted in change?_ Look over the issues that your group have discussed. Pick one, and create a list of reasons some people support it and reasons other people do not. Interview people with different opinions on the subject to get personal reactions to include in the chart.

_____

_____

_____

_____

_____

_____

_____

_____

_____

_____

TAKE ACTION

MAKE CONNECTIONS The years 2008 to 2016 were filled with a number of societal changes that challenged notions of American values and cultural beliefs. Some of these changes have resulted in new laws, new interpretations from the Supreme Court, and new outlooks. They have also resulted in an increasingly divided country.

DIRECTIONS: Working in a group, discuss one current piece of legislation that demonstrates a connection to the Essential Question: *How have disputes over ideas, values, and politics resulted in change?* Together, write an outline of how that issue was resolved through legislation or a Court decision and why that legislation or decision was controversial. What does it say about changing ideas and values? Groups can then share their outline with the class.